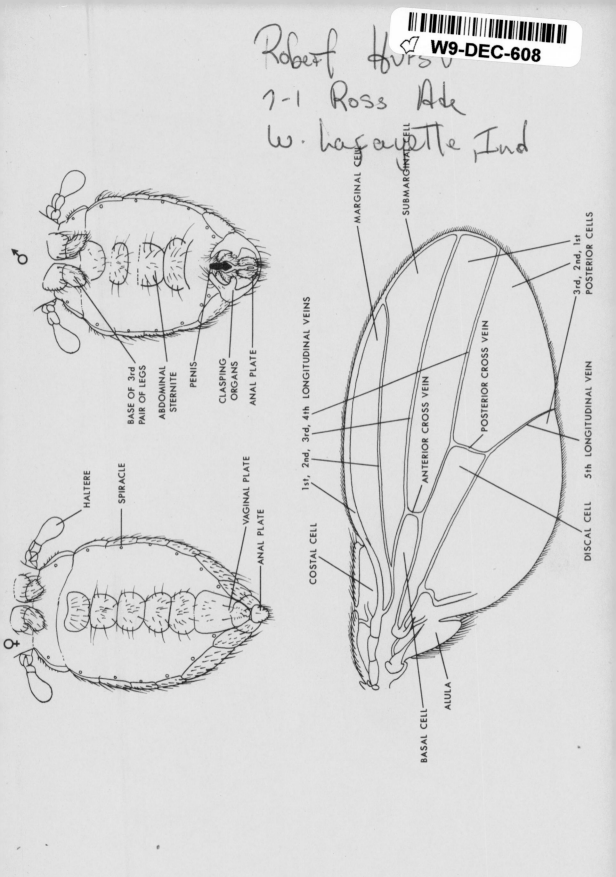

♂

BASE OF 3rd
PAIR OF LEGS

ABDOMINAL
STERNITE

PENIS

CLASPING
ORGANS

ANAL PLATE

♀

HALTERE

SPIRACLE

VAGINAL PLATE

ANAL PLATE

MARGINAL CELL

SUBMARGINAL CELL

1st, 2nd, 3rd, 4th LONGITUDINAL VEINS

3rd, 2nd, 1st
POSTERIOR CELLS

ANTERIOR CROSS VEIN

POSTERIOR CROSS VEIN

5th LONGITUDINAL VEIN

COSTAL CELL

DISCAL CELL

BASAL CELL

ALULA

GENETICS

The deoxyribonucleic acid double helix. The two ribbons represent two parallel polynucleotide chains coiled in right-handed helices about a common axis. The chains are held together by specific hydrogen bonds between opposite purines and pyrimidines. The distance between adjacent nucleotide pairs is 3.4 Å. The molecule may contain as many as 25,000 of these nucleotide pairs. Within the nucleus the DNA is intimately associated with a basic protein which presumably occupies the narrow groove between the nucleotide chains. Under this arrangement the phosphoric acid residues of DNA are neutralized by the basic amino acids of the histone. It has been suggested that template ribonucleoprotein chains can be synthesized within the wide groove of the DNA helix. 1, purine; 2, pyrimidine; 3, phosphoric acid residue; 4, deoxyribose; and 5, a hydrogen bond linking a purine and a pyrimidine.

GENETICS

ROBERT C. KING, Ph. D.

ASSOCIATE PROFESSOR OF BIOLOGY

NORTHWESTERN UNIVERSITY

Illustrated by E. JOHN PFIFFNER

STAFF ARTIST · CHICAGO NATURAL HISTORY MUSEUM

New York · OXFORD UNIVERSITY PRESS · 1962

TO

THOSE WHO MEAN THE MOST,

AMANDA, VIOLET, VAUGHAN, AND ARCHIE

PREFACE

Genetics, the study of heredity, is of great antiquity. It dates back to the work of the primitive agriculturalists who thousands of years ago in the ancient centers of civilization domesticated the various plants and animals we use to this day. Paradoxically, modern genetics is one of the most youthful of the major biological sciences. It originated with the rediscovery in 1900 of a scientific article originally published in 1866 by a young Augustinian monk named Gregor Mendel. This paper described a hypothesis which originated from a bold piece of abstract thinking combined with elegant experimentation. Mendel's experimental analysis (which will be outlined further on in this text) constitutes one of the very greatest achievements in pure science, and a vast array of theoretical and practical consequences followed.

We now know that the genetic machinery of living things generally consists of units called genes. Genes are immense when compared to most biologically important molecules, but even so they are too small to be seen with the light microscope. It appears that many genes exert their influence in living systems by controlling steps in chains of biochemical reactions through the production of organic catalysts called enzymes. Genes have the ability to reproduce themselves; that is they can gather from their immediate environment many smaller molecules and can combine these to form replicas of themselves. Furthermore, a gene molecule can undergo a physical or chemical change termed a mutation, and the mutated gene often will reproduce its new pattern just as faithfully as it previously copied the original pattern.

Only living things are able to reproduce and to evolve. These abilities are in the final analysis bound to the ability of their genes to replicate their original and their mutated patterns. Since the science of genetics boils down to the study of genes and their operations, genetics becomes the most basic of all biological sciences, and its study often can give insight into the most fundamental biological problems: the origin of life, the origin of cellular differentiation during embryogenesis, and the origin of the diverse species which now inhabit or once inhabited our planet.

In a complex atomic age man cannot understand his own nature and his kinship with his fellow beings, or plan for his future without some knowledge of genetics. In various branches of applied science genetics is indispensable. For example, the geneticist has redesigned the genetic material of certain plants, animals, and microorganisms in various ways which benefit mankind. The production of a disease-resistant race of wheat may yield savings to the farmer measured in the millions of dollars. Genetics is equally useful to the pure scientist, such as the physical geochemist who is interested in the origin of autocatalytic systems under conditions similar to those postulated to have existed when the earth was young, the biochemist studying enzymatic reactions, or the anthropologist studying interrelations between different races of man. A knowledge of genetics is helpful to the evolutionist studying the long-range changes living things have undergone during the past 0.5 billion years, and to the physician who is interested in the differences in the proneness to various infectious and degenerative diseases exhibited by different individuals. Given a knowledge of the genetic background of his patient, the physician of the future may be able to detect and treat diseases before they show clinical symptoms and to reduce human suffering accordingly.

Thus genetics may, and indeed has, stimulated many diverse disciplines in both the natural and the social sciences; and genetics has received much in return. The fact that genetics has attracted mathematicians, physicists, chemists, physicians, and other scientists of diverse backgrounds to contribute to its development is one of the chief reasons for its prodigious growth.

You should be aware of the fact that in this book you will be exposed to only a minute fraction of the information available to the geneticist. I must choose one or two examples to illustrate a certain phenomenon, although perhaps one hundred other examples would also serve, but, in any text, space is limited. Genetic information is accumulating at such a rate that a *Drosophila* geneticist, for example, finds it hard to keep abreast of this highly prescribed area. In the fifty years that flies of this genus have been studied, a vast literature of 20,000 technical publications has arisen. In thirty countries in 200 laboratories some 1000 scientists are currently engaged in research involving such fruit flies. Research in microbial genetics (a science only twenty years old) is proceeding even more rapidly.

To understand the operations of genetic material one must digest information from a wide variety of scientific areas. One must know what chromosomes look like, what chemicals comprise them, and how they reproduce themselves and are passed on to future generations of cells. One must have some knowledge of the types of reproduction carried on by the various species which are the favorites of geneticists. With this background one can learn about the intimate properties of those chromosomal segments called genes; how they control the biochemistry and consequently the morphology and physiology of the organism, and how they behave in the gene pool of the species to control its evolution.

R. C. K.

Evanston, Illinois
December 1961

ACKNOWLEDGMENTS

Critical comments on the manuscript were provided by Professors D. F. Poulson, W. K. Baker, and J. A. Moore; while E. G. Vanoucek and Helen Pakeltis gave helpful suggestions from the student's point of view. Useful criticisms were received from H. Swift for Chapter 2 and from D. Calhoun for Chapters 6 and 7. Appendix C was compiled with help from Doctors D. Y.-Y. Hsia and R. E. Tashian. During the construction of Figure 10-4 we relied heavily upon advice from Professor E. B. Lewis and upon new cytological localizations by C. L. Ward for certain third chromosomal mutants. Doctors H. Kubitschek, S. B. Pipkin, and R. C. Von Borstel provided information or material used in preparing the illustrations in Figures 4–8, 12–1, and 12–5, respectively, and R. G. Burnett took the photographs used in Figures 1–2 and 1–3. The authors and publishers who generously granted permission for the use of copyright materials have been acknowledged in the legends accompanying figures and tables. Pauline Kirchner with great skill prepared most of the graphical illustrative material. The collaboration with E. John Pfiffner, whose drawings so enrich the book, was certainly the pleasantest aspect of the project.

CONTENTS

1 Methods for Studying Cellular Morphology and Physiology, 3

2 Cell Structure, 13

3 Chromosome Dynamics, 31

4 Some Favorite Organisms of Geneticists, 44

5 Fundamental Hereditary Laws, 65

6 Modification of Classical Genetic Ratios, 79

7 Quantitative Inheritance, 89

8 Linked Genes and Linkage Groups, 103

9 Crossing Over and Genetic Mapping, 113

10 Chromosomal Aberrations, 129

11 Variation in the Number of Chromosomes, 155

12 Sex Determination, 168

13 Mutation, 185

14 Genes and the Biochemistry of the Organism, 213

15 The Interaction of Genic and Nongenic Hereditary Units, 249

16 Developmental Genetics, 262

17 Evolution and Population Genetics, 296

APPENDIX

A Chronology, 325

B Periodicals Which Often Contain Articles Oriented Toward Genetics and Cytology, 329

C Some Laboratories Engaged in Studies of Human Genetics Throughout Canada, Mexico, and the United States, 330

D Drosophila Culture, 332

E Motion Pictures or Film Strips Which Illustrate Material Covered in Specific Chapters, 332
   Useful Material for Laboratory Use, 333

INDEX, 335

GENETICS

Chapter 1

Methods for Studying Cellular Morphology and Physiology

Magnifying systems

Every living organism is or starts life as a single cell, and it is therefore to the cell and the structures which comprise it that we eventually must return to seek the answer to almost every biological problem. However, living cells are difficult to study because they are generally small and transparent. Naturally, cytologists, the scientists who study cell structure and function, would like not only to be able to see at higher magnifications the morphology and behavior of cells, but also to learn what types of molecules make up the various cellular components and what chemical reactions are taking place within cells. Fortunately, we live in an age in which remarkable advances are being made daily in the production and perfection of various physical and chemical techniques for gathering such information.

Most of what we know concerning cells comes from the study with the light microscope (see Fig. 1–1) of stained slices or sections of dead tissues. The resolving power of any magnifying system gives its ability to reveal fine detail, and this ability is generally measured as the minimum distance between two lines or points at which they are resolved as two rather than as a single blurred object. The light microscope has a resolving power of 0.2 microns[1] and a useful magnification of a little over 1000 times.

---

[1] 1 micron (μ) = 0.001 mm.; 1 millimicron (mμ) = 0.001 μ

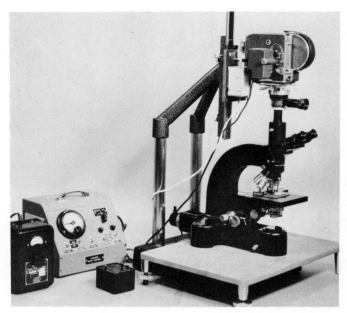

Figure 1–1 A Leitz Ortholux light microscope equipped for taking phase contrast, time lapse motion pictures.   (Courtesy of W. H. Kessel, Scientific Instruments, Chicago.)

The other magnifying system commonly used by cytologists is the electron microscope (see Fig. 1–2) which has a resolving power 100 times that of the light microscope. The electron microscope uses beams of electrons which are focused in a vacuum by a series of magnetic lenses. Because the ability of electrons to penetrate tissue is very weak, very thin tissue preparations are required, for which purpose special slicing machines called ultramicrotomes (see Fig. 1–3) have had to be developed. Such special microtomes can cut sections of tissues embedded in plastic at least 400 times thinner than the 10-micron sections generally used for light microscopy.

Preparation of tissues

Fairly standard techniques are employed in preparing cells for observation with the light microscope. First the cells are preserved by placing them in a fixative. Such solutions precipitate the proteinaceous enzymes of cells and so prevent autolysis, destroy bacteria which might produce decay of the tissue, and cause many of the cellular constituents to become insoluble. The tissue is washed to remove the fixative and is then run through a series of ethanol (ethyl alcohol) solutions of increasing concentration. After the water has been completely extracted, the ethanol is extracted with a substance, such as benzene, which mixes with both ethanol and paraffin.

Eventually the benzene is replaced with hot melted paraffin, and the paraffin is allowed to cool to form a solid block. A microtome is used to cut sections from the block; these sections are affixed to a microscope slide, and the paraffin is dissolved away by a solvent such as xylene. The xylene is replaced by ethanol, this in turn by ethanol-water solutions, and finally by water. Now the tissue slices may be subjected to any one of a multitude

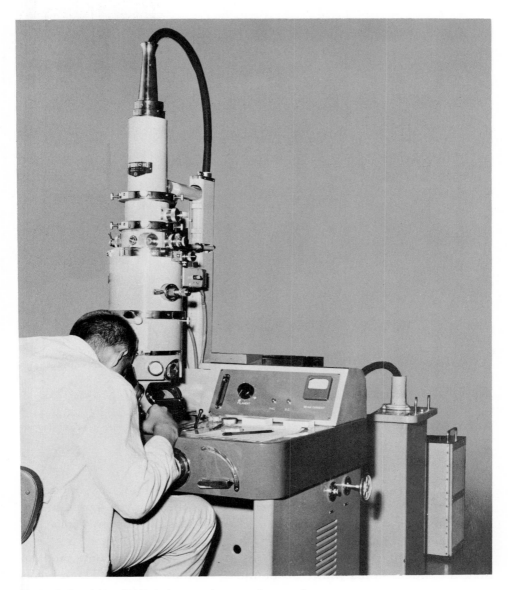

Figure 1–2   A Hitachi HS 6 electron microscope in operation.

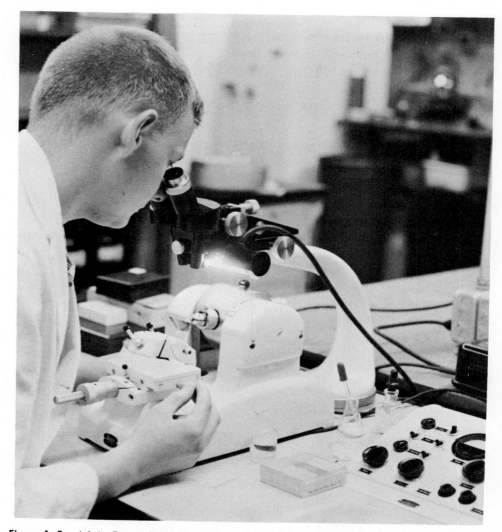

Figure 1–3 A Leitz-Fernandez-Moran ultramicrotome in operation. Each time the specimen rotates 360° a section ¼₀th of a micron in thickness is cut from the face of the specimen block by the stationary glass knife.

of chemical treatments. Various cellular constituents may be stained with dyes, extracted with solvents, or digested by purified enzyme preparations. The tissue is next dehydrated with a series of ethanol-water solutions, and the ethanol is replaced by xylene. The tissue is covered by a drop of a resinous mounting medium and a coverslip is placed over the entire preparation; the slide is stored while the mounting medium hardens. The result of this laborious process is a fairly permanent preparation which may be subjected to microscopic examination whenever desired. However, the student should be continually reminded that the cell has undergone many drastic changes during the procedures which are required to produce the preparation, and therefore that he must exercise caution in interpreting what he sees.

Cytophotometry

The cytochemist uses various chemicals which react with specific molecules to be found within cells to produce a colored product. Such techniques allow qualitative studies of the localization within cells of various inorganic and organic compounds. In many cases it is possible to get quantitative estimates as to the amounts of the stained material within a cell by the use of special cytophotometric methods. The techniques are simple in principle but difficult in practice and often involve expensive equipment. The image of a cell is magnified several hundred times with a microscope and projected upon an iris diaphragm (see Fig. 1–4). By regulating the diameter of the diaphragm opening, one can project light from a small area of the cell upon a sensitive photoelectric cell which measures the amount of light striking it. A fraction of the light passing through a stained object (the nucleus, for example) will be absorbed, and under these conditions less light will strike the photocell than if the stained object were not present. It is consequently possible to determine the amount of light transmitted by any light-absorbing structure in the cell. A monochromator is generally used to select light of any one of a number of specific wave lengths for a given measurement. For a given type of absorbing material the amount of light absorbed varies directly with the concentration of the light-absorbing material. Such cytophotometric techniques have been used by Ris, Swift, and others to study variations which characteristically occur in the nucleoprotein contents of cells during mitosis and meiosis. You will learn more about nucleic acids and nucleoproteins in the next chapter.

Certain chemical structures in complex molecules selectively absorb specific wave lengths of light. Nucleic acid, for example, shows a maximum absorption for light of 260 mμ wave length and a minimum for light of wave length 230 mμ (see Fig. 1–5). Cytospectrophotometric methods allow the determination of the characteristic absorption curves of the molecules making up specific cellular structures. One simply makes measurements of the type described above while varying the wave length of the light used.

If one wishes to use ultraviolet light, a microscope equipped with quartz lenses is required, because glass filters out this radiation. There are many instances in which such ultraviolet absorption microspectrophotometry is the only means available for obtaining information about the nature of certain chemical constituents of cells.

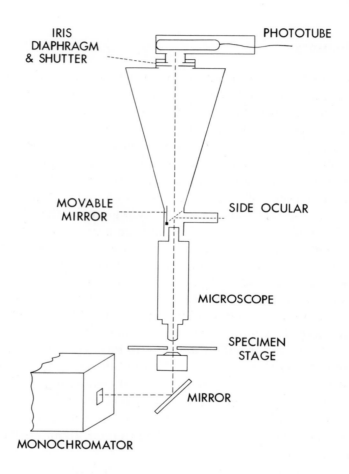

Figure 1–4 A simplified diagram of the optical system of a microspectrophotometer. Light of a given wave length is selected by a monochromator and projected through a tissue section mounted on a microscope. The magnified image may be viewed through the side ocular or projected on the photocell which measures the amount of light reaching it. The size of the spot of light reaching the photocell may be regulated by the iris diaphragm.   (Redrawn from C. P. Swanson, *Cytology and Cytogenetics,* copyright 1957, Prentice-Hall, Inc., Englewood Cliffs, N. J.)

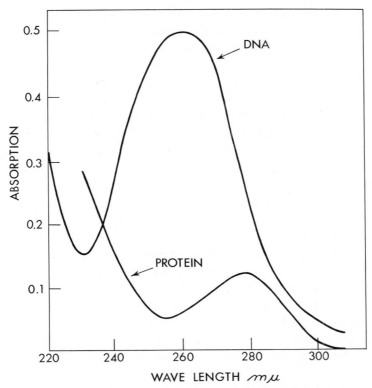

Figure 1-5   Ultraviolet absorption curves for DNA and for protein solutions. The protein used was serum albumin. Note the striking differences in the shapes of the two curves.   (From *Radiation Biology,* Vol. II, edited by A. H. Hollaender, McGraw-Hill Book Co. After Thorell, 1947.)

Autoradiography

The cytologist often wishes to gather information about the sequences of reactions a given chemical undergoes while in a cell and the regions in the cell where these reactions occur. Thus a chemical may enter a cell as a water-soluble substance and be converted at some later time into a more complex insoluble compound and stored in a specific cellular organelle. Information about such processes can be obtained by using chemicals which are tagged with radioactive atoms. For example, a chemical reaction may be carried out which causes some sizable fraction of the molecules of the substance under study to have one of their hydrogen atoms replaced

---

[2] All isotopes of a given element contain the same number of protons in their nuclei and hence have almost identical properties. They differ, however, in the number of neutrons in the nucleus and consequently in their mass. Radioactive isotopes are unstable and undergo spontaneous disintegration or decay, generally forming new elements and emitting radiation.

by an atom of the radioactive isotope[2] of hydrogen, tritium. In the vast majority of cases the cell cannot distinguish a molecule carrying a radioactive atom from its normal counterpart. Tritium atoms undergo radioactive decay at a specific rate, and during this process they are transformed into another element (helium) and concurrently emit low energy electrons. Such electrons travel extremely short distances (about 1 μ on the average in photographic emulsion) before exhausting their energy. Thus the location of the tritium-labeled molecules can be detected by the electrons they liberate. Each electron can activate silver grains in a photographic emulsion, and these grains will appear as black specks when viewed with a light microscope after the film has been processed with a photographic developer. The method of autoradiography allows the localization of radioactive isotopes in tissue sections. The tissue slices are covered by a fine-grain, photographic emulsion in a photographic dark room, and the preparations are then left to expose for a suitable period of time to allow a fraction of the radioactive atoms to decay and liberate electrons which sensitize silver grains in the emulsion. The film is developed subsequently, and the preparation is examined to note the location of developed silver grains above various cellular structures. Developed grains generally occur within one micron of the labeled atoms which lie close to the emulsion. If cells are killed after being grown for differing times upon some labeled chemical, and autoradiographic studies are made subsequently, one can trace the movement of the labeled atoms as a function of time. An example of the

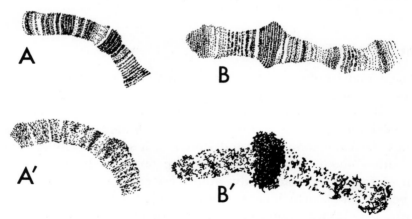

Figure 1–6   The distal end of chromosome C of *Rhynchosciara angelae* at two different stages of larval life. A and B show squashed chromosomes stained with a dye specific for nucleic acids. A' and B' show the corresponding segments of chromosomes (containing newly synthesized, radioactive DNA) radioautographed without any staining. A and A' are from full-grown larvae; whereas B and B' are from larvae at a prepupal stage, about six days older. Note that a chromosomal segment has increased in diameter during the interval between A and B, and that it is this puffed region which contains the greatest concentration of newly synthesized DNA.   (After Ficq and Pavan.)

usefulness of autoradiography to cytologists is shown in Figure 1–6. Here we are able to visualize the distribution of a specific tritium-labeled chemical compound in various regions of a chromosome isolated from a cell of a specific tissue. The amount of labeled material is seen to increase in specific chromosomal regions during the development of the organism. Information as to the nature of the compounds in which the labeled atoms reside can be obtained by extracting the tissue slices with various solvents or by digesting them with specific enzymes and determining subsequently whether or not the radioisotope has been removed from the tissue.

Phase-contrast microscopy

Living cells generally contain transparent structures of varying shapes, thicknesses, and refractive indices[3] surrounded by a transparent medium. A light ray passing through a transparent particle of higher refractive index than the surrounding medium will be changed in phase with respect to a light ray passing through the surrounding medium. The phase-contrast microscope utilizes an optical system which converts these phase variations into variations in light intensities. Thus a transparent mitochondrion lying in a transparent cytoplasm is invisible when viewed with the light micro-scope, since the eye cannot detect the phase variations; but may appear as a particle which is darker or brighter than its background when viewed with phase-contrast optics. The phase-contrast microscope allows the cytologist to observe the behavior of living, dividing cells. With phase-contrast optics it is possible to take time-lapse motion pictures of living cells and to gain a much clearer understanding of the dynamic processes cells undergo (see Fig. 1–1).

---

[3] The refractive index of a substance is the ratio of the velocity of light in a vacuum to its velocity in the substance in question.

1–1. List some of the newer techniques for gathering information about cell morphology and physiology.

1–2. The biochemist studies genetic material in terms of nucleic acids. Such molecules have a diameter of 2–3 mμ. The cytologist studies genetic material in terms of chromosomes which are 1 or 2 μ in diameter. Can you suggest how the gap between these two levels of organization can be bridged?

BIBLIOGRAPHY

Baker, J. R.   1958   Principles of Biological Microtechnique. Wiley, New York.

Casselman, W. G. B.   1959   Histochemical Technique. Wiley, New York.

Conn, H. J.   1961   Biological Stains, 7th ed. Williams & Wilkins Co., Baltimore, Md.

Ficq, A., and C. Pavan   1957   Autoradiography of polytene chromosomes of *Rhynchosciara angelae* at different stages of larval development. Nature *180*: 983–4.

Oster, G., and A. W. Pollister   1955   Physical Techniques in Biological research, Vols. 1–3. Academic Press, New York.

Pearse, A. G. E.   1960   Histochemistry, Theoretical and Applied, 2nd ed. Little, Brown, Boston.

Pollister, A. W.   1955   A critique of cytochemical methods. *In* Radiation Biology, Vol. II, Chap. 6. A. Hollaender, editor. McGraw-Hill, New York.

Richards, D. W.   1954   The Effective Use and Proper Care of the Microscope. American Optical, Buffalo 15, New York.

Ris, H.   1957   Chromosome structure. *In* The Chemical Basis of Heredity, W. D. McElroy and B. Glass, editors. Johns Hopkins Press, Baltimore, Md.

Swift, H.   1953   Nucleoproteins in the mitotic cycle. Texas Rep. Biol. & Med. *11*: 755–74.

Chapter 2

Cell Structure

The chemical components of tissue

The world we live in is composed of matter which in turn is composed of a finite number of chemical elements. Ninety-two chemical elements occur in nature, but only a relatively few of the lighter elements are biologically important. In fact four elements, hydrogen, oxygen, carbon, and nitrogen make up 99 per cent of living tissue. For each nitrogen atom in tissue there are approximately 3 carbon, 15 oxygen, and 30 hydrogen atoms. Seven other chemical elements: potassium, phosphorus, sulfur, sodium, chlorine, magnesium, and calcium together make up about 1 per cent of tissue. In addition certain elements are required in trace amounts (iron, manganese, copper, zinc, iodine, cobalt, fluorine, and molybdenum).

The major classes of biochemical compounds found in tissues are the proteins, carbohydrates, and lipids. Proteins are complex nitrogenous substances of high molecular weight which on decomposition yield simpler compounds called amino acids. Proteins may be simple or conjugated. Conjugated proteins are proteins which are combined with other organic molecules. Nucleoproteins, for example, are basic proteins combined with nucleic acids. Unlike proteins, the majority of carbohydrates contain no nitrogen. One generally finds only carbon, hydrogen, and oxygen in these compounds. Complex carbohydrates or polysaccharides are polymers of simpler units called monosaccharides. Lipids are a heterogeneous group of biochemical substances which are variably soluble in organic solvents like alcohol and sparingly soluble in water. Lipids include fats, oils, waxes, phospholipids, sterols, carotenoids, and some other less common compounds.

As is seen in the following table, characteristic animal and plant tissues vary considerably in the relative abundance of the various major classes of constituent chemicals.

	WATER	PROTEIN	LIPID	CARBOHYDRATE	ASH
animal	60%	20%	15%	1%	4%
plant	60%	5%	1%	30%	4%

These differences are due to the fact that in animals proteins often function as structural elements and fats as energy reserves, whereas in plants, carbohydrates often take over both functions. The interested reader is referred to the biochemistry texts listed at the end of this chapter for structural formulas of the various organic compounds mentioned in this chapter.

The components of a generalized cell

The majority of cells contain a nucleus (see Fig. 2–1A and 2–1C) which is often spherical. It is filled with a gelatinous nucleoplasm in which the chromosomes are dispersed, and is surrounded by a double-walled envelope. In surface view the nuclear envelope is seen to contain numerous annuli. These circular areas when seen in cross section look like pores. However, since the nucleus is impermeable to large protein molecules, it is suspected that in the living state the annular "pores" are plugged with material of some sort.

The nucleus floats in the cytoplasm which in the case of animal cells secretes an outer plasma membrane which is generally thin, delicate, flexible, and capable of regeneration. The plasma membrane contains proteins and lipids. In plants the cytoplasm secretes a cell wall which generally is impregnated with substances such as cellulose, lignin, and waxes and is thick and relatively rigid. The extensibility of this cell wall may be modified, however, by the influence of certain plant growth hormones.

The cytoplasm is generally slightly acidic and is about 85 per cent water. About 10 per cent of its weight is made up of soluble globular proteins having a diameter of about 3 mμ and of insoluble fibrous proteins having the dimensions (100 $\times$ 1 $\times$ 0.5 mμ). The tensile strength, elasticity, and viscosity of the cytoplasm are accounted for in part by the underlying fabric of fibrous protein molecules which are held together by chemical bonds of various sorts to produce a "brush heap" configuration. Cytoplasm undergoes cyclic changes in viscosity which presumably arise from reversible chemical reactions which vary the amount of cross linking between and

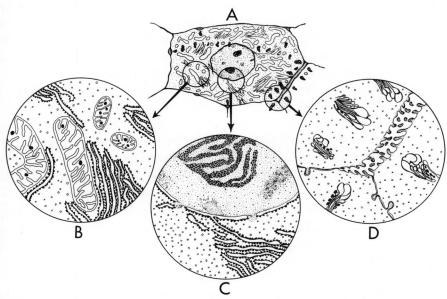

Figure 2-1   (A) A generalized cell as seen through the light microscope. (B) An area in the cytoplasm as seen in an electron micrograph demonstrating endoplasmic reticulum and mitochondria. (C) An area adjacent to the nucleus as seen with the electron microscope. Note that the double-walled nuclear envelope surrounding the nucleus is interrupted at two regions by "pores." The outer wall of the nuclear envelope is studded with ribosomes and is in one region continuous with the endoplasmic reticulum. Within the nucleoplasm are dispersed the denser chromosomes and a central nucleolus. (D) An area where three adjacent cells intersect as seen in an electron micrograph. Note the manner in which the plasma membranes of the cells are thrown into interdigitating microvilli. Five clusters of Golgi material are present.   (Redrawn after Novikoff in *Science*, 1956, by permission of the American Association for the Advancement of Science.)

within macromolecules. Within the cytoplasm are found various organelles (mitochondria, plastids, the endoplasmic reticulum, the Golgi apparatus, and the centrosome).

Cytoplasmic organelles

The mitochondria (see Fig. 2–1B) are universal, self-reproducing constituents of cells. They are spherical or rod-shaped and may change from one form to another. When viewed in living cells with a phase microscope they are seen to be in constant motion. Small rods may unite into larger ones or large rods may fragment, and the fragments may later grow in length. The liver cell of the rat contains about 1000 mitochondria, which are 1–4 μ long and 0.3–0.7 μ in diameter. A longitudinal section through such a mitochondrion shows that it is surrounded by a double limiting membrane, the total thickness of which is about 16 mμ. This membrane is semipermeable and can be readily stretched. The inner membrane has parallel ridges projecting from it which divide the mitochondrion into a series of compartments. These ridges often do not meet in the center of the mitochondrion, however, and therefore access to all compartments is generally possible by way of a central canal. About one-fourth of the protein and fat of the cells of rat liver is contained in the mitochondria. The mitochondrion contains batteries of dozens of different enzymes, some of which are firmly attached in specific patterns to the walls of the compartments and some of which float in the intramitochondrial fluid. Note that the enzymes of the mitochondrial wall may serve at one time both structural and catalytic functions. Most of the energy required by cells is stored as an energy-rich compound called adenosine triphosphate (ATP). The mitochondria manufacture ATP and so may be said to "secrete energy." The mitochondria are the power plants of the cell and supply it with most of its usable energy.

The plastids are characteristic of plant cells and may have arisen in the past from endosymbiotic blue-green algae. Plastids are self-reproducing, but in many cases their behavior is under the control of nuclear genes. Different types of plastids are named in accordance with the characteristic chemicals they contain. Chloroplasts carry chlorophyll and are intimately concerned with the process of photosynthesis, while amyloplasts, chromoplasts, and elaioplasts elaborate starch, pigments, and oil, respectively. A more detailed description of chloroplasts is given in Chapter 15.

Electron microscopic studies of areas of the cytoplasm which stain with basic dyes have shown that these regions often contain sheets of double-layered membranes which in some cases are continuous with the outer membrane of the nuclear envelope. This membranous system is called the endoplasmic reticulum (see Fig. 2–1B and 2–1C). The membranes are studded with submicroscopic particles (ribosomes) 10 to 20 mμ in diameter. The membranes are composed of protein and phospholipid, whereas the particles are ribonucleoprotein. Ninety per cent of the total ribonucleic acid of rat liver cells is in the ribosome fraction, which appears to be the major site of protein synthesis in the cell. On the other hand, the membrane of the endoplasmic reticulum is essential for the formation of certain lipids.

The Golgi apparatus is identified in electron micrographs as a complex, made up of closely packed, broad, flattened sacs (designated as cisternae) and swarms of small vesicles (see Fig. 2–1D). The Golgi apparatus is distinguished from the endoplasmic reticulum by the arrangement of the membranous vesicles and by the lack of ribonucleoprotein granules. It appears that the Golgi apparatus is a segregating system capable of collecting and sequestering substances synthesized elsewhere in the cell. These systems are conspicuous in the secretory cells and appear *de novo* at various stages in the development of these and other cells.

Since the centrosome performs a vital function during the division of the animal cell, further discussion of its behavior will be reserved until the section on mitosis.

The chemistry of the nucleus

The nucleus contains threadlike bodies called chromosomes which stain with basic dyes such as toluidine blue or methyl green. The interested reader is referred to the histochemistry texts listed at the end of the preceding chapter for details as to the dyes and staining procedures referred to in this chapter. Chromosomes are rich in nucleoproteins (basic proteins attached to nucleic acids). Nucleic acids are of two general types: deoxyribose nucleic acid (DNA) and ribose nucleic acid (RNA). These acids are named after the sugars that characterize them: 2-deoxy-D-ribose and D-ribose, respectively. These five-carbon or pentose sugars differ only in the atoms attached to the number 2 carbon. The OH group of ribose is replaced by an H atom in the case of deoxyribose.

D-RIBOSE   2-DEOXY-D-RIBOSE

The two nucleic acids differ in the types of organic bases they contain. Both have the purines adenine and guanine and the pyrimidine cytosine. However, generally RNA is characterized by the pyrimidine uracil and DNA by thymine. Relatively small quantities of some other pyrimidines are occasionally isolated from DNA from various sources. A purine or pyrimidine base condensed with a pentose or deoxypentose sugar is called a *nucleoside*. A purine or pyrimidine base condensed with a pentose or deoxypentose sugar and phosphoric acid is called a *nucleotide*.

Figure 2–2 illustrates the fashion in which a DNA molecule is built. It consists of a poly-sugar-phosphate backbone from which the purines and pyrimidines project. The backbone is formed by bonds between the phosphate molecule and carbon 3 and carbon 5 of adjacent pentoses. The nitrogenous base extends from carbon 1 of each sugar. According to this model as proposed by Watson and Crick (see frontispiece) DNA forms a double helix which is held together by hydrogen bonds between specific pairs of bases (thymine to adenine and cytosine to guanine). The resulting polymer may have a molecular weight as high as 100,000,000. Note that each strand in the double helix is complementary to its partner strand rather than identical with it. Subsequent to their separation each strand evidently can serve as a template upon which a new complementary strand is formed.

Knowledge concerning the molecular configuration of RNA is still relatively rudimentary, but the molecule is apparently single stranded. DNA molecules generally have much higher molecular weights and are more homogeneous in size than RNA molecules isolated from the same organism. Recent Nobel Prizes have been awarded to S. Ochoa and A. Kornberg for their studies on the *in vitro* enzymatic synthesis of RNA and DNA, respectively.

It is suspected that a basic protein lies in the narrow groove that spirals around the DNA molecules (see frontispiece) and that the component basic amino acids of the protein neutralize the phosphoric acid residues of the DNA. Two main types of basic proteins have been found associated with chromosomes: one of low molecular weight (protamine) and one of high molecular weight (histone). In addition there occurs an acidic protein of high molecular weight. In the chromosome each of the ultimate fibrils consists of two complementary DNA molecules intertwined about the basic protein. These fibrils are 3–4 mμ in diameter and several micra long. Bundles of these units form elementary chromosome fibrils 20 mμ in diameter, and bundles of these in turn form the microscopically visible chromosome thread or chromonema of 0.5–1 μ diameter. Whether or not a single DNA molecule extends the entire length of the chromosome is a matter of debate.

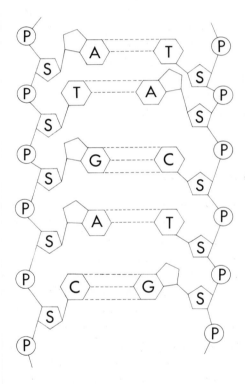

Figure 2-2   A diagrammatic representation of the ladderlike DNA molecule. The "uprights" of the ladder consist of alternating phosphate (P) and deoxyribose sugar (S) groups. The "cross rungs" consist of purine-pyrimidine base pairs which are held together by hydrogen bonds (represented here by dashed lines). Note that the AT pairs are held together less strongly than the GC pairs. In reality the ladder is twisted into a right-handed double helix. Each nucleotide pair is rotated 36° with respect to its neighbor. Thus ten successive nucleotide pairs complete one full turn of the helix. Only five nucleotide pairs are shown. A DNA molecule of molecular weight 25,000,000 would be made up of approximately 40,000 nucleotide pairs. A, T, G, and C equal adenine, thymine, guanine, and cytosine, respectively.

The localization of DNA and RNA in cells can be determined by certain staining procedures. The Feulgen test which utilizes Schiff's reagent as a stain is specific for DNA when properly performed. Azure B (at pH4) stains the two nucleic acids different colors. Cytochemical studies using staining procedures of the type just mentioned have demonstrated that DNA is restricted to the chromosomes. Chromosomes also contain a relatively small amount of RNA. RNA is found in high concentration in the nucleolus and in the cytoplasmic ribosomes.

Deoxyribose nucleic acid has been described in considerable detail, but it merits all the attention one can bestow, since a great body of evidence indicates that the genetic material of most organisms is made of DNA. Considerably less is known of the role played by RNA, but the hypothesis which is most favored currently is that RNA molecules serve as a series of templates which carry copies of sections of the "master plan" which is stamped into the nuclear DNA. The RNA templates move into the cytoplasm where they are involved in the control of the synthesis of enzymes and other vital proteins. The actual sequence of purine and pyrimidine bases in DNA and RNA may represent part of the code out of which the "blueprints" are constructed. More precise speculations as to the operation of this code are given on page 224.

Chromosome morphology

The chromonema or chromosome thread undergoes a characteristic coiling cycle which may be the result of cyclical changes in the chemical links between DNA and its basic protein partner. The coiling behavior of chromosomes may be experimentally modified by treatment with metabolic poisons like KCN. When at a relatively extended state the chromonema has a series of microscopically visible beadlike swellings along its length called chromomeres (see Fig. 2–3). Chromomeres may represent regions where the elementary chromosome fibrils form compact gyres instead of running along in an easy spiral path roughly parallel to the axis of the chromonema. Chromosomes are generally terminated by unipolar segments sometimes called telomeres, and chromosomes normally contain a specialized segment the centromere,[1] which during mitosis is associated with the traction fiber.[2] Certain chromosomes contain an additional specialized segment, the nucleolus organizer which is associated with the spherical nucleolus (see Fig. 2–3). Nucleoli are repositories of RNA-histone, enzymes, and simpler

---

[1] The term kinetochore is synonomous with centromere.
[2] The function of the traction fiber is described on page 32.

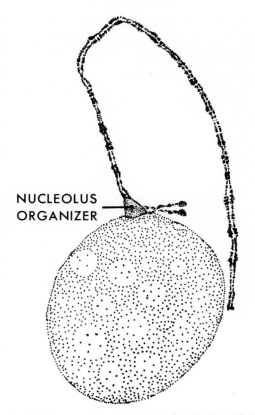

NUCLEOLUS
ORGANIZER

Figure 2-3 Chromosome 6 in meiotic prophase in maize showing its nucleolus organizer in contact with a large, spherical nucleolus. Note the intertwined chromonemata and the numerous chromomeres along their length. (Redrawn by permission from *Fundamentals of Cytology* by L. W. Sharp, copyright 1943, McGraw-Hill Book Co., Inc.)

compounds. That the nucleolus organizer actually synthesizes the nucleolar RNA has been demonstrated by autoradiographic studies utilizing radioactive precursors of RNA.

Giant chromosomes

Certain giant chromosomes serve as the major source of information as to the micromorphology of chromosomes. The longest are so-called lampbrush chromosomes which are found in the primary oocytes of vertebrates and often reach lengths of over 800 μ. A series of loops arise from the main chromosomal axis (see Figs. 2-4A and 2-4B) and are responsible for the fuzzy appearance of the chromosome. Careful microscopic examination shows that many of the chromomeres have paired lateral loops extending

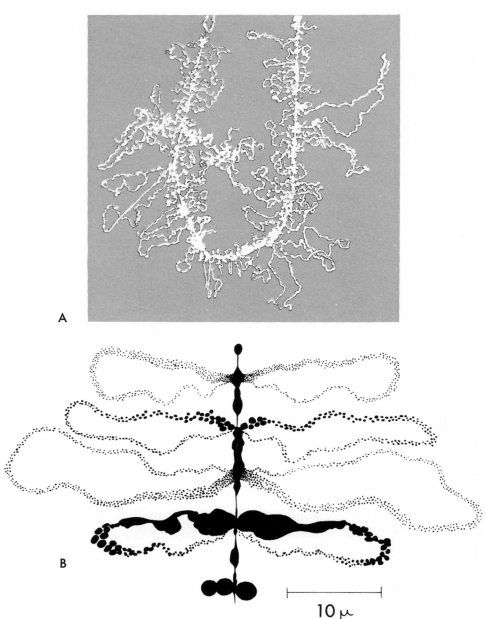

Figure 2-4   (A) A drawing of a living lampbrush chromosome from the primary oocyte of a newt. Note the main chromosomal axis from which arise many meandering filaments. (B) Careful observation at higher magnifications reveals that the meandering filaments are paired lateral loops arising from the chromomeres. Each loop consists of a ribonucleoprotein matrix surrounding a submicroscopic axis which contains DNA. The loops are asymmetric in the sense that the matrix is more abundant at one end (the thick insertion) than at the other (the thin insertion). Gall and Callan have postulated that the loop axis is being spun out of the chromomere at the thin insertion and is winding up again into the chromomere at the thick insertion.   (After J. G. Gall.)

from them (see Fig. 2–4B). As the egg grows these loops increase in circumference. Later as the chromosomes contract the loops disappear. The loops are composed of a central filament of submicroscopic dimensions upon which are encrusted granules rich in RNA. The chromomeres contain DNA. Gall and Callan have proposed that the chromomeres continuously synthesize materials and that these products are organized into paired loops consisting of locus-specific RNA protein granules. These granules continually break away from the loops and enter the nucleoplasm. The granules later enter the cytoplasm when the nuclear membrane breaks down, and here they may control the synthesis of various types of proteins.

The polytene (many stranded) chromosomes found in specific tissues of certain fly maggots are the other favorite giant chromosomes for cytological study. Polytene chromosomes arise as the result of continued chromosomal multiplication without concurrent nuclear division. This process results in the production of 2^x chromosomes, where x gives the number of multiplication cycles. In the case of the salivary-gland cell nuclei of fully grown larvae of *Drosophila melanogaster,* as many as ten consecutive multiplication cycles have occurred to produce a total of 1024 chromosomes. These remain associated parallel to each other and so produce a giant chromosome which is a many-stranded cable. Figure 2–5 shows the paired fourth chromosomes

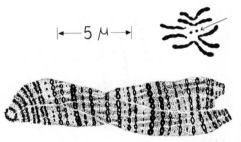

Figure 2–5 Drawings of chromosome 4 from a larval salivary-gland cell nucleus of *Drosophila melanogaster* and, on the same scale, of the entire group of oogonial chromosomes at metaphase. In the oogonial group the fourth chromosomes are represented by the small black dots, in which no structural details can be seen under the highest magnification of the light microscope. In contrast the paired polytene chromosomes show a wealth of detail.   (After C. B. Bridges, reprinted by special permission of the *Journal of Heredity.*)

of *Drosophila melanogaster* as seen in a salivary-gland cell nucleus and in an oogonial metaphase. The magnification is the same in both. Note in the case of the salivary chromosomes the characteristic pattern of transverse bands which are thought to represent aligned chromomeres from the constituent parallel strands. In certain insects a comparison can be made between the banding patterns of chromosomes isolated from different tissues. When this is done (see Fig. 2–6) the patterns are found to be remarkably similar, although the degree of polyteny and consequently the

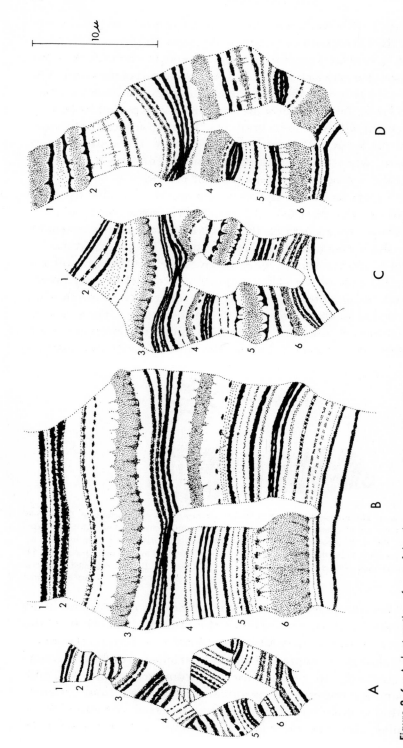

Figure 2-6 A short section of one of the chromosomes of the midge, *Chironomus*, (A) from a cell of the intestine, (B) salivary gland, (C) excretory tubule, and (D) rectum. Note the similarities in banding pattern and the dissimilarities in chromosomal thickness. (After Beermann.)

A   B   C   D

10 μ

thickness of the chromosomes may differ. Certain regions of certain chromo-somes in the cells of specific tissues undergo reversible changes in circum-ference during larval development such as those shown in Figure 2–7. In other tissues this same chromosomal segment will be quiescent. These puffs presumably represent areas of intense chromosomal synthesis of compounds required during specific developmental stages. Autoradiographic and cytophotometric studies have shown that puff formation is generally accom-panied by RNA synthesis and more rarely by DNA synthesis at the site of the puff.

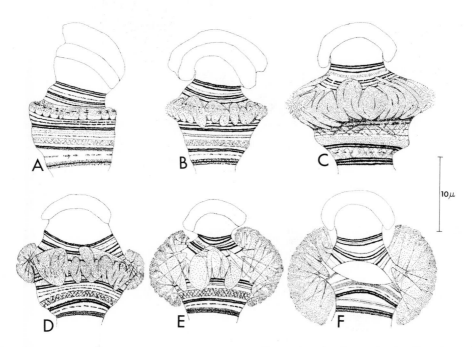

Figure 2–7   The development of a chromosomal puff in a larval salivary-gland cell nucleus of *Chironomus tentans*. This reversible phenomenon occurs at a specific developmental stage. The puff is rich in RNA.   (Redrawn from Beermann, 1952.)

Two types of chromatin are plainly visible in the salivary gland chromo-somes shown in Figure 2–8. The banded regions of the chromosomes are said to contain euchromatin, while the condensed, vesiculate, darkly stained regions contain heterochromatin. Heterochromatin is generally found in the vicinity of the centromere and the nucleolus organizer, although it occurs interstitially. Heterochromatic regions of different chromosomes tend to adhere together. This results in the production of a

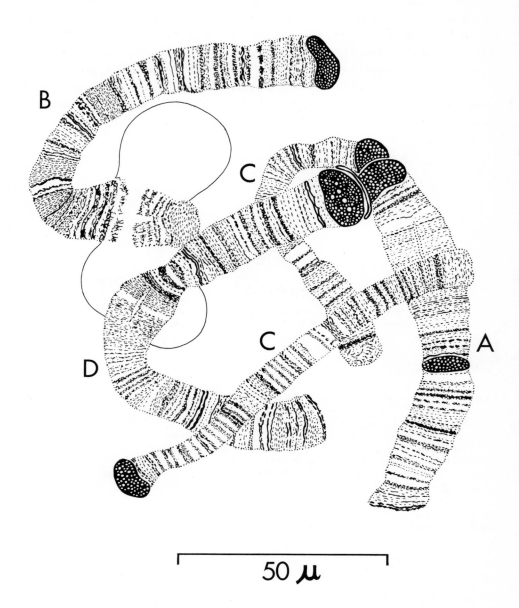

$$50 \mu$$

Figure 2–8 Chromosomes from a squashed salivary gland cell of 'Cecidomyia' serotinae showing the tendency of vesiculate, darkly stained, heterochromatic chromosomal elements to adhere. Note that the homologous C chromosomes are not synapsed and that the B chromosome forms a nucleolus.

(From *Animal Cytology and Evolution* by M. J. D. White, 1954, Cambridge University Press.)

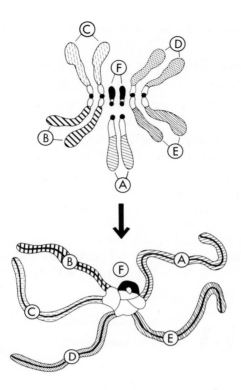

Figure 2–9 A schematic representation of the chromosomes of *Drosophila melanogaster* as seen at metaphase of mitosis (above) and in the nuclei of salivary gland cells of mature larvae (below). The chromosome limbs are shown with differing degrees of shading. (A) X-chromosomes; (B, C) left and right arms of the second chromosomes; (D, E) left and right arms of the third chromosomes; and (F) the fourth chromosome. The heterochromatic parts of the chromosomes are shown in white. In the salivary gland nucleus the heterochromatin adheres to form the chromocenter. The centromeres of the metaphase chromosomes, which are invisible in the salivary gland chromosomes, are shown in black.

(By permission from *Principles of Genetics* by Sinnott, Dunn, and Dobzhansky, copyright 1958, McGraw-Hill Book Co., Inc.)

heterochromatic body, the chromocenter, from which project the euchromatic chromosome arms (see Fig. 2–9). Occasionally a chromosome may be composed primarily of heterochromatin. Such chromosomes are called heterochromosomes and appear to be relatively inert from a genetic standpoint. The Y-chromosome of many species is a heterochromosome. The function of heterochromatin and the precise manner in which it differs chemically and physically from euchromatin are still matters of speculation.

2–1.   Give a description of the structure and function of the various cytoplasmic organelles.

2–2.   What major classes of biochemicals are found in tissue?

2–3.   How does RNA differ from DNA? What role does each play in the cell?

2–4.   What information have we gained from the cytological study of giant chromosomes?

2–5.   Biochemists sometimes speak of the RNA they make enzymatically *in vitro* as "nonsense RNA." What do you suppose they mean by this?

2–6.   If two parallel threads are coiled together, two types of spiral arrangements can be produced. In the paranemic situation the two threads coil in opposite directions, and the two threads can be easily separated laterally without uncoiling. In the plectonemic situation the two threads coil in the same direction, and the two threads cannot be separated unless uncoiled. If the two DNA strands in the Watson-Crick helix are coiled in the plectonemic fashion, what complexities does this situation engender? (See reference to Delbruck and Stent.)

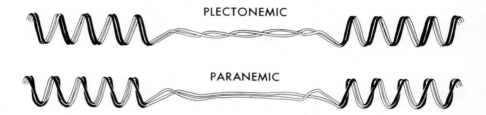

PLECTONEMIC

PARANEMIC

2–7.   The backbone of the DNA molecule is formed by bonds between the phosphate molecule and carbon atoms 3 and 5 of adjacent pentoses. However, the sugar molecules point in opposite directions in the two strands. The link between the base and the sugar is between carbon 1 of the pentose and the number 3 nitrogen of a pyrimidine base or the number 9 nitrogen of a purine. Twin DNA strands are held together by hydrogen bonds between specific pairs of bases. Hydrogen bonds link the oxygen attached to the number 6 carbon of thymine and guanine to a hydrogen attached to the amino group of the number 6 carbon of adenine and cytosine, respectively. Hydrogen bonds link the hydrogen attached to the number 1 nitrogen of guanine and thymine to the number 1 nitrogen of cytosine and adenine, respectively. The oxygen attached to carbon 2 of cytosine is bonded to a hydrogen of the NH_2 group attached to the 2 carbon of guanine. With this information draw a segment of the DNA double molecule containing thymine and guanine in one chain and adenine and cytosine in the adjacent strand.

2–8.   The procedure developed by Feulgen and Rossenbeck in 1924 for the cytochemical detection of DNA involves hydrolysis in 1 N HCl at 60°C for 15
minutes. The hydrolysis splits purine-deoxyribose bonds, removes the purine
bases, and exposes the deoxyribose. This sugar, unlike ribose, exists largely in
a noncyclic form with a terminal aldehyde group. If the colorless Schiff reagent
is now added, it combines with the exposed aldehyde groups to form a colored
complex. The test is useful only because the colored product of the reaction fails
to diffuse away but remains bound to the chromosomes. What is the cause of this
attachment?

2–9.   Kornberg and his colleagues have identified an enzyme system which synthesizes DNA *in vitro*. The system requires the deoxyribonucleoside triphosphates
of adenine, guanine, cytosine, and thymine; magnesium ions; an enzyme of
bacterial origin; and a small amount of single-stranded, polymerized DNA.
Speculate on the function of this "primer" DNA.

2–10. Construct a DNA molecule from the Potter kit (see Bibliography). Where is
the "narrow groove" in which the basic protein is thought to lie? Note the wide
groove. It is speculated that RNA may pair with DNA in this groove.

BIBLIOGRAPHY

Beermann, W.   1952   Chromomerenkonstanz und spezifische Modifikationen der
Chromosomenstruktur in der Entwicklung und Organdifferenzierung von
Chironomus tentans. Chromosoma *5*: 139–98.

Beermann, W.   1961   Ein Balbiani-Ring als Locus einer Speicheldrüsenmutation.
Chromosoma *12*: 1–25.

Brachet, J., and A. E. Mirsky, editors   1961   The Cell, II. Cells and their component parts. Academic Press. New York.

Chargaff, E., and J. N. Davidson, editors   The Nucleic Acids, Vols. 1, 2, 1955; Vol.
3, 1960. Academic Press, New York.

Delbruck, M., and G. S. Stent   1957   On the mechanism of DNA replication. In
The Chemical Basis of Heredity, W. D. McElroy and B. Glass, editors. Johns
Hopkins Press, Baltimore, Md.

Feulgen, R., and H. Rossenbeck   1924   Mikroskopisch-chemischer Nachweis einer
Nucleinsäure von Typus der Thymonucleinsäure und die darauf beruhende
elektive Färbung von Zellkernen in mikroskopischen Präparaten. Z. physiol.
Chem. 135: 203–48 (The original description of the Feulgen procedure.)

Frey-Wyssling, A.   1953   Submicroscopic Morphology of Protoplasm and Its Derivatives, 2nd ed. Elsevier, New York.

Fruton, J. S., and S. Simonds   1958   General Biochemistry, 2nd ed. Wiley, New York.

Gall, J. G.   1956   On the submicroscopic structure of chromosomes. Brookhaven
Symposia in Biology *8*: 17–32.

Hannah, A. 1951 Localization and function of heterochromatin in *Drosophila melanogaster*. Advances Genet. *4*: 87–125.

Kornberg, A. 1960 Biologic synthesis of DNA. Science *131*: 1503–8.

Lowman, F. G. 1956 Electron-microscope studies of *Drosophila* salivary-gland chromosomes. Chromosoma *8*: 30–52.

Miescher, F. 1869 On the chemical composition of pus cells. *In* Great Experiments in Biology, M. L. Gabriel and S. Fogel, editors, 1960. Prentice-Hall, Englewood Cliffs, N. J. (The report of the discovery of nucleic acid.)

Mitchell, J. S., editor 1960 The Cell Nucleus. Academic Press, New York.

Novikoff, A. B. 1956 Electron microscopy: cytology of cell fractions. Science *124*: 969–72.

Ochoa, S., and L. Heppel 1957 Polynucleotide synthesis. *In* The Chemical Basis of Heredity. W. D. McElroy and B. Glass, editors. Johns Hopkins Press, Baltimore, Md.

Palade, G. E., and P. Siekevitz 1956 Liver microsomes. J. Biophys. Biochem. Cytol. *2*: 171–200.

Palay, S. 1958 The morphology of secretion. *In* Frontiers of Cytology, S. Palay, editor. Yale University Press, New Haven, Conn.

Pelling, G. 1959 Chromosomal synthesis of RNA as shown by incorporation of uridine labeled with tritium. Nature *184*: 655–6.

Picken, L. 1960 The Organization of Cells and Other Organisms. Oxford University Press, New York.

Potter, V. R. 1960 Nucleic Acid Outlines, Vol. I. Burgess Publ. Co., Minneapolis, Minn.

Potter, V. R. 1960 DNA model kit. Burgess Publishing Co., 426 S. 6th St., Minneapolis 15, Minn. (Very useful for getting a clear idea of DNA structure in three-dimensional terms.)

Roth, J. S., editor 1959 Enzymes of polynucleotide metabolism. Ann. New York. Acad. Sc. *81*: 511–804.

Schrader, F. 1936 The kinetochore or spindle fiber locus in *Amphiuma tridactylum*. Biol. Bull. *70*: 484–98.

Sharp, L. W. 1943 Fundamentals of Cytology. McGraw-Hill, New York.

Watson, J. D., and F. H. C. Crick 1953 Molecular structure of nucleic acids. Nature *171*: 737–8. (The classic paper on the subject.)

Watson, M. L. 1955 The nuclear envelope. J. Biophys. Biochem. Cytol. *1*: 257–70.

Zubay, G., and P. Doty 1959 The isolation and properties of deoxyribonucleoprotein particles containing single nucleic acid molecules J. Mol. Biol. *1*: 1–20.

Chapter **3**

Chromosome Dynamics

In the preceding chapter two types of rather specialized chromosomes were described. Because of their giant size these chromosomes are favorites of cytologists, and it is assumed that they display many morphological features common to all chromosomes. Unfortunately, little can be seen of the chromosomes in the nuclei of nondividing cells of most species. However, in preparation for cell duplication chromosomes coil compactly upon themselves and become visible. The chromosome complement of most species can then be readily determined, and it has been demonstrated that the chromosomes are generally constant in number for the somatic cells of a given species of organism. Chromosome numbers vary from two to several hundred. A very extensive listing of chromosome numbers is given in Spector's handbook.

Chromosome replication

Nondividing or *interphase* cells are generally found more frequently in tissues than are actively dividing cells (see Fig. 3–1A). The reticulate, interphase nucleus is surrounded by a nuclear envelope, a nucleolus is often present within the nucleus, and a centrosome may be present just outside the nucleus. The centrosome contains a granule called the centriole which is stained by various basic dyes. The cells of higher plants, however, generally lack centrosomes. Chromosome replication occurs in the nuclei of those interphase cells which are preparing to undergo nuclear duplication or mitosis. Evidence for this replication comes from cytophotometric studies which show a doubling in the amounts of the DNA and basic histone contained in the interphase nucleus.

Studies by Taylor of the distribution of newly synthesized tritium-labeled DNA in the chromosomes of various plants have shown that each interphase chromosome is functionally double. When duplication occurs, two new units are synthesized from low molecular weight precursors to form a quadripartite structure. Upon separation each daughter bipartite chromosome is found to possess a new and an old unit. There is evidence that the two units of the bipartite chromosome are not identical but are complementary, perhaps in a manner reminiscent of the complementarity of the two strands in the DNA molecule. It will be recalled that in the DNA double helix the sequence of the purine and pyrimidine bases in one molecule determines the complementary sequence in the adjacent strand. Lima de Faria has performed experiments similar to those of Taylor which demonstrate that DNA synthesis occurs at different times in euchromatin and heterochromatin.

Mitosis (nuclear duplication)

Mitosis is generally divided into four phases: prophase (0.60), metaphase (0.05), anaphase (0.05), and telophase (0.30). The numbers in parentheses give the relative fraction of the total mitotic time generally spent in each stage. Actual mitotic times vary greatly but are generally no shorter than 10 minutes. During mitotic prophase (Fig. 3–1B-D) the centrosome divides and the two daughter centrosomes move apart. The chromosomes become visible within the nucleus because they coil up to produce a series of compact gyres. Each chromosome is longitudinally double except in the region of the centromere, and each half chromosome is called a chromatid. The nucleolus disappears and later so does the nuclear envelope. Recent studies with the electron microscope have shown that the nuclear envelope is converted into endoplasmic reticulum and stored in the cytoplasm at this point. A mitotic apparatus now comes into being (Fig. 3–1E) which consists of three components: the asters which form about each centrosome, the gelatinous spindle, and the traction fibers which connect the centromeres of the various chromosomes to either centrosome. In the cells of higher plants both the centrosome and the astral rays are missing, but the spindle and traction fibers are present. During *prometaphase* the chromosomes move about within the spindle (Fig. 3–1D) and eventually arrange themselves in the equatorial region of the spindle (Fig. 3–1E). At this stage

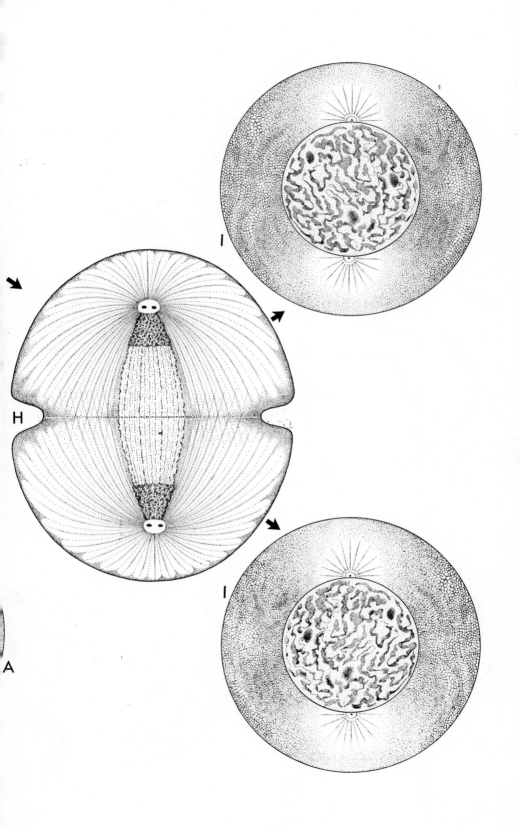

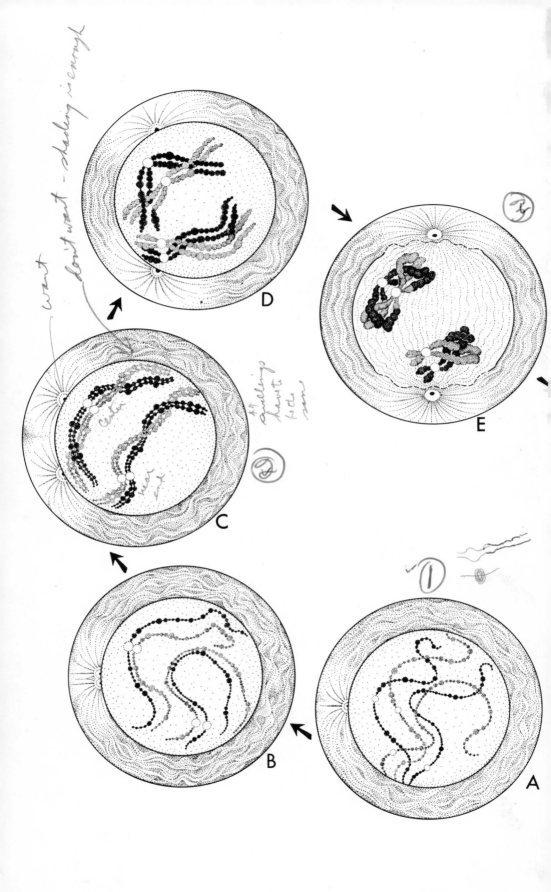

want

don't want - shading is enough

Center

near end

swellings haven't to the zero

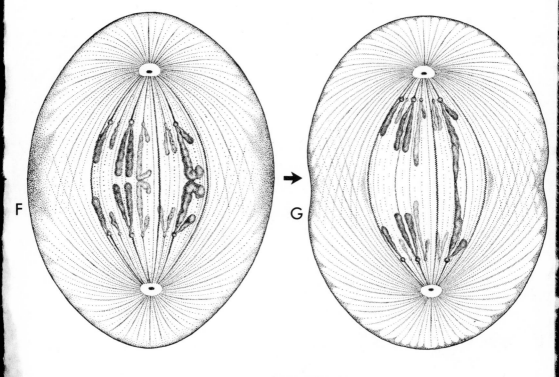

F   →   G

MITOSIS

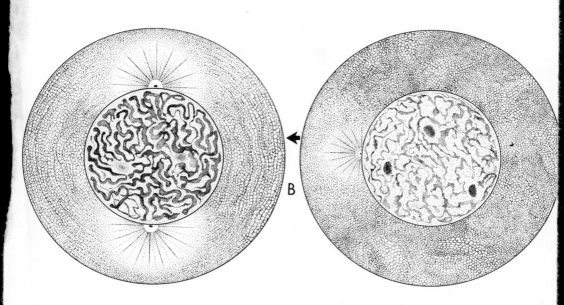

B ←

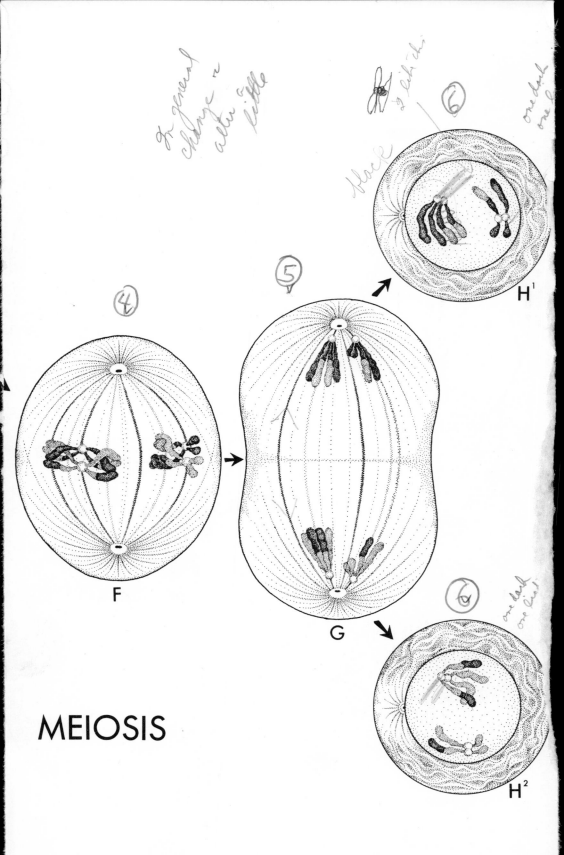

MEIOSIS

a black and a
white in each one

Black

white

7

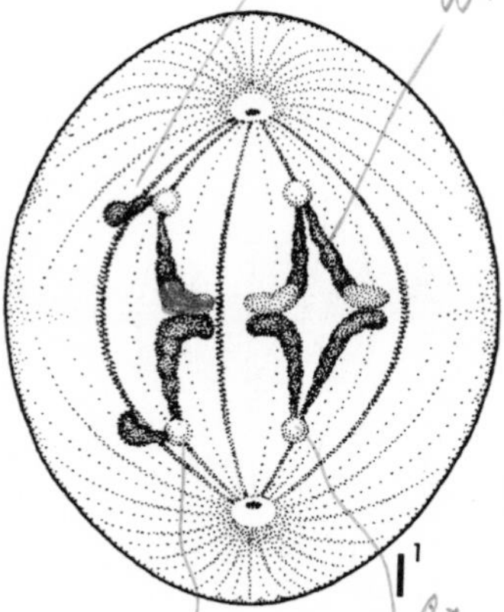

8

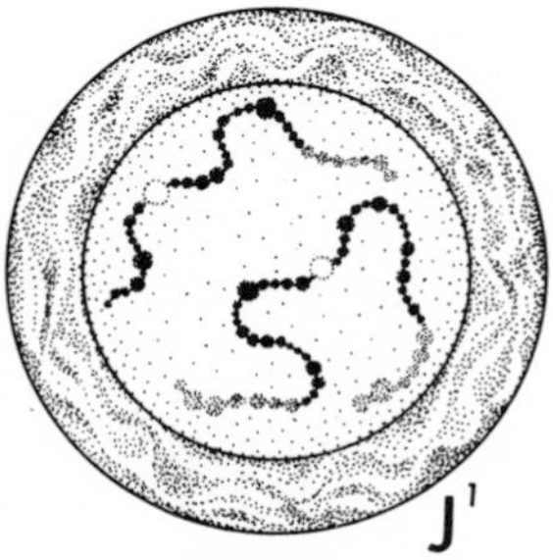

9

black

white

I¹

J¹

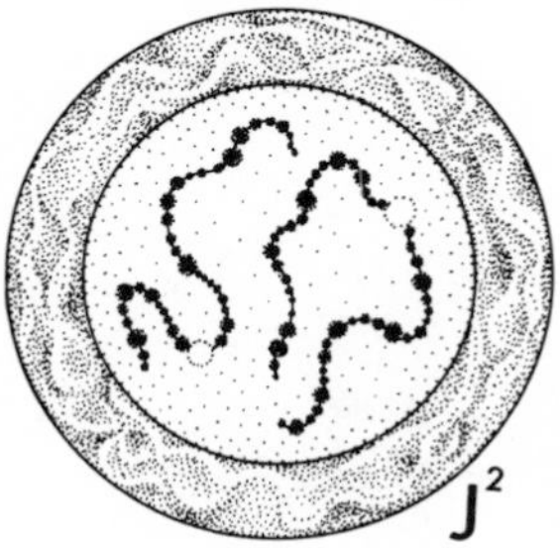

J²

Black

White

separated slightly

7

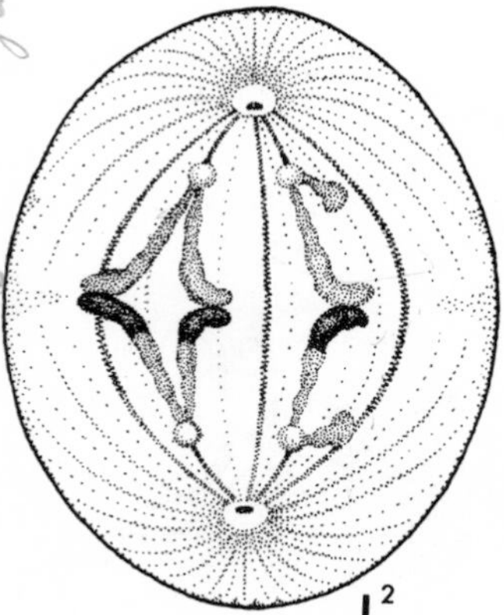

I²

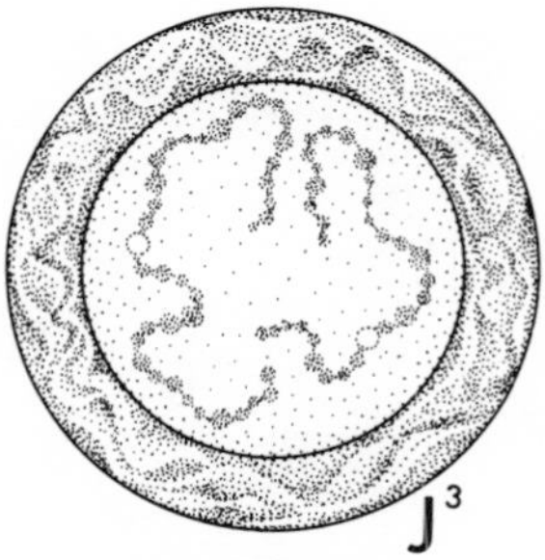

J³

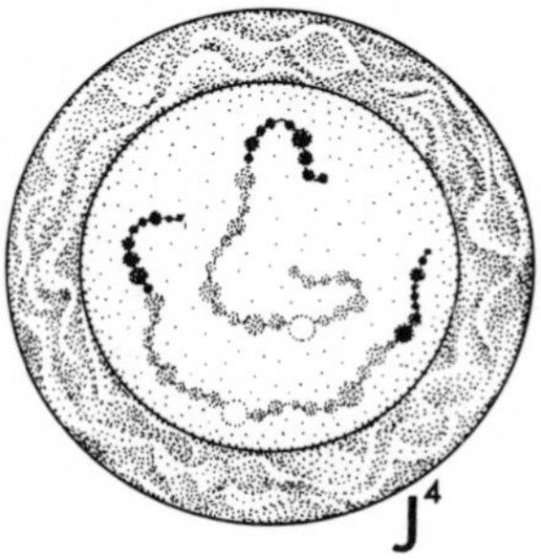

J⁴

make
like

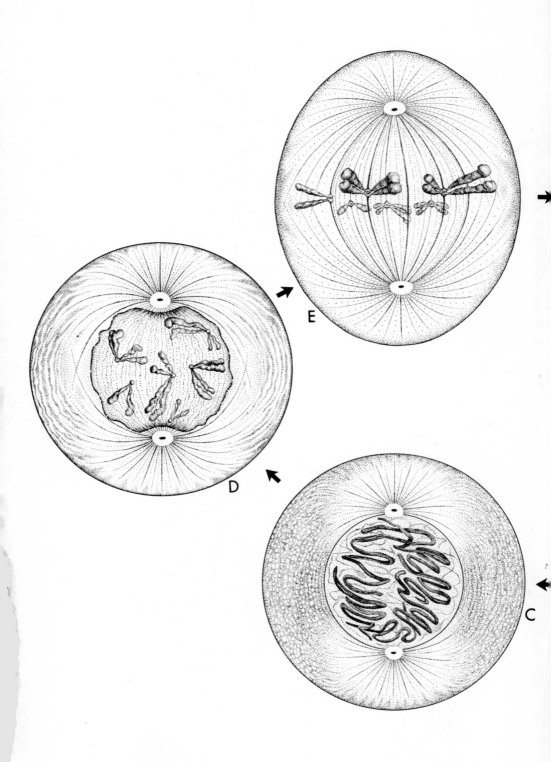

E

D

C

Figure 3–1

(A) Late interphase in a cell about to undergo mitosis. The chromosomes which are uncoiled and maximally extended give the nucleus a reticulate appearance. Three nucleoli are present. A centrosome encompassed by astral rays and containing a median centriole is seen at the surface of the nuclear envelope.

(B) Early prophase. By this time the centrosome has divided and the daughter centrosomes have come to lie at opposite poles. The chromosomes are coiling up into compact gyres and as a result look shorter and thicker. The nucleoli disperse.

(C) Late prophase. By this time the chromosomes are clearly visible, and each is obviously double. The nucleoli are no longer visible.

(D) Prometaphase. The chromosomes have reached their maximal thickness and minimal length. Each of the six chromosomes is longitudinally double except in the region of the centromere. Each half chromosome is called a chromatid. The chromosomes move about and gradually come to lie in the equatorial plane. The nuclear envelope begins to break down, and a mitotic apparatus begins to take shape.

(E) Metaphase. The nuclear envelope has disappeared. The chromosomes are arranged equatorially. A mitotic apparatus is present which consists of the centrosomes and their encompassing astral rays, a gelatinous spindle made up of fibers which extend between the centrosomes, and traction fibers which extend from each centrosome to the chromosomal centromere. Each centromere has divided, and thus a chromosome comprised of two chromatids has been converted into two daughter chromosomes. These adhere for a brief period.

(F) Early anaphase. The chromosome pairs start to be pulled apart by the traction fibers. The longer daughter chromosomes still adhere at their distal segments. Each chromosome complement is seen to consist of two metacentric, two telocentric, and two submetacentric chromosomes.

(G) Late anaphase. The chromosomes are now nearing the poles, and the cell is beginning to pinch in two.

(H) Telophase. The cleavage furrow is more pronounced. The spindle is degenerating. The chromosomes have coalesced, and new nuclear envelopes are forming about them. The centrioles have divided as the centrosome prepares for the next mitosis.

(I) Daughter cells resulting from cytokinesis which contain approximately equal amounts of cytoplasm and identical chromosomal complements. That these daughter cells are themselves about to undergo mitosis is evident from the fact that the daughter centrosomes have completed their poleward migrations.

Figure 3-3

(A) A primary spermatocyte in leptonema. The organism has two pairs of chromosomes (one metacentric and one submetacentric). The maternal and paternal homologous chromosomes are drawn in differing shades. The centromeres are represented by open circles. Note that the chromosomes are oriented with one of their ends in contact with one region of the nuclear membrane, forming a *bouquet* configuration. The chromosomes are uncoiled and maximally extended. In this state the chromomeres and chromonemata can be seen readily. A centrosome encompassed by astral rays is present.

(B) During zygonema synapsis of homologous chromosomes takes place. This pairing begins at one or more points and extends "zipperlike" until complete. Subsequently the cell contains two bivalents. The centrosome has divided into two daughter centrosomes.

(C) During pachynema each paired chromosome splits into two sister chromatids except at the region of the centromere. As a result the bivalents are converted into tetrads. The centrosomes move apart.

(D) During diplonema in each tetrad one pair of sister chromatids begins to separate from the other pair. However, at certain regions the chromatids are prevented from separating by places where interchanges have taken place. The points where the chromatids form cross-shaped configurations are called chiasmata.

(E) Diakinesis. The chromatids are now shorter and thicker, and terminalization is occurring. The centrosomes have reached the poles, and the nuclear envelope is beginning to disappear.

(F) Metaphase I. The tetrads are arranged at the equator of the spindle.

(G) Late anaphase I. The chromosomes have separated and have moved to each pole. However, the centromeres have not divided. As a consequence maternal and paternal chromosomal material has been separated (except in regions distal to points of crossing over).

(H^1, H^2) Secondary spermatocytes containing dyads.

(I^1, I^2) Early anaphase II. Centromeres divide and allow separation of sister chromatids.

(J^1, J^2, J^3, J^4) The four spermatids containing monads. Chromosomes once again uncoil and elongate. (J^1) and (J^4) each contains one single and one double crossover chromatid.

(*metaphase*) the two chromatids are ready to be separated and to move under the action of the traction fibers to the poles of the spindle. During *anaphase* the centromere becomes functionally double, and the chromatids are converted to independent chromosomes which separate and move to opposite poles (Figs 3–1F and 3–1G). Treatment of dividing cells with the alkaloid colchicine poisons the spindle and prevents anaphase movements of chromosomes. During *telophase* the spindle disappears and reconstitution of the two daughter nuclei from the anaphase chromosomes begins (Fig. 3–1H). As nuclear envelopes form around each of the two groups of daughter chromosomes they return to their extended state, and nucleoli reappear. The new nuclear membranes in the daughter cells are formed by fusion of elements of the endoplasmic reticulum. Next cytokinesis occurs and the cytoplasm is divided into two parts by a cleavage furrow in the case of animal cells (Fig. 3–1H) or by a cell plate in the case of plant cells. The result of mitosis and cytokinesis is the production of two daughter cells with precisely the same nuclear content and approximately equal amounts of cytoplasm.

The appearance of a given chromosome at anaphase depends upon the location of its centromere. Chromosomes which appear as rods are said to be *telocentric,* that is, the centromere is very close to one end of the chromosome. V-shaped chromosomes are *metacentric.* Since in this case the centromere is at the middle of the chromosome, the chromosomal arms are of equal length. A *submetacentric* chromosome has arms of unequal length since the centromere is nearer one end than the other. *Acentric* and *dicentric* chromosomes have no centromere and two centromeres, respectively. As we shall see later (p. 141), such chromosomes are rapidly eliminated from dividing cells.

Chromosomal duplication is followed generally by nuclear division and this by cytoplasmic division or *cytokinesis.* However, rare cases occur in which chromosomal replication is not followed by nuclear division, and in which nuclear division is not followed by cytokinesis.

Recently techniques have been developed by Mazia and Dan for isolating the mitotic apparatus from large quantities of sea urchin eggs. Chemical studies of the mitotic apparatus are currently under way and have shown that protein makes up 95 per cent of the dry weight of the structure, and that chemical bonds linking sulfur atoms together are responsible for the characteristic orientation of the protein fibers within the apparatus.

Another important advance has been the discovery of a series of chemicals related to purine which initiates mitosis and cytokinesis. The best known of these is called *kinetin,* and its action has been described by Das, Patau, and Skoog.

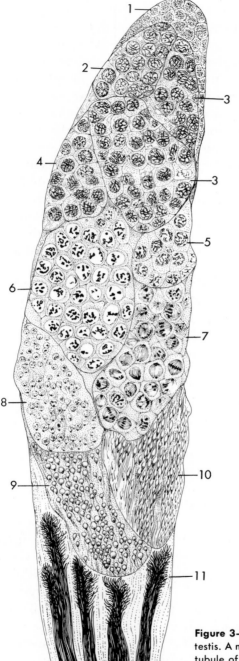

Figure 3–2 Spermatogenesis in a grasshopper testis. A median longitudinal section through one tubule of the testis is shown. The spermatocytes contained in various cysts are in the same developmental stage. 1, spermatogonia; 2, spermatocytes in leptonema; 3, zygonema; 4, pachynema;

Meiosis

In most sexually reproducing organisms the doubling of the gametic (haploid) chromosome number which accompanies syngamy is compensated for by a halving of the resulting zygotic (diploid) chromosome number at some other point during the life cycle. These changes are brought about by a single chromosomal duplication followed by two successive nuclear divisions. The entire process is called meiosis or the reduction divisions, and it normally occurs during animal gametogenesis or sporogenesis in plants.

Figure 3–2 illustrates the histological situation in the testis of a grasshopper. The testis is composed of a series of tubules, one of which is shown in the drawing. The apical region of the tubule contains mitotically active spermatogonia. Proximal to the spermatogonia are found cysts containing 128 primary spermatocytes which arose from a single spermatogonium that underwent seven consecutive divisions. All cells in a given cyst are in the same stage in meiotic prophase, and cells in more proximal cysts are at more advanced stages.

Meiotic prophase is generally divided into five consecutive stages: *leptonema, zygonema, pachynema, diplonema,* and *diakinesis* (Fig. 3–3).

The Leptotene stage

During this stage the chromosomes are maximally extended and the chromomeres are often clearly visible. The chromosomes are often all oriented with one of their ends in contact with one region of the nuclear membrane, forming the so-called bouquet configuration.

The Zygotene stage

The chromosomes in somatic cell nuclei are generally present as pairs, one member of which was contributed by the male and one by the female parent. Such homologous chromosomes generally do not pair in somatic tissue. During the zygotene stage of meiotic prophase, however, pairing or *synapsis* of homologous chromosomes does take place. This pairing often begins at one or more points and extends "zipperlike" until complete. The nature of the pairing force is an enigma. When synapsis is finished the apparent number of threads is one-half what it was before, and the visible bodies in the nucleus are now *bivalents* rather than single chromosomes.

5, diplonema; 6, diakinesis; 7, metaphase I; 8, early spermatids; 9, spermatids developing tails; 10, spermatids with elongating heads; and 11, bundles of mature spermatozoa. A 100 micron line is drawn at the base of the tubule to indicate the magnification.

The Pachytene stage

During this stage each paired chromosome splits into two sister chromatids (except at the region of the centromere). The doubling of the amount of DNA actually occurred much earlier. As a result of the longitudinal division of each homologous chromosome into two chromatids there exist in the nucleus groups of *tetrads* (groups of four chromatids lying parallel to each other). During pachynema, exchanges may occur between homologous but not sister chromatids. This process is called *crossing over* and results in the production of crossover chromatids which contain genetic material of both maternal and paternal origin.

The Diplotene stage

In each of the tetrads one pair of sister chromatids begins to separate from the other pair, as though the synaptic force holding the homologues together were replaced by a repulsive force. At one or more points the chromatids are prevented from separating by places where interchanges have taken place (*chiasmata*). The longer the chromosome the more chiasmata are observed. The chiasmata slip along toward the ends, so the position of a chiasma no longer coincides with that of the original crossover. As this *terminalization* proceeds all the chiasmata are forced toward the ends of the chromosomes.

Diakinesis

The chromosomes begin to coil up and so become shorter and thicker. The result is a group of compact tetrads lying well spaced out in the nucleus, often near its membrane. Terminalization is completed, and the nucleolus disappears.

Division I

The nuclear envelope disappears, and the tetrads are arranged at the equator of the spindle. The separation of chromosomes is a *reductional* one; that is, the separation is of maternal from paternal chromosomal material with the exceptions of regions distal to where crossing over has occurred. Division I produces two *secondary spermatocytes* which contain *dyads* surrounded by a nuclear envelope.

Division II

After a short interphase during which the chromosomes do not uncoil the nuclear membrane disappears, and the dyads arrange themselves upon the metaphase plate. The second division is *equational* (again with the exception of chromosomal regions distal to points of crossing over); the centromere divides and thus allows the separation of sister chromatids. Division II produces four *spermatids* which contain *monads* surrounded by a nuclear membrane. Meiosis therefore provides a mechanism whereby (1) an exchange of material may take place between homologous chromosomes and (2) each gamete receives but one member of each chromosome pair.

Spermiogenesis

Figure 3–4 shows representative stages during the formation of mature sperm from spermatids. The apical acrosome which is secreted by the Golgi material contains enzymes which function to digest the various substances which coat unfertilized eggs. In many cases a considerable amount of cytoplasm is extruded from the spermatid during its transformation into a slender sperm. The genetic material is converted into a solid crystalline structure which shows no trace of the constituent chromosomes. A transformation of histone to protamine often occurs in the nucleoproteins during an advanced stage of spermiogenesis.

Early in spermiogenesis the centrosomal apparatus separates into a centriole which stays attached to the nuclear envelope and a ring centriole which moves peripherally and becomes oriented to permit passage of the flagellar filaments. The filamentous flagellum is formed as an extension of the proximal centriole. Electron microscopic studies of sperm tails of many different animals show that they generally contain a bundle of ten pairs of fibrils of which one pair is central and nine are peripheral. Cilia from a ciliated epithelium have a similar fibrillar structure and also arise from centriolelike bodies. Centrioles are themselves short cylinders containing nine pairs of peripheral filaments disposed about a central cavity. The sperm of some organisms contain an additional quiescent centriole which functions subsequent to fertilization. Surrounding the proximal region of the tail filament is a two-stranded helical structure, the *nebenkern* which arises from clumped mitochondria plus some elements of endoplasmic reticulum. The nebenkern may function to supply the ATP required for sperm motility.

Observations by Tahmisian and Devine upon abnormal spermatogenesis in irradiated grasshoppers suggest that the attachment of the centriole to the nuclear envelope is required for synthesis of the flagellum. Furthermore

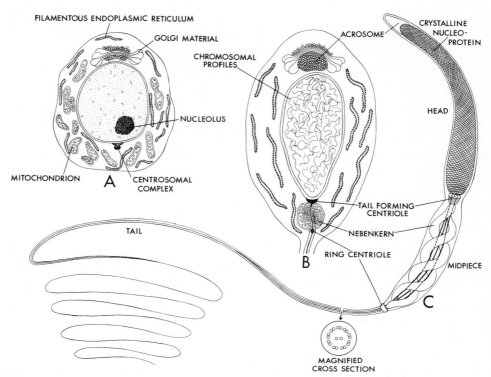

FILAMENTOUS ENDOPLASMIC RETICULUM
GOLGI MATERIAL
CHROMOSOMAL PROFILES
ACROSOME
CRYSTALLINE NUCLEO-PROTEIN
HEAD
NUCLEOLUS
MITOCHONDRION
A
CENTROSOMAL COMPLEX
TAIL FORMING CENTRIOLE
NEBENKERN
B
RING CENTRIOLE
TAIL
MIDPIECE
C
MAGNIFIED CROSS SECTION

Figure 3–4   Representative stages during the conversion of a spermatid into a mature sperm.

the form of the nucleus appears to be determined in part by the acrosome. Normally one acrosome is present and there is an axial symmetry from acrosome to centriole. Multiple acrosomes are sometimes seen in irradiated sperm, however. Under such circumstances the nucleus elongates under each acrosome, and the result is a multilobed sperm head. Multiple centrioles are also observed in irradiated sperm. If they contact the nucleus, these form filament bundles all of which are incorporated into one posterior tail, provided an apical acrosome is present. The situation is different, however, in sperm lacking an acrosome but containing multiple centrioles. Under these circumstances polarity is absent and tails develop at random or at diametrically opposed regions.

Oogenesis

In the male four products of meiosis generally form mature, functional sperm, whereas in the female generally only one of the four products is functional. The meiotic divisions give rise to four haploid nuclei, but cytokinesis does not occur, and later three of the nuclei, the polar nuclei, degenerate. During its development the oocyte is often associated with accessory cells which play an important part in the formation of yolk (*vitellogenesis*). In some cases it is the follicle cells that envelop the egg which perform this service, whereas in other cases special nurse cells which are daughters of the oocyte synthesize nutritive materials and pour them into the oocyte. The egg which results is generally the largest cell of the body, and the eggs of some organisms reach phenomenal sizes. An ostrich egg, for example, may have a volume of 500 cc.

Fertilization

Fertilization begins with the collision between sperm and egg (Fig. 3–5) and ends with production of the diploid fusion nucleus. The sperm activates the egg and so starts a chain of reactions which ends in cytokinesis, and it also contributes a haploid set of paternal chromosomes and a centriolar apparatus (since in most eggs the asters and centrosomes degenerate after the second reduction division). Various organisms differ in the relative

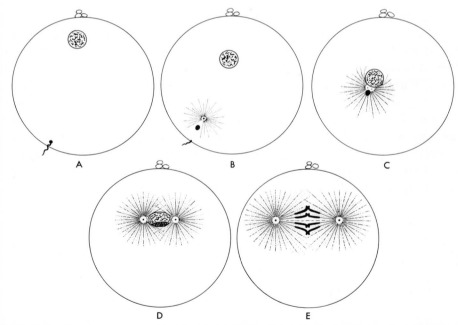

Figure 3–5   Some events accompanying and following fertilization. (A) The sperm penetrates the oocyte. Note extruded polar nuclei. (B) A centrosome originating from the sperm organizes an aster. The sperm head and the female nucleus approach each other. (C) The centrosome begins to divide. The haploid male and female pronuclei are almost in contact. (D) The nuclei fuse and the two centrosomes organize a mitotic apparatus. (E) The duplicated maternal and paternal chromosomes arrange themselves on the metaphase plate and then are pulled apart. Cytokinesis follows.   (Redrawn from Wilson's *The Cell in Development and Heredity*, Macmillan.)

maturity of the egg at the time of fertilization. In certain annelids, fertilization may begin before the egg has commenced its first reduction division, whereas in sea urchins fertilization occurs subsequent to metaphase II and the elimination of the polar bodies. There is no indication that either the tail or the midpiece of the sperm plays any roll in fertilization once the egg and sperm have made contact. The sperm nucleus or male pronucleus moves toward the center of the egg, leaving its tail behind. A centrosome containing a single centriole organizes an aster. The centriole divides, the centrosome splits in two, and the daughter centrosomes move apart, as the male and female nuclei approach each other and fuse. This fusion or syngamy restores the diploid chromosomal complement. The nuclear envelope next disappears and embryogenesis commences with the first mitosis.

Parthenogenesis

Fertilization is not a universal phenomenon among higher organisms, since there are many animals which can reproduce parthenogenetically, that is, the females can produce unfertilized eggs which will undergo embryogenesis and yield eventual adults. Various hymenoptera (the honey bee is a good example) exhibit *arrhenotokous parthenogenesis,* the phenomenon where unfertilized eggs produce haploid males and fertilized eggs produce diploid females. Under such conditions meiosis occurs normally during oogenesis, but males possess an anomalous meiotic mechanism. Pairing of chromosomes does not occur, and following chromosomal duplication a single mitotic division produces two haploid spermatids. In most lower hymenoptera two sperm are formed from each spermatocyte in the manner just described. In bees, however, one spermatid degenerates and as a result only one functional spermatozoan is formed from any spermatocyte.

3–1. What is mitosis and what does it accomplish?

3–2. What is meiosis and what does it accomplish?

3–3. Describe how a spermatid is transformed into a sperm.

3–4. What would be the consequences if a sexually reproducing organism failed to undergo meiosis and produced diploid gametes as a result?

3–5. Can you conceive of a reason why in the egg three of the four products of meiosis are nonfunctional?

3–6. Some related species of plants have chromosome numbers which form a series (14, 28, 42, etc.). What does this suggest about the evolutionary history of different species?

3–7. In many organisms more than one sperm enters the egg, but only one unites with the female pronucleus and the rest degenerate. Fankhauser has shown in amphibia that an accessory sperm nucleus will divide if the portion of the egg containing it is separated by a constriction from the portion containing the zygote nucleus. What does this suggest as to the mechanism which causes the degeneration of accessory sperm?

3–8. If at telophase a chromosome fragment is not incorporated into the regenerating nucleus, it may form a tiny micronucleus. What information does this give us about the origin of the nuclear envelope?

3–9. During meiosis heterochromatic chromosome regions are often compact and densely stained while the more extensive euchromatic regions are diffuse and take up little stain. The heterochromatin is said to show positive heteropyknosis. What does this imply about the coiling cycles of euchromatin and heterochromatin?

3–10. It is known that chromosomes exposed to X-rays often fragment. It has been suggested that a tiny chromosome fragment which subtends a centromere may function as a centriole. When irradiated cells undergo cytokinesis one often observes multipolar mitoses. Can you suggest how these might arise?

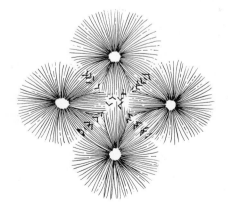

3–11. Steffensen has shown that if certain plants are grown upon magnesium-deficient nutrient solutions one observes an increased chromosome fragmentation in germ cells but not in somatic cells. What does this finding indicate?

3–12. The position of the centromere determines what shape the chromosome will display at anaphase. Thus chromosomes with terminal or nearly terminal centromeres look like rods, while those with a centromere in the middle look V-shaped. Some plants and animals, however, have a diffuse centromere which extends the length of the chromosome. What type of anaphase behavior would you expect chromosomes with such diffuse centromeres to display?

3–13. What do the following terms signify? Resolving power, micron, microtome, fixative, cytophotometry, autoradiography, phase-contrast microscope, lipid, plastid, Golgi material, histone, template, chromonema, telomere, nucleolus, heterochromatin, kinetin, terminalization, bivalent, dyad, reductional division, vitellogenesis, syngamy, parthenogenesis, chromatid, polar body.

3–14. Various rotifers, insects, crustacea, and nematodes exhibit a rare type of parthenogenesis called *thelytoky*. Here unfertilized eggs yield females, and males may be absent entirely. Discuss the advantages and disadvantages of such a system.

3–15. In certain organisms a cyclical variety of thelytokous parthenogenesis has become established. Some aphid species, for example, reproduce parthenogenically for several generations during the summer, but revert to sexuality in the fall. Speculate as to the cytological details of such cyclical reproductive behavior. Consult White's book for details.

BIBLIOGRAPHY

Anderson, N. G.   1956   Cell division. Quart. Rev. Biol. *31*: 169–99; 243–69.

Barrer, R., S. Joseph, and G. A. Meek   1960   The origin and fate of the nuclear membrane in meiosis. Proc. Roy. Soc. *152B*: 353–66.

Bloch, D. P., and H. Y. C. Hew   1960   Schedule of spermatogenesis in the pulmonate snail *Helix aspersa,* with special reference to histone transition. J. Biophys. Biochem. Cytol. *7*: 515–32.

Bloch, D. P., and H. Y. C. Hew   1960   Changes in nuclear histones during fertilization and early embryonic development in the pulmonate snail, *Helix aspersa.* J. Biophys. Biochem. Cytol. *8*: 69–81.

Brachet, J., and A. E. Mirsky, editors   1961   The Cell, III. Chromosomes, mitosis and meiosis. Academic Press, New York.

Colwin, L. H. and A. L. Colwin   1961   Changes in the spermatozoan during fertilization in *Hydroides hexagonus* (Annelida). I. Passage of the acrosomal region through the vitelline membrane. J. Biophys. Biochem. Cytol. *10*: 231–54.

Das, N. K., K. Patau, and F. Skoog   1956   Initiation of mitosis and cell division by kinetin and indoleacetic acid and in excised tobacco pith tissue. Physiologia Plantarum *9*: 640–51.

Fankhauser, G. 1925 Analyse der physiologischen Polyspermie des Triton-Eies auf Grund von Schnürungs-Experimenten. W. Roux' Archiv Entwickungsmechanik *105*: 510–80.

Gall, J. G. 1961 Centriole replication. A study of spermatogenesis in the snail *Viviparus*. J. Biophys. Biochem. Cytol. *10*: 163–93.

Gatenby, J. B., and T. N. Tahmisian 1959 Centriole adjunct, centrioles, mitochondria, and ergastoplasm in Orthopteran spermatogenesis. (An electron microscope study.) La Cellule *60*: 105–35.

Gross, P. R., editor 1960 Second conference on the mechanisms of cell division. Ann. New York Acad. Sc. *90*: 345–613.

Lima de Faria, A. 1959 Differential uptake of tritiated thymidine into hetero- and euchromatin in *Melanoplus* and *Secale*. J. Biophys. Biochem. Cytol. *6*: 457–66.

Mazia, D. 1961 Biochemistry of the dividing cell. Annual Review Biochem. *30*: 669–88.

Porter, K. R., and R. D. Machado 1960 Studies on the endoplasmic reticulum, IV. Its form and distribution during mitosis in cells of onion root tip. J. Biophys. Biochem. Cytol. *7*: 167–80.

Runnstrom, J., B. E. Hagstrom, and P. Perlmann 1959 Fertilization. *In* The Cell *1*: 327–97. Academic Press, New York.

Schrader, F. 1953 Mitosis, 2nd ed. Columbia University Press, New York.

Spector, W. S., editor 1956 Handbook of Biological Data. Chromosome numbers, pp. 92–6. Saunders, Philadelphia.

Steffensen, D. 1953 Induction of chromosome breakage at meiosis by a magnesium deficiency in *Tradescantia*. Proc. Nat. Acad. Sc. *39*: 613–20.

Swanson, C. P. 1957 Cytology and Cytogenetics. Prentice-Hall, Englewood Cliffs, N. J.

Tahmisian, T. N., and R. L. Devine 1961 The influence of X-rays on organelle induction and differentiation in grasshopper spermatogenesis. J. Biophys. Biochem. Cytol. *9*: 29–45.

Taylor, J. H. 1960 Chromosome reproduction and the problem of coding and transmitting the genetic heritage. American Scientist *48*: 365–82.

Taylor, J. H. 1960 Asynchronous duplication of chromosomes in cultured cells of the Chinese hamster. J. Biophys. Biochem. Cytol. *7*: 455–65.

White, M. J. D. 1954 Animal Cytology and Evolution, 2nd ed. Cambridge University Press, Cambridge, England.

Wilson, E. B. 1928 The Cell in Development and Heredity. Macmillan, New York.

Chapter 4

Some Favorite Organisms
of Geneticists

In Chapters 1 and 2 some of the tools currently available for study of cells were described and mention was made of what cytological studies tell us about the components of cells. You now know what the various nuclear and cytoplasmic organelles look like, what they are made of, and how they behave in the resting cell. In Chapter 3 the dynamic changes that somatic and sexual cells undergo in order to reproduce themselves were outlined. In this chapter a description will be given of seven organisms which have provided vast amounts of useful information concerning the operation of the genetic machinery. These species are themselves some of the favorite biological tools manipulated by geneticists.

Drosophila melanogaster

From the standpoint of genetics *Drosophila melanogaster* is the best known of all organisms and the one most commonly used in an elementary genetics laboratory. Because of this latter fact a more detailed description of this species will be given than for the others. A catalogue of the advantages of the fruit fly follows: (1) The fly is small, anatomically complex, readily handled, and breeds prolifically in the laboratory. (2) Conditions for culturing *Drosophila* are simple, cheap, and readily controlled (see Appendix D). Flies can be raised by the hundreds in half-pint milk bottles or by the tens of thousands in population cages. (3) The life cycle is short. (4) Many mutants have been described, and this information is readily available. (5) The number of chromosomes is small. (6) The chromosomes of the salivary gland cells of the mature larva are gigantic and show a characteristic banding. The homologous chromosomes pair in most somatic tissues, including the salivary gland. As will be elucidated later this behavior makes possible the identification of chromosomal rearrangements and the mapping of deficiencies and, as a result, the cytological localization of genes. (7) Homologous chromosomes do not undergo crossing over in the germ cells of the male. This greatly simplifies the genetic procedures employed. (8) A satisfactory, but complex synthetic medium has been developed for the aseptic growth of *Drosophila* by J. H. Sang and others. (9) An encyclopedic body of information is readily available for this species, from which the worker can proceed to still unexplored areas of research. (10) Collections of hereditary variations exist, and stocks of various mutants are readily available to all workers in the field. (11) A yearly bulletin (*Drosophila Information Service*) is published which lists all publications concerning *Drosophila* that year, the stock lists of the major laboratories, the addresses of all *Drosophila* workers, descriptions of new mutants and genetic techniques, research and teaching notes. As a result *Drosophila* workers can keep abreast of the work going on throughout the world.

Life cycle of Drosophila melanogaster

The fruit fly undergoes complete metamorphosis. The stages of its life cycle are: the egg, larva, pupa, and adult. At 25°C development may be subdivided as follows: embryonic stage, one day; first instar[1] larva, one day; second instar, one day; third instar, two days; pupa, four days; total, nine days. At room temperature the total developmental time is about two weeks.

PRE-ADULT STAGES. The egg is about 0.19×0.50 mm. (weight 1×10^{-5} gm.). Immediately following entrance of the sperm the meiotic divisions are completed, and the egg nucleus is formed. The other nuclei form polar nuclei which degenerate. The sperm nucleus and egg nucleus fuse to form a zygote nucleus which proceeds to undergo mitotic divisions.

Embryonic development results in the formation of a white, segmented, wormlike creature, the larva or maggot. The larvae feed constantly and burrow through the food, leaving numerous channels and furrows. The larval organs are shown in Figure 4–1. The salivary glands of larval *Drosophila* produce digestive juice and also a secretion which is used to glue the insect to the substratum when it undergoes puparium formation. The polytene chromosomes in nuclei of cells of these glands in the third instar larva have been previously described.

---

[1] instars: the periods between molts (i.e. a first instar larva undergoes molt 1 and is transformed into a larger, second instar larva).

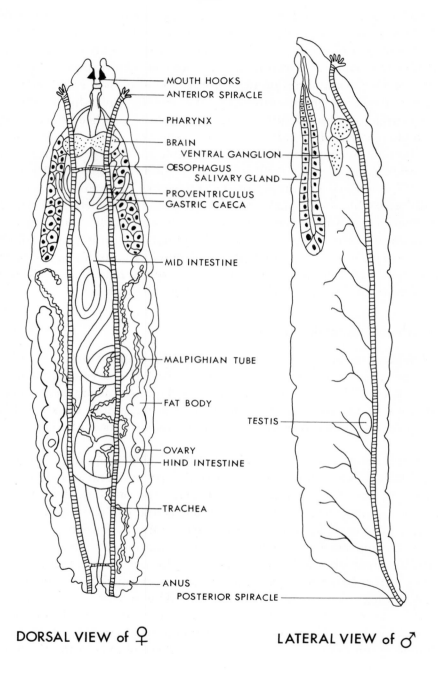

MOUTH HOOKS
ANTERIOR SPIRACLE

PHARYNX

BRAIN
VENTRAL GANGLION
ŒSOPHAGUS
SALIVARY GLAND
PROVENTRICULUS
GASTRIC CAECA

MID INTESTINE

MALPIGHIAN TUBE

FAT BODY

OVARY
HIND INTESTINE

TRACHEA

TESTIS

ANUS
POSTERIOR SPIRACLE

DORSAL VIEW of ♀   LATERAL VIEW of ♂

Figure 4–1 A diagrammatic illustration of some of the organ systems of the third instar larva of *Drosophila melanogaster*. The ventral ganglion is not shown in the female and the fat body and alimentary canal of the male are not shown.

When the larvae are preparing to pupate, they creep from the culture medium and glue themselves to some relatively dry surface. *Drosophila* pupate within the last larval skin, which is at first soft and white but slowly hardens and darkens in color. Immediately following pupation most larval tissues undergo histolysis and are destroyed by phagocytes. More or less simultaneously embryonic structures called imaginal discs grow to produce sections of the adult organism (which is fitted together like a mosaic).

THE ADULT. Adult flies are 2–3 mm. long. Females weigh about 1.5 mg. when mature; males 0.8 mg. (see Fig. 4–2 and front endpaper). The compound eyes are each composed of about 740 *ommatidia* (facets) in the male and about 780 in the female. Three single eyes (the *ocelli*) are arranged in

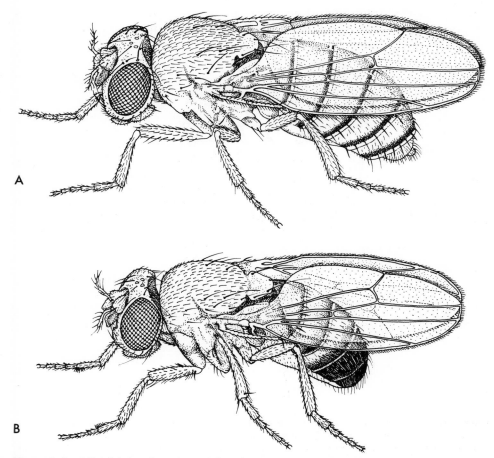

Figure 4–2   (A) Adult female and (B) adult male of *Drosophila melanogaster*.   (Redrawn after H. J. Muller, The Harvey Lectures *43*: 169.)

a triangular pattern on top of the head. The thorax is composed of three fused segments: the prothorax (bearing the first pair of legs), the mesothorax (bearing the second pair of legs and the wings), and the metathorax (bearing the third pair of legs and the trisegmented *halteres*). The wing has a characteristic pattern of five longitudinal veins and two crossveins. Large bristles and small hairs grow in a definite pattern over the body. The external genitalia of the two sexes are strikingly different. Males have (on the foreleg only) a *sex comb* consisting of a row of bristles arranged like the teeth of a comb, whereas females lack this organ.

The internal reproductive system of the female is shown in Figure 4–3. Each of the two ovaries is comprised of a group of egg tubes (ovarioles). In the distal portion of the ovariole is located the germarium, which contains follicular cells, oogonia, and nests containing compact groups of 16 cells which arise as the result of four consecutive, synchronous divisions of an oogonium. Proximal to the germarium are four to eight egg chambers (depending on the age of the adult fly), each larger than the preceding one.

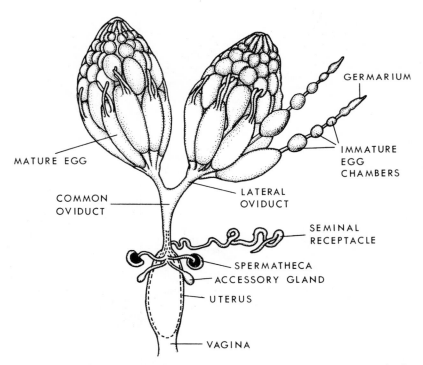

Figure 4–3 The reproductive system of a female *Drosophila melanogaster*. Two ovarioles have been pulled loose from the right ovary. The uterus contains a mature egg (shown as a dashed outline). Sperm stored in the seminal receptacle and spermathecae enter the egg before it leaves the uterus.

(After A. Miller)

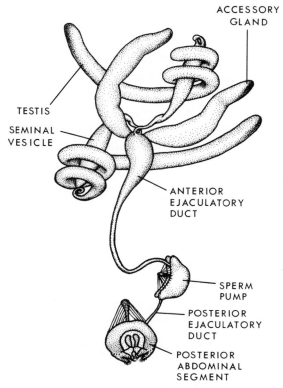

ACCESSORY
GLAND

TESTIS

SEMINAL
VESICLE

ANTERIOR
EJACULATORY
DUCT

SPERM
PUMP

POSTERIOR
EJACULATORY
DUCT

POSTERIOR
ABDOMINAL
SEGMENT

Figure 4–4   The reproductive system of a male *Drosophila melanogaster*.   (After A. Miller)

Each consists of 15 *nurse cells,* the oocyte, and an envelope of follicle cells. The nurse cells nourish the oocyte, which grows until it increases in volume by over 100,000 times. Eventually the nurse cells degenerate, leaving the fully grown primary oocyte (the "mature" egg). Crossing over presumably occurs in the germarium in the 16-cell nests which are not as yet surrounded by follicle cells.

In the male (see Fig. 4–4) each of the two testes is a tube with the basal half helically coiled. The mature testis contains germ cells in various stages of maturation, but spermatozoa and spermatids are most common. Spermatogonia are limited to the extreme tip of the testis.

Mating generally occurs during the first day of adult life, and females start ovipositing during the second day. During its ten-week lifetime a fertilized female can produce 3000 eggs (about 30 times her own weight). Generally 95 per cent of the eggs laid hatch. Under optimal conditions a geneticist can breed a maximum of 30 generations yearly.

Zea mays

Corn is a member of the grass family (the Gramineae) and is *monoecious,* that is, it bears male and female flowers on the same plant. The staminate (male) flowers are borne in the tassels which terminate the stems; whereas the pistillate (female) flowers are borne in the ears which are formed at the base of the upper branches. In plants it is conventional to refer to the haploid stage as the *gametophyte* and the diploid phase as the *sporophyte.* The maize plant is the sporophyte, and each cell nucleus contains 20 chromosomes.

The life cycle of maize is shown in the back endpaper. Meiosis occurs in the *microsporocytes* (microspore mother cell, D of back endpaper) in the tassels; and occurs in the *megasporocyte* (megaspore mother cell, I) in each of the ovules in the ear. During microsporogenesis, meiosis (E-F) results in four haploid microspores. Within each microspore a mitotic duplication yields two nuclei one of which duplicates mitotically in its turn. Since cytokinesis does not occur, each microspore is transformed into a pollen grain containing three haploid nuclei (G). The average tassel produces about 25,000,000 such pollen grains.

The corn ear can be thought of as a fused group of inflorescences each bearing a double row of flowers. Since each flower will eventually produce a kernel, the kernels will be arranged in double rows extending the length of the ear. The style of each flower develops into a silk while within the pistil a single ovule is differentiated. It is within the ovule that a megaspore mother cell is formed. The nuclear events occuring within the megaspore mother cell are shown in J through L of back endpaper. During megasporogenesis, meiosis results in four haploid nuclei of which three degenerate. Then follow three consecutive, synchronous, mitotic divisions with the result that the female gametophyte (or embryo sac) so formed contains eight haploid nuclei (M).

When a pollen grain (or male gametophyte) lands on a silk it germinates (H) and sends out a pollen tube which grows down the silk to the embryo sac. The tube contains the three haploid nuclei, one of which functions as the tube or vegetative nucleus, while the other two sickle-shaped, sperm nuclei participate in the double fertilization which follows. In the embryo sac two of the eight nuclei move toward the center of the embryo sac and remain in contact. These identical polar nuclei are later fertilized by one of the sperm nuclei and a triploid fusion nucleus is produced which gives rise to the endosperm of the kernel. The cluster of three apically arranged nuclei divide until a group of 20 to 40 antipodal cells are formed. These later degenerate. The remaining cluster of three basal nuclei forms the nuclei of the two synergids and the egg. The latter is fertilized by the remaining sperm nucleus to form the diploid embryo (N). The synergids later degenerate.

The development of the kernel takes about 50 days from double fertilization to maturity. During this period a 1400-fold increase in volume takes place. The ear (B) may have as many as 1000 kernels, each of which represents an independent fertilization. The kernel (C) consists of the relatively small diploid embryo, the triploid endosperm, and a tough diploid outer covering of maternal origin, the *pericarp*. At the apical end of the kernel one can often observe the scar marking the original point of attachment of the silk. The surface cells of the endosperm contain aleurone grains and oil. The remaining cells contain starch. The embryo has a central axis terminated by a primary root on the basal end and a stem at the apical end. The scutellum or first leaf serves to digest and absorb the endosperm during the growth of the embryo and seedling.

The adult corn plant which grows from the seedling is rather large, generally averaging 7 feet in height. The plant takes about four months to mature.

Zea mays is the plant for which the most genetic information is available. It is a species of great economic importance, for the world crop is worth hundreds of millions of dollars annually. The species is completely dependent upon man for its propagation, since under natural conditions its seeds would not be dispersed.

Neurospora crassa

This fungus grows as a ground pad composed of filaments or *hyphae* which are tangled together to form a mass called the *mycelium*. The hyphae branch and fuse. Since there are perforations in the hyphal cross walls, the mycelial cytoplasm is continuous. Hyphal cells are multinucleate and each nucleus is haploid. Under certain conditions hyphal fusions may occur between different strains of *Neurospora*. This process (*heterocaryon* formation) results in a hyphal cell which contains nuclei of different genetic constitutions in the same cytoplasm.

The organism can be propagated through transfers of fragments of the mycelium. Aerial hyphae constrict to produce asexual haploid spores which are of two types: oval macroconidia, which are multinucleate, and smaller, spherical uninucleate microconidia. When asexual spores are incubated upon fresh medium they will germinate and form a new mycelium. The organism will grow upon a minimal medium containing sucrose, ammonium tartrate, ammonium nitrate, potassium dihydrogen phosphate, magnesium sulfate, sodium and calcium chloride, biotin, and small quantities of trace elements (B, Cu, Fe, Mn, Mo, and Zn). The medium may be supplemented with yeast extract, malt extract, casein hydrolyzate, or an extract of ground *Neurospora* for optimal growth.

   The mold exists as two mating types, A and a. When placed upon an appropriate medium either type will produce fruiting bodies called *protoperithecia* (see Fig. 4–5). These are small bodies from the bases of which extend receptive hyphae called *trichogynes*. Mating occurs when a nucleus of opposite mating type from a conidium or mycelial fragment fuses with a trichogyne. The nucleus moves down the trichogyne, dividing as it goes.

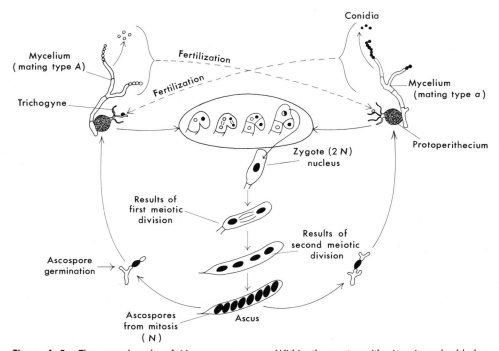

Figure 4–5 The sexual cycle of *Neurospora crassa*. Within the protoperithecium is embedded a haploid, female sex organ (the ascogonium). The ascogonium is a coiled, globous, multinucleate, lateral outgrowth from a hypha, and it is enveloped by a mass of sterile hyphae. The apex of the ascogonium is prolonged into a receptive filament called a trichogyne. When there are conidia of opposite mating type in the vicinity, the trichogynes grow to and unite with them. The haploid conidial nucleus moves down the trichogyne, dividing as it goes. Ultimately the conidial nuclei reach the ascogonium. The ascogonium subsequently buds off numerous hyphae called proasci, the cells of which contain two haploid nuclei, each of opposite mating type. These nuclei are descendants of ascogonial and conidial nuclei. The ultimate cell of a branch of a proascus is shown in the center of the figure. It is highly magnified relative to the rest of the figure. The apical binucleate cell is arched. The haploid nuclei within it divide in unison, and subsequently cell walls are laid down. As a result the terminal cell of the branchlet is uninucleate, the penultimate cell is bínucleate, and the antepenultimate cell is uninucleate. Fusion of haploid nuclei occurs in the penultimate cell which subsequently enlarges to many times its original size to form the ascus. Meiosis occurs within the ascus. The mature fruiting body (perithecium) contains many mature asci. Haploid ascospores released from an ascus will germinate and produce new mycelia.   (After Wagner and Mitchell.)

The newly formed nuclei enter projections in the fruiting body called proasci where they fuse with haploid maternal nuclei to produce diploid zygotic nuclei. Meiosis follows immediately to produce four haploid nuclei which undergo a subsequent mitotic division. Cell walls develop around each nucleus and as a result each is converted into an oval, sexual *ascospore* about 28 micra long. The eight ascospores are contained in a thin-walled ascus sac which holds them in a definite order established by the direction of the nuclear segregations during meiosis. The mature fruiting body or *perithecium* contains as many as 300 ascus sacs, and the ascospores are shot from the mature spore sacs and are carried long distances by air currents. Although strains of the same mating type will not cross they will form heterocaryons.

Many techniques are available for the isolation of nutritional mutants of *Neurospora*. Spores are allowed to germinate upon minimal medium. Normal spores germinate and send out a mycelial network. These are then filtered off and the remaining germinated spores that show poor development are grown upon a supplemented medium, where each produces enough mycelia to allow further propagation. The specific nutritional requirement of each is then determined by systematic attempts to grow the mold on a series of minimal media to which one or another individual pure amino acid or vitamin is added.

The scientific literature resulting from experiments with *Neurospora* forms the foundation of biochemical genetics.

Paramecium aurelia

Paramecium aurelia is a cigar-shaped, ciliated protozoan about 40μ broad and 130μ long. Its genetic machinery consists of two diploid *micronuclei*, each about 3μ in diameter, and a single *macronucleus* ($20\mu \times 50\mu$) which contains about 500 complete sets of chromosomes. The macronucleus appears to control the physiology of the organism, whereas the micronuclei function in reproduction.

Under optimal conditions the organism can reproduce asexually by binary fission once every five hours. During this process the macronucleus constricts in the middle and separates into two halves, the micronuclei divide mitotically, and finally the organism pinches in two to produce a posterior and an anterior daughter cell.

The sexual process of *conjugation* (see Fig. 4–6) occurs when animals of different mating type but of the same variety are brought together under suitable culture conditions. At $27°C$ the process lasts five to six hours. Animals pair side by side, and the macronucleus breaks down into a series

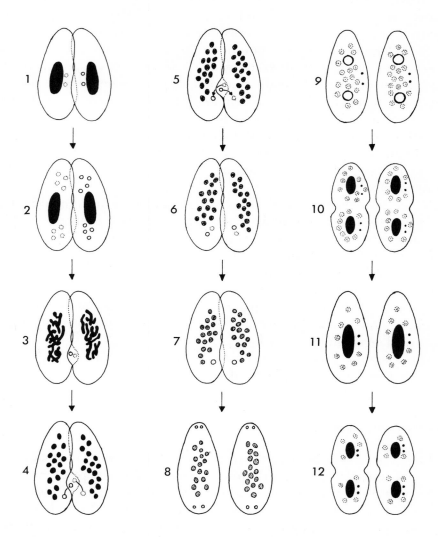

Figure 4–6 Nuclear changes accompanying conjugation in *Paramecium aurelia*. (1) Two parental animals, each with one macronucleus and two diploid micronuclei. (2) Formation of eight haploid nuclei from the micronuclei of each conjugant. (3) Seven nuclei in each conjugant disappear; the remaining nucleus resides in the paroral cone; the macronucleus breaks up into fragments. (4–7) The nuclei in the paroral cones divide mitotically, forming "male" and "female" gamete nuclei. The female nuclei pass into the interior of the parental animals, while the male nuclei are transferred to the partners. Male and female haploid nuclei fuse. (8) Each fusion nucleus divides twice mitotically. (9) Two of the four nuclei so formed differentiate into macronuclear anlagen (white circles) while the other two become micronuclei. (10–12) Transverse fission of the exconjugants produces four animals (two of which are shown in 11). Fragments of the old macronucleus are gradually lost. In (12) transverse fission begins in the animals seen previously in (11). (Redrawn from *Genetics of Paramecium aurelia* by G. H. Beale, 1954, published by Cambridge University Press.)

of 50 or more fragments which eventually degenerate. Each of the two micronuclei undergoes meiosis with the result that eight haploid nuclei are formed, but seven of them degenerate. The nucleus which survives always lies within the *paroral cone*. This is a protuberance formed in the oral region of the conjugating ciliate which juts into the body of the partner. The "protected" nucleus undergoes a mitotic division to produce two gamete nuclei. One of these, the stationary or female gamete nucleus, returns to the interior of the conjugant, whereas the other migratory or male gamete nucleus passes into the cytoplasm of the mate. The gamete nuclei of the mate behave in an identical fashion. The partners separate, and fusion of the haploid nuclei occurs immediately in each exconjugant. The fusion nucleus undergoes two mitotic divisions. An exconjugant now contains four diploid nuclei, and two are included in each daughter cell after transverse fission. One nucleus increases tremendously in volume to produce a macronucleus. The second divides to produce two micronuclei.

Paramecium aurelia can also undergo nuclear reorganization without pairing of animals. This process is called *autogamy,* or internal self-fertilization. Autogamy is identical to conjugation except that there is no pairing, and as a consequence no fusion of nuclei from different animals; instead, the identical haploid nuclei produced by one animal fuse together. Autogamy, therefore, constitutes a very extreme form of inbreeding. *Paramecium aurelia* can be maintained indefinitely without conjugation, but autogamy occurs at regular intervals and cannot be prevented.

Paramecium is a favorite of geneticists interested in the relations between nucleus and cytoplasm in hereditary processes. The fact that the composition of the genetic machinery may be modified through autogamy and conjugation while the cytoplasm remains relatively unchanged makes this organism ideal for such studies.

The coli-phage system

The colon bacillus, *Escherichia coli,* is a rod-shaped organism about 20μ long and 0.8μ wide, containing two or four nuclei. The vast majority of the nuclei are haploid and contain a single chromosome. Reproduction is generally asexual, that is, the genetic material replicates and separates and subsequently the bacterium undergoes transverse fission. The organism can live and multiply on a simple medium which contains glucose and ammonium chloride plus trace amounts of some other compounds. The generation time under optimal conditions is about 20 minutes.

Numerous mutant strains have been recovered, and bacteria from many of these strains are *auxotrophs,* that is, they can be grown only upon minimal medium which has been supplemented with various growth factors such as amino acids or vitamins. Such bacteria have lost the ability to grow on minimal medium because they can no longer manufacture growth factors from the simpler raw materials provided in minimal medium. In addition there are strains which differ in their resistance to poisons, viruses, and antibiotics, in their fermentative abilities, and in their serological properties.

Genetic transfer in *E. coli* is unidirectional. In the K_{12} strain of *E. coli* there are found two mating types F^- ("female") and F^+ ("male"), and a particular strain of the F^+ has been isolated in which mating is relatively common. This strain is called *Hfr* (high frequency of recombination). Mating pairs of bacteria adhere and a narrow bridgelike connection can be seen between them (see Fig. 4–7). The *Hfr* parent slowly forces a portion of its chromosome into the F^- recipient. One specific end of the DNA string always enters the recipient first. The total DNA length transferred is five to ten times the length of the bacterium. Consequently the DNA being transferred must unwind. The rate of transfer is about 1000 nucleotide units per second. The result is an F^- bacterium which is partially diploid (a *heterogenote*), since it contains both its own chromosome and a portion of the *Hfr* chromosome. This partially diploid condition is unstable, however, and duplicate material is eventually eliminated. If the transferred genetic material undergoes crossing over with the genetic material of the host, it may be retained.

F^+ individuals contain an infective factor called F which determines male sexuality and which is extra chromosomal (but not isolable as a cell-free virus particle). F^- individuals infected with F particles become F^+. F particles are transferred from F^+ to F^- individuals during transient matings which do not involve chromosome transfer. The *Hfr* mating type carries the F particle on the chromosome end transmitted last during fertilization.

Bacteriophages

Most organisms are preyed upon by viruses (see Table 4–1), and *E. coli* is no exception. The *B* strain of *E. coli,* for example, is attacked by at least seven bacterial viruses (*bacteriophages*). A virulent T_2 phage attaches itself to the surface of the bacterium by its "tail" and through it injects most of its nucleic acid into the host. The proteinaceous virus shell remains behind. When naked virus is inside the host reproducing itself it is said to be in the *vegetative* state. When a 37°C incubation temperature is used the bacterium

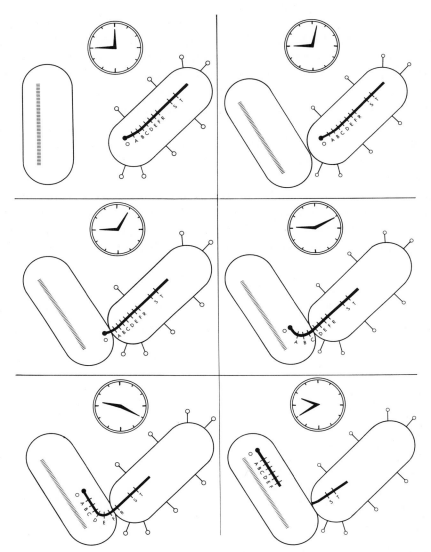

Figure 4–7   A diagrammatic representation of the sequence of events thought to occur during uni-directional genetic transfer in *Escherichia coli*. The *Hfr* individual slowly forces a portion of its chromo-some into the *F⁻* recipient. The inserted chromosome ruptures at point R. The result is the production of a partially diploid heterogenote. The chromosome of the *F⁻* cell is represented by a shaded line. To enable the *Hfr* and *F⁻* cells to be distinguished under the electron microscope the *Hfr* cells are marked with bacteriophage particles. This is done by adding inactivated phage to the *Hfr* cells before they are mixed with *F⁻* cells. Although the phage particles are dead they still adhere to the surface of the bacterial host. The diagram is oversimplified in a number of ways. Only one chromosome is shown, although it is known that each bacterium has between two and four identical chromosomes. Furthermore, each chromosome is much longer than the one shown, and each is in the form of a ring. The ring opens at the point of the attachment of an F particle to the chromosome. It is the region bearing the sex factor which enters the *F⁻* recipient last. About two hours are required for the trans-mission of the entire chromosome.   (After Wollman and Jacob, *Scientific American*, July, 1956)

bursts open and 100 mature phage particles are liberated twenty-one minutes after the attachment of T_2 phage to the bacterial surface. These phages infect other bacteria and so initiate a chain reaction. The bacteria are generally grown on the surface of an agar gel in petri dishes. An area where several thousand bacteria have been destroyed shows up as a clear circular area or *plaque* (see Fig. 4–8). Different bacteriophages are distinguished by the morphology of the plaque they produce, their appearance under the electron microscope, the length of the latent period (the time between infection and liberation of new phage), their burst size (the average number of progeny liberated), and by differences in their serological properties.

If a bacterium is infected simultaneously by three genetically different bacteriophages, the progeny often include viruses which contain genes derived from all three parents. To explain this phenomenon Visconti and Delbruck proposed that the bacteriophages multiply upon entering the host

TABLE 4–1   The size, shape, and major host of representative virulent viruses (after Luria).

VIRUS	SHAPE	DIMENSIONS (mμ)*	MAJOR HOST
Fowl pox	brick-shaped	260 × 320	chicken (arthropod vectors)
Molluscum contagiosum	brick-shaped	260 × 330	man
Herpes zoster (shingles)	brick-shaped	260 × 330	man
Vaccinia	brick-shaped	210 × 260	cow
Rabbit papilloma	spherical	44	rabbit
Rous sarcoma	spherical	70-80	chicken
Mouse milk factor	spherical	130	mouse
Mouse encephalitis	spherical	28	mouse
Equine encephalomyelitis	spherical	42	horse (spread by mosquitoes and mites)
Polyhedrosis	rod-shaped	40 × 280	silkworm
Tobacco mosaic	rod-shaped	15 × 300	tobacco
bushy stunt	spherical	22	tomato
yellow mosaic	spherical	20	turnips (spread by beetles)
bacteriophage T_1	prismatic head, rod-shaped tail	head 50, tail 10 × 150	*E. coli* (strain *B*)
bacteriophage T_2, T_4, T_6	prismatic head, rod-shaped tail	head 65 × 95, tail 25 × 100	*E. coli* (strain *B*)
bacteriophage T_5	prismatic head, rod-shaped tail	head 65, tail 10 × 170	*E. coli* (strain *B*)
bacteriophage T_3, T_7	prismatic	45	*E. coli* (strain *B*)

* Determined by electron microscopy for dry and possibly flattened particles.

and that the replicating units so formed mate repeatedly. Mating occurs in pairs and is at random with respect to the pairing partner. During any given mating cycle a segment of genetic material originating from one parent can exchange with that from a second parent. The phages eventually mature, and subsequent to lysis of the host, recombinant and nonrecombinant viruses are liberated.

However, it should be stressed that not all bacteriophages are virulent. It may be that mutually beneficial virus-host relationships are the most abundant, but since these are the most difficult to detect, they have been overlooked. Nonvirulent or *temperate* phages may infect sensitive bacteria, but rarely or never cause lysis. Phage *lambda* of *E. coli* is one such temperate phage. Recent studies have shown that temperate phages do not multiply within the host bacterium. Instead the virus attaches itself as a *prophage* to a specific region of the host chromosome and duplicates only when the host chromosome duplicates. Many specific sites for different prophages exist on the chromosome of *E. coli*. However, one prophage is known which seems

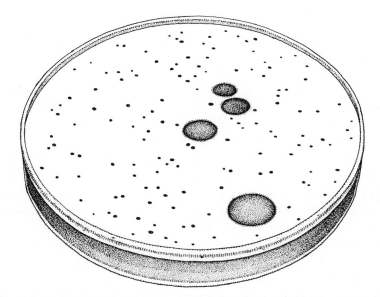

Figure 4–8 A petri dish containing a gel in which is suspended nutrient broth. Covering the surface of the medium is a white "lawn" composed of countless bacteria. The circular clear plaques represent regions where populations of bacteria have been destroyed by bacterial viruses. The numerous small plaques are from T_6 bacteriophage, while the four large plaques are produced by T_7. The petri dish cover has been removed. In order to obtain such a preparation a layer of 1×10^8 bacteria was deposited upon the nutrient agar in the petri dish, and a small number of bacteriophage particles was spread over these. The bacteria multiply to form a layer with holes in it at the points at which a phage particle was present initially. The initial phage particle is adsorbed to a bacterium and after a short period this bacterium is lysed, releasing about 100 new phage particles. These in turn attack neighboring bacteria and produce more phage. The process continues until visible holes appear.

free to take a position anywhere. A bacterium which is capable of carrying a virus in the prophage condition is said to be *lysogenic*. If lysogenized bacteria are exposed to ultraviolet light, the prophage they contain enters the vegetative state and subsequently destroys the cell. If during the mating process a chromosome segment carrying a prophage is inserted into a nonlysogenic bacterium, the prophage becomes virulent and destroys the cell. Thus, whether a virus is virulent or temperate depends upon the host it infects.

Lysogenized bacteria often exhibit changed physiological properties. The diphtheria bacterium, for example, produces its characteristic toxin only when carrying a prophage. In this case viral genes are responsible for the phenotype of the host. Another property the provirus confers upon its bacterial host is immunity against external viruses of the same type. Such viruses are absorbed and genetic material is injected, but this material does not multiply vegetatively within the lysogenized bacterium.

A phage may first infect a nonlysogenic bacterium and replicate its genetic material within the host. During this period the host chromosome may fragment, and some of these fragments may become incorporated into the maturing phage. Following lysis of the host, liberated phages may infect lysogenic bacteria and transport pieces of the chromosome of the original bacterium (the *transduced elements*) to the new host. A transduced element may remain free in the new host bacterium, in which case it will not multiply and will be passed to one or the other of two daughter bacteria whenever cell division occurs. On the other hand, the transduced fragment may synapse with homologous material in the host chromosome and replicate itself in phase with the host chromosome. About one-third of the time all or part of the transduced element may become integrated into the host chromosome by crossing over, and about two-thirds of the time both old and new genetic elements may remain together to produce a partially diploid, unstable condition. The process described above, in which a fragment of the genetic material of the host can be carried by a virus to a second host where it is integrated into the genetic material of the second host is called *transduction*. The sex factor F when integrated into the bacterial chromosome (as is the case in the *Hfr* strain) is also able to pick up adjacent genes of the host chromosome. The new unit formed by F and a few bacterial genes may subsequently return to the autonomous state and be transmitted during conjugation as an infectious unit.

From the previous discussion it can be seen that among certain bacteria there exists a class of genetic elements that are not essential constituents of the cell, since they may be absent from it. However, when they are present they may exist in two alternative states, either as autonomous units replicating independently of the bacterial chromosome, or as integrated units attached to the bacterial chromosome with which they replicate. For this class of genetic elements of which phage lambda and the sex factor *F* are examples the term *episomes* has been proposed by Jacob and Wollman.

Studies on the coli-phage system have revolutionized genetics, bacteriology, and virology.

Man as an object for genetic research

Man (*Homo sapiens*) would appear to be a poor organism for genetic research when compared with the five species described in this chapter. Our species has a long generation time, a small family size, and a large number of small chromosomes. Standardization of the environment and controlled matings are impossible. However, many human matings of interest to geneticists actually have been studied, and the construction of pedigrees is often possible although laborious (see Fig. 4–9). One should recall that more is known about the anatomy, physiology, biochemistry, and behavior of man than of any other organism. For this reason types of inherited traits can be studied which would be undetectable in any other species.

Nature has provided geneticists with a useful tool in the study of their own species in the form of one-egg (monozygotic or identical) and two-egg (dizygotic or fraternal) twins. Approximately 40,000 twins are born yearly in the United States alone, and of these, 13,000 are monozygotic. Twins reared together generally share equivalent environments. Thus by contrasting identical twins who have identical genetic endowments with fraternal

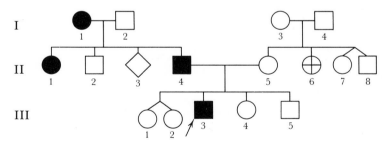

Figure 4-9 A sample pedigree. Females are symbolized by circles and males by squares. Individuals showing the trait are symbolized by solid figures. Offspring are presented beneath the parental symbols in order of birth from left to right. The arrow points to the *propositus*, the person through whom the pedigree was discovered. The sex of individual II–3 is unknown. II–6 died at an early age. II–7 and II–8 were dizygotic twins. III–1 and III–2 were identical twins.

twins who are genetically dissimilar the geneticist can estimate the relative roles played by environment and heredity in the conditioning of various phenotypes (see pp. 267, 288). Finally, techniques have recently been developed by Puck and others for the study of the genetics of human cells grown in tissue culture which promise to revolutionize the entire area.

TABLE 4–2   A comparison of reproduction among six favorite organisms of geneticists

SPECIES	REPRODUCTION	HAPLOID CHROMOSOME NUMBER	GENERATION TIME	WHERE CROSSING OVER OCCURS	REMARKS
Homo sapiens	sexual	23	20 years	primary spermatocytes & oocytes	bisexual & diploid
Drosophila melanogaster	sexual	4	10 days	primary oocyte only	bisexual & diploid
Zea mays	sexual	10	2 generations per year	micro- & mega- sporocytes	diploid & monoecious
Neurospora crassa	generally asexual	7	2 weeks	in diploid fusion nucleus	usually haploid
Paramecium aurelia	generally asexual	a large number	5 hours	in each member of a con- jugating pair	diploid
Escherichia coli	generally asexual	1	20 minutes	in hetero- genote produced by mating or transduction	usually haploid

4–1. List the advantages of each of the organisms described in this chapter for genetic research.

4–2. What advantages might haploid organisms have over diploid organisms in genetic research?

4–3. In corn, how many chromosomes are found in (1) a root tip nucleus, (2) an endosperm cell nucleus, (3) a microsoporocyte nucleus, and (4) a synergid nucleus?

4–4. Contrast autogamy with conjugation in *Paramecium aurelia*.

4–5. What do the following terms signify? Aleurone, conidia, ascospore, macronucleus, monoecious, sporophyte, metamorphosis, micropyle, imaginal disc, tarsus, ovariole, heterogenote, burst size, temperate phage, prophage site, transduction, embryo sac, scutellum, plaque, trichogyne, heterocaryon formation, exconjugant, paroral cone.

BIBLIOGRAPHY

Adelberg, E. A., editor   1960   Papers on Bacterial Genetics. Little, Brown, Boston.

Allen, G., editor   1960   Symposium on cytology and cell culture genetics in man. Amer. J. Human Genetics *12*: 97–138.

Beale, G. H.   1954   The Genetics of *Paramecium aurelia*. Cambridge University Press, Cambridge, England.

Bridges, C. B., and K. S. Brehme   1944   The mutants of *Drosophila melanogaster*. Carnegie Institution of Washington, Publ. 522. Washington, D. C.

Burnett, F. M., and W. M. Stanley   1959   The Viruses, Vol. 2. Academic Press, New York.

Demerec, M., editor   1950   Biology of *Drosophila*. Wiley, New York.

Hayes, W., and R. C. Clowes, editors   1960   Microbial Genetics. 10th Symposium of the Society for General Microbiology. Cambridge University Press, Cambridge, England. (See articles by Hayes on the bacterial chromosome, by Kellenberger on the physical state of the bacterial nucleus, and by Jacob, Schaeffer, and Wollman on episomes.)

Herskowitz, I. H.   1952   Bibliography on the Genetics of *Drosophila*. Part 2. Commonwealth Agricultural Bureau, Farnham Royal, Slough, Bucks., England.

Herskowitz, I. H.   1958   Bibliography on the Genetics of *Drosophila*, Part 3. Indiana University Press, Bloomington, Ind.

Jacob, F., and J. Monod   1961   Genetic regulatory mechanisms in the synthesis of proteins. J. Molec. Biol. *3*: 318–56.

Kiesselbach, T. A.   1949   The structure and reproduction of corn. U. Nebraska Coll. Agric., Agricultural Exper. Sta. Research Bull. No. 161.

Luria, S. E.   1953   General Virology. Wiley, New York.

Muller, H. J.   1939   Bibliography on the Genetics of *Drosophila*. Oliver & Boyd, Edinburgh, Scotland.

Novitski, E.   1960   The Drosophila Information Service *34*. Prepared at the Department of Biology, University of Oregon, Eugene.

Penrose, L. S., and H. L. Brown, eds.   1961   Recent Advances in Human Genetics. J. A. Churchill, London.

Puck, T. T.   1957   The mammalian cell as a microorganism. *In* Rhythmic and Synthetic Processes in Growth, D. Rudnick, editor. Princeton University Press, Princeton, N. J.

Ryan, F. J.   1950   Selected methods of *Neurospora* genetics. Methods in Medical Research *3*: 51.

Sang, J. H.   1956   The quantitative nutritional requirements of *Drosophila melanogaster*. J. Exper. Biol. *33*: 45–72.

Sprague, G. F., editor   1955   Corn and Corn Improvement. Academic Press, New York.

Stanier, R. Y., M. Douderoff, and E. A. Adelberg   1957   The Microbial World. Prentice-Hall, Englewood Cliffs, N. J.

Stent, G. S., editor   1960   Papers on Bacterial Viruses. Little, Brown, Boston.

Stern, C.   1960   Principles of Human Genetics, 2nd edition. Freeman, San Francisco.

Visconti, N., and M. Delbruck   1953   The mechanism of genetic recombination in phage. Genetics *38*: 5–33.

Wenrich, D. H., et al., editors   1954   Sex in Microorganisms. American Association for the Advancement of Science, Washington, D. C.

Weijer, J.   1952   A catalogue of genetic maize types together with a maize bibliography. Bibliographia genetica *14:* 189–425.

Wichterman, R.   1953   The Biology of *Paramecium*. Blakiston, New York.

Chapter 5

Fundamental Hereditary Laws

Introduction

A fertilized egg divides into two cells, then four, and finally in the case of man after a succession of 40 to 50 division cycles have elapsed an infant containing 25 trillion cells is produced. Each somatic cell of the completed organism contains, in its nucleus, chromosomes which are present as pairs. Each member of a chromosome pair is a replica of one of the chromosomes contributed at syngamy by the mother or father to the original fusion nucleus of the fertilized egg. In the same way each of the linearly arranged genes on the maternal chromosome has a partner gene at the same locus on the paternal chromosome. Let us now consider a single gene lying at some specific chromosomal locus. The gene may exist in a number of different forms or states. Let us set up a hypothetical situation in which this gene exists in but two states: either as a normal, functioning gene or as an inactivated form of the gene. Presumably the inactive form arose from the active one by a mutational event. The active gene, which we may symbolize arbitrarily by A^a, is called the normal or wild type *allele* of the gene. The inactive gene, symbolized by A^i, is called the inactive allele of the gene A. Let us assume further that gene A^a is responsible for the production in some unspecified fashion of a growth hormone. Gene A^i can still reproduce itself, but cannot produce the hormone.

If A^a and A^i are the only states in which gene A can exist, then there can occur only three types of organisms carrying a pair of A genes; A^aA^a, A^aA^i, and A^iA^i. Haploid gametes produced by such diploid organisms can contain but one A gene. A^aA^a and A^iA^i individuals are called *homozygous* and can produce but one type of gamete; whereas A^aA^i individuals are called *heterozygous,* since they can produce two differing types of gametes, those bearing gene A^a and those bearing A^i. We would expect the A^iA^i individual to be a dwarf, since it can produce no growth hormone. However, if one dose of the A^a gene produces sufficient growth hormone for normal development, then both A^aA^a and A^aA^i individuals will have normal stature. Thus it may be impossible to distinguish A^aA^a from A^aA^i individuals visually, but, of course, they are different genetically and can be distinguished by the types of offspring they produce. Geneticists use the term *phenotype* to designate the external appearance of organisms, and *genotype* to designate their genetic constitution. Thus A^aA^a and A^aA^i individuals have different genotypes but identical phenotypes.

In Figure 5–1 a series of three mating schemes (I, II, and III) is shown in the symbolic fashion commonly used by geneticists. In I, an A^aA^a male is mated with or crossed to an A^aA^a female. (Note the male and female symbols, which originate from the zodiac signs for Mars—the shield and spear ♂—and for Venus—the looking glass ♀.) The two individuals mate (indicated by an X) and produce the offspring below the arrow. P_1 stands for parental generation and F_1 for first filial generation. The progeny of the F_1 individuals would be called the F_2 generation, and so on. It is obvious that homozygous parents "breed true," that is, they produce only offspring like themselves. Thus in I, tall parents produce tall offspring; in II, dwarf parents produce dwarf offspring. Heterozygous parents, however, produce some offspring which are different in phenotype from their parents. Note that in III, three-fourths of the offspring are tall like the parents while one-fourth is dwarf. Why this is so is shown by the checkerboard in IV. The

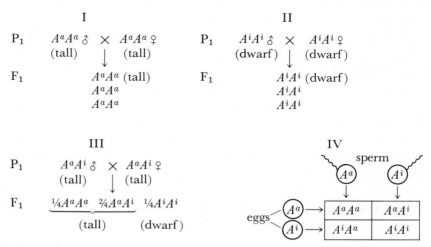

Figure 5–1

four squares (containing two letters each) represent the four classes of fertilizations that can occur as the result of collisions between a sperm and an egg. Remember that the sperm and egg populations each contain equal numbers of two different types of gametes (A^a and A^i), and sperm-egg collisions occur at random, that is, there is no tendency for one type of egg to be fertilized by one type of sperm more frequently than by sperm of the second type. The tall individuals which make up three-fourths of the progeny belong to two genotypic classes. One-third of the talls is homozygous; two-thirds are heterozygous. The homozygous tall offspring when bred together will breed true as shown in I; whereas the heterozygous progeny when bred together will behave as did their parents (see III).

Mendel's monohybrid cross

If we now refer to the experiments described by Gregor Mendel in 1865, the parallel between his observed results and the above model will become apparent. Mendel used as his experimental organism the garden pea, *Pisum sativum*. He obtained from seedsmen a tall strain of peas, the plants of which at maturity were between 6 and 7 feet high, and a second dwarf strain whose plants at maturity were ¾ to 1½ feet in height. Mendel self-fertilized these monoecious plants and found that both strains bred true for six generations. When tall and dwarf plants were crossed, however, the progeny were all tall. Upon self-fertilization the F_1 tall individuals produced an F_2 which contained tall and dwarf progeny in a 3:1 ratio (787 tall to 277 dwarf). Mendel showed that these dwarf progeny bred true. However, he found that by self-fertilizing the tall individuals and studying their progeny he could group the F_2 tall plants into two categories. Of 100 tall plants tested 28 or approximately one-third produced upon self-fertilization only tall progeny; whereas 72 or approximately two-thirds produced tall and short offspring in a 3:1 ratio.

The fact that the dwarf characteristic was masked in the F_1 heterozygote (which was produced by crossing inbred tall and short plants together) led to the concepts of *dominance* and *recessiveness*. The symbolism adopted at this stage in the development of genetics was to use a capital letter to designate the dominant factor (T for tall) and to use the same letter but a small one for the recessive factor (t for dwarf). The F_1 heterozygote may therefore be symbolized by Tt, the homozygotes by TT and tt. Mendel's experiment therefore could be represented symbolically as shown in Figure 5–2. In the same fashion our earlier scheme involving the genes A^a and A^i could be rewritten using this type of symbolism. In this case A^a and A^i could be symbolized by T and t, respectively.

The fact that the dwarf character emerged in the F_2 demonstrated that the recessive factor was not modified in the F_1 hybrid. The factor was present in the hybrid (although its expression was masked by the dominant factor), since the hybrid transmitted the recessive factor to half its offspring.

$$P_1 \qquad TT \text{ (tall)} \times tt \text{ (short)}$$
$$\downarrow$$
$$F_1 \qquad Tt \text{ (tall)}$$
$$\text{self-fertilized}$$
$$\downarrow$$
$$F_2 \qquad 1\,TT : 2\,Tt : 1\,tt$$
$$\text{(3 tall)} : \text{(1 short)}$$

Figure 5–2

At the time Mendel was conducting his experiments cytology was in a very primitive state, and the gymnastics performed by chromosomes during gametogenesis and fertilization had yet to be observed and interpreted. Mendel's contributions to science are all the more remarkable because of the meager foundation upon which he was forced to build. He showed that the male and female parents contributed factors (we now call these factors genes) to the offspring and that these factors were somehow responsible for the production of certain sharply defined morphological characteristics (such as plant height). Furthermore each parent contained a pair of factors, but passed only *one* member of the pair to its offspring. The factors retained their individuality from generation to generation and were not modified in the hybrid. The factors contributed by the parents united at random when the progeny were produced. Mendel's analysis of his data led to the recognition of the distinction between phenotype and genotype and homozygosity and heterozygosity.

Mendel in 1865 could not arrive at a mechanism to explain how his factors produced their characteristic phenotypes, and the fact that certain genes were recessive and others dominant was very mysterious. In our model the recessive gene was inactive, the dominant allele was active in the production of a growth hormone, and only one dose of the dominant allele supplied sufficient hormone for the attainment of normal height.

Let us now set up a hypothetical model situation in which the gene T is responsible for the production of five units of growth hormone; whereas the gene t produces but one unit. Each unit of hormone allows the individual to grow one foot in height. Figure 5–2 may now be rewritten as shown in Figure 5–3. In this case the homozygous dominant (TT) and the heterozygote (Tt) could be distinguished from each other, and early geneticists would have said that T was not completely dominant to t, since T could not completely mask t.

P$_1$ TT (10 ft. tall) × tt (2 ft. tall)
                                    ↓
F$_1$ Tt (6 ft. tall)
                               self-fertilized
                                    ↓
F$_2$ 1TT (10 ft. tall):2Tt (6 ft. tall):1tt (2 ft. tall)

Figure 5–3

Finally let us construct a situation in which T produces five units of the hormone, whereas t produces 4.9 units. Now TT individuals would be 10 feet, Tt individuals 9.9 feet, and tt individuals 9.8 feet tall. However, it very well could be impossible to control environmental conditions to ensure all members of the population of individuals getting the same amounts of nutrients, and as a result the variations in height due to differences in nutrition might well mask the subtle differences due to genotype. In such a case one would never recognize the existence of T and t.

It should follow from the above discussion that (1) dominance and recessiveness are relative terms and that (2) a recessive allele generally performs its physiological function less well than the dominant allele (or not at all). Furthermore unless there exists an abnormal allele which is inactive (*amorphic*) or functions imperfectly (is *hypomorphic*) when compared to the normal allele, we cannot detect the existence of the normal gene. Thus, if dwarf strains of peas did not exist, we would not know that plant height is genetically controlled. The detection of inherited conditions therefore depends upon the ability of the scientist to control and reduce environmental fluctuations, to produce by inbreeding genetically homogeneous strains which differ from each other by one or only a few characteristics, to develop refined methods of accurately measuring the differences between strains, and to keep meticulous records of pedigrees. In other words, the present-day geneticist need only follow the example set by the elegant experimentation of Gregor Mendel in the latter part of the nineteenth century.

Mendel's dihybrid cross

Mendel next went one step further in his experimental analysis by observing the progeny of dihybrid crosses (crosses which involve two different gene pairs simultaneously). For our purposes it is sufficient to discuss only the experiment in which he studied the inheritance of seed color and seed shape. In the first case the two contrasting phenotypes were yellow and green; in the second, smooth and wrinkled. It so happened that the genes controlling the two different classes of morphological characteristics were located on different chromosomes. Strains of peas that were known to breed true were used in the following series of crosses which yielded the following results.

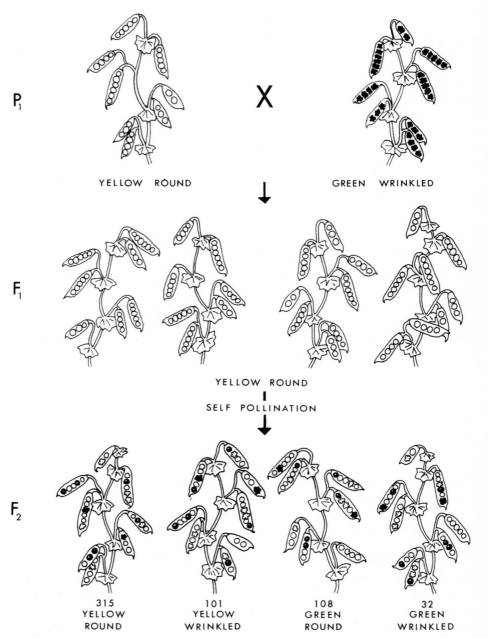

Figure 5–4

The F_1 data demonstrate that yellow is dominant to green and round is dominant to wrinkled. Note that two new phenotypic combinations (yellow wrinkled and green round) appear in the F_2.

If we use the same method of symbolic representation we did for the earlier monohybrid cross, the following scheme emerges:

$$P_1 \quad Y\,Y\,R\,R \times y\,y\,r\,r$$
$$\downarrow$$
$$F_1 \quad Y\,y\,R\,r$$

Figure 5–5

The F_1 individuals are thus doubly heterozygous. The gametes they produce must contain a gene for seed color and one for seed shape. However, these gametes can belong to any one of four types: *YR, Yr, yR,* and *yr.* Male and female gametes unite at random. As before, we can predict the results by using a checkerboard. However, the checkerboard will now have 16 squares instead of four, since 16 different types of fertilizations can occur.

MALE GAMETES

		Y R	Y r	y R	y r
		(1)	(2)	(3)	(4)
	Y R	Y Y R R	Y Y R r	Y y R R	Y y R r
		(5)	(6)	(7)	(8)
FEMALE	Y r	Y Y r R	Y Y r r	Y y r R	Y y r r
GAMETES		(9)	(10)	(11)	(12)
	y R	y Y R R	y Y R r	y y R R	y y R r
		(13)	(14)	(15)	(16)
	y r	y Y r R	y Y r r	y y r R	y y r r

Figure 5–6

It is now possible to regroup the individuals represented by each square into four phenotypic classes. Yellow round individuals contain at least one *Y* and one *R* gene; yellow wrinkled contain at least one *Y* but no *R* gene; green round, at least one *R* but no *Y* gene; and green wrinkled individuals contain only genes symbolized by small letters (see Table 5–1). Thus the four phenotypic classes are predicted to be present in the F_2 population in a 9:3:3:1 ratio. Mendel's F_2 population contained 556 individuals. The

TABLE 5–1   Phenotypic Classes.

YELLOW ROUND	YELLOW WRINKLED	GREEN ROUND	GREEN WRINKLED
(1) Y *Y* R *R*	(6) Y *Y* r *r*	(11) y *y* R *R*	(16) y *y* r *r*
(2) Y *Y* R *r*	(8) Y *y* r *r*	(12) y *y* R *r*	
(3) Y *y* R *R*	(14) y *Y* r *r*	(15) y *y* r *R*	
(4) Y *y* R *r*	$\frac{3}{16} = 0.1875$	$\frac{3}{16} = 0.1875$	$\frac{1}{16} = 0.0625$
(5) Y *Y* r *R*			
(7) Y *y* r *R*			
(9) y *Y* R *R*			
(10) y *Y* R *r*			
(13) y *Y* r *R*			
$\frac{9}{16} = 0.5626$			

The numbers in parentheses refer to the appropriate square in the checkerboard (Fig. 5–6).

observed and the expected numbers of individuals in each phenotypic class are presented in Table 5–2.

The agreement between the values Mendel observed and the expected values is very close, and this gives one confidence that a valid method was

TABLE 5–2

	YELLOW ROUND	YELLOW WRINKLED	GREEN ROUND	GREEN WRINKLED
Observed	315	101	108	32
Expected	313	104	104	35
Deviation	+2	−3	+4	−3

used in analyzing the data. The results of Mendel's dihybrid crosses demonstrated the independent assortment of gene pairs. This is precisely the result one would expect on the basis of chromosomal segregation during gametogenesis (refer back to pp. 35–37) provided the genes in question resided on different chromosomes. As is shown in Figure 5–7 the classes of gametes produced depend entirely upon arrangements of the chromosome bivalents at metaphase I. If the configuration is the one diagrammed under A, then capital-letter genes are included in one secondary gametocyte and small-letter genes in the other. However, the B configuration has an equal chance of occurring, and this produces *Yr* and *yR* gametes.

If we refer back to Figure 5–6, we can now regroup the individuals represented by each square into nine genotypic classes. The numbers in parentheses refer to the appropriate square in the checkerboard (see Table 5–3). It follows that the phenomenon of dominance has converted a 4:2:2:2:1:1:1:1 genotype ratio into a 9:3:3:1 phenotypic ratio. The classical 9:3:3:1 ratio which has been observed over and over again in the

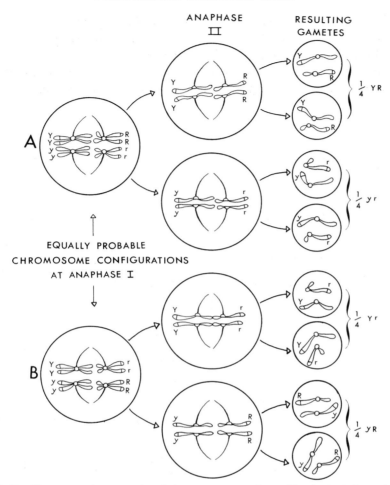

Figure 5-7 Chromosomal segregation during gametogenesis resulting in the independent assortment of gene pairs.

TABLE 5-3   Genotypic Classes

DOUBLY HETEROZYGOUS	HETEROZYGOUS, HOMOZYGOUS	DOUBLY HOMOZYGOUS
YyRr (4,7,10,13)*	*YYRr* (2,5)	*YYRR* (1)
	YyRR (3,9)	*YYrr* (6)
	Yyrr (8,14)	*yyRR* (11)
	yyRr (12,15)	*yyrr* (16)

* Note that the four classes of zygotes have identical genotypes although they arise from different types of encounters between male and female gametes. For example in (4) of Table 5–1 the female gamete contributes the *Y* and *R* genes, whereas in (13) it is the male gamete which contributes *Y* and *R*.

F_2 of dihybrid crosses involving many different species is the result of independent assortment of the gene pairs during gametogenesis followed by random pairing of male and female gametes and the conversion of the nine genotypic classes of zygotes produced into four phenotypic classes of adults because of dominant genes masking their recessive alleles.

TABLE 5–4

SEGRE-GATING GENE PAIRS	NUMBER OF PHENO-TYPIC CLASSES†	PHENO-TYPIC RATIOS	NUMBER OF GENO-TYPIC CLASSES	GENO-TYPIC RATIOS	SQUARES*	FREQUENCY OF MOST COMMON PHENOTYPIC CLASS	FREQUENCY OF MOST COMMON GENOTYPIC CLASS
1	2	3:1	3	2:1:1	4	$\frac{3}{4}$ A	*Aa* $\frac{2}{4} = \frac{1}{2}$
2	4	$(3:1)^2 =$ 9:3:3:1	9	$(2:1:1)^2 =$ 4:2:2:2:2: 1:1:1:1	16	$\frac{9}{16}$ AB	*Aa Bb* $\frac{4}{16} = \frac{1}{4}$
3	8	$(3:1)^3 =$ 27:9:9:9: 3:3:3:1	27	$(2:1:1)^3 =$ 8:4:4:4:4: 4:4:2:2:2: 2:2:2:2:2: 2:2:2:2:1: 1:1:1:1:1: 1:1	64	$\frac{27}{64}$ ABC	*Aa Bb Cc* $\frac{8}{64} = \frac{1}{8}$
4	16	$(3:1)^4 =$ 81:27:27: 27:27:9: 9:9:9:9:9: 3:3:3:3:1	81	$(2:1:1)^4 =$ 16:8:8:8: 8:8:8:8:8: 4:4:4:4:4: 4:4:4:4:4: 4:4:4:4:4: 4:4:4:4:4: 4:4:4:4:2: 2:2:2:2:2: 2:2:2:2:2: 2:2:2:2:2: 2:2:2:2:2: 2:2:2:2:2: 2:2:2:2:2: 2:1:1:1:1: 1:1:1:1:1: 1:1:1:1:1: 1:1	256	$\frac{81}{256}$ ABCD	*Aa Bb Cc Dd* $\frac{16}{256} = \frac{1}{16}$
n	2^n	$(3:1)^n$ ‡	3^n	$(2:1:1)^n$ ‡	4^n	$3^n/4^n$	$2^n/4^n$

† also equivalent to the kinds of gametes

* number of squares in checkerboard = number of different types of encounters between male and female gametes

‡ refer to Figure 5–8 for the method used to expand these ratios

Multifactor crosses

As one would expect, the situation becomes more complex when dealing with the results of crosses involving three and four segregating gene pairs (see Table 5–4). In the case of a cross between individuals of genotype *Aa Bb Cc*, for example, 64 types of encounters between male and female gametes occur. The checkerboard method of determining genotypes and phenotypes becomes laborious here, and a shorter method is used. The method, shown in Figure 5–8, simply takes either the classical 3:1 pheno-

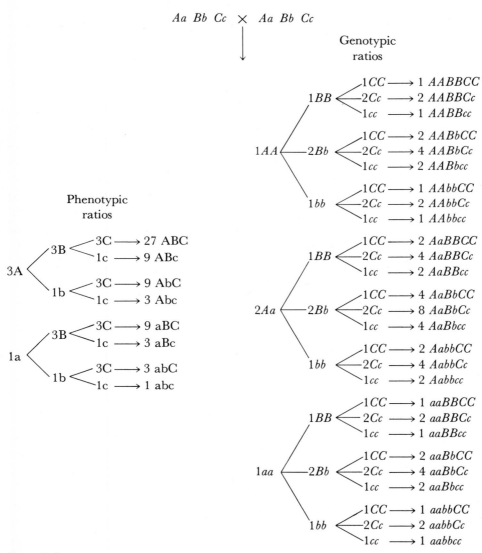

Figure 5–8

typic or the $2:1:1$ genotypic ratio produced by a single pair of factors
and expands it for each consecutive gene pair.

If we take an organism (like man) with a fairly large number of chromosome pairs (23), we can calculate the number of phenotypic and genotypic
classes of offspring produced by individuals heterozygous for a single pair
of alleles in each chromosome pair. The number of phentotypic classes is
2^{23} or 8×10^6; the number of genotypic classes is 3^{23} or 9×10^{10}. This
last value is larger than the number of seconds in 1000 years (3×10^{10}).
It follows that an astronomical amount of variability is likely to be found
among the offspring produced by two unrelated parents. Geneticists
generally have to content themselves with the study of monohybrid,
dihybrid, and trihybrid crosses, because the labor involved becomes pro-
hibitive if more pairs of alleles are studied simultaneously.

The test cross and the back cross

If one crosses a heterozygote to an individual containing only recessive
alleles of the genes in question, the segregation and assortment of the
allelic pairs during gametogenesis in the heterozygote can be determined
by observing the phenotypes of the offspring. Such a cross is called a *test
cross,* and it is often used, since it avoids the confusion due to the masking
effect of dominant alleles and markedly reduces the labor involved. Note,
for example, that the phenotypic classes shown in the second F_1 generation
of Figure 5–9 are identical in frequency to the gamete types produced by

I P_1 $AABBCC ♀ \times aabbcc ♂ \longrightarrow F_1\ AaBbCc ♂ ♂$ and $♀ ♀$

II P_1 $AaBbCc ♀ \times aabbcc ♂$ (test cross)

F_1 ⅛ $AaBbCc$ ⅛ $AaBbcc$ ⅛ $AabbCc$ ⅛ $Aabbcc$
        ⅛ $aaBbCc$ ⅛ $aaBbcc$ ⅛ $aabbCc$ ⅛ $aabbcc$

(The heterozygous individuals shown in cross II were derived from the F_1 of cross I)

Figure 5–9

the F_1 female. Also contrast the number of different types of encounters
between male and female gametes in the situation shown in cross II of
Figure 5–9 with that given in Table 5–4 for three segregating gene pairs
(8 versus 64). The *back cross* is defined as a cross between an F_1 individual
and its parent or an individual of genotype identical to the parent. Thus
the second P_1 cross shown in Figure 5–9 is both a test cross and a back
cross. A cross between an $Aa\ Bb\ Cc\ F_1 ♂$ and its $AA\ BB\ CC$ mother would
be a back cross but not a test cross. It is obvious that the two terms are not
synonyms and should not be confused.

5–1. What do the following terms signify? Dominance, recessiveness, allele, F_2, genotype, phenotype, heterozygote, homozygote, dihybrid cross, test cross.

5–2. In *Drosophila melanogaster* there exists a mutant strain called *dumpy* in which the flies have wings which are obliquely truncated. When a normal female is crossed to a dumpy male all the offspring have normal wings. When brother-sister matings are made between F_1 flies, an F_2 is produced containing 173 dumpy and 526 normal flies. When an F_1 female is crossed back to the P_1 male, 97 dumpy and 106 normal offspring are produced. Diagram such a succession of crosses. What conclusions can you draw as to the inheritance of wing morphology in *Drosophila?*

5–3. A mutation called *Curly* (*Cy*) exists in *Drosophila* which causes the wings to curl up. When a *Cy* male is mated to a virgin *Cy* female the F_1 population contains 207 *Cy* and 101 normal flies. Can you propose a hypothesis to explain these results? How would you test this hypothesis?

5–4. In a plant called the four o'clock, strains are known with red, pink, or white flowers. The cross pink × pink gives an F_1 population which contains 25 per cent red, 50 per cent pink, and 25 per cent white plants. What can you conclude as to the inheritance of flower pigmentation?

5–5. A satisfactory, experimental model can be made in the following way which illustrates the F_2 results of Mendel's dihybrid cross. Take two nickels and two dimes, shake them up thoroughly in a container, toss them on a table, and score the results. After 100 tosses total your results and place them in column 6. Let heads represent the dominant character; tails the recessive, and let nickels and dimes control seed color and seed shape, respectively. Your observations should be in reasonable agreement with the expected values shown in column 5. The $4:2:2:2:2:1:1:1:1$ predicted ratio is equivalent to that shown in Table 5–3.

CLASS	NICKELS	DIMES	CORRESPONDS TO	EXPECTED	OBSERVED
1	H T	H T	*YyRr*	25.00	
2	H H	H T	*YYRr*	12.50	
3	T T	H T	*yyRr*	12.50	
4	H T	H H	*YyRR*	12.50	
5	H T	T T	*Yyrr*	12.50	
6	H H	T T	*YYrr*	6.25	
7	T T	H H	*yyRR*	6.25	
8	H H	H H	*YYRR*	6.25	
9	T T	T T	*yyrr*	6.25	
	H = Heads;	T = Tails.		Total 100.00	100

5–6. In chickens there exists an allelic pair of genes *F* and *f* which effects the morphological development of feathers and on another chromosome a pair of genes *Bl* and *bl* which effects the coloration of the plumage. Individuals with normal feathers are genotypically *ff*. *FF* individuals are "extreme frizzle" with brittle, curly feathers which wear off easily; whereas *Ff* individuals are "mild frizzle" with curly feathers which are much more nearly normal. *FF* and *Ff* individuals are easily distinguished. *Bl Bl* chickens have "white-splashed" plumage, *bl bl* chickens are black, and *Bl bl* are of an intermediate coloration called "blue." Let us assume that an extreme frizzle, white-splashed hen and a normal, black rooster mate and produce offspring, and that these interbreed. What phenotype ratios will be observed in the F_1 and F_2 populations? If F_1 females are back crossed to their father what phenotypic ratios will appear in their offspring?

5–7. In a meadow there exists a population of mature plants of the same species. Members of the population vary greatly in size. How could you demonstrate whether or not this variability was genetically determined?

5–8. The fact that different human beings live in different sensory worlds was demonstrated by A. L. Fox, who discovered that persons differ in their ability to taste the chemical phenythiocarbamide (PTC). Tasters may have children who are nontasters. What do you conclude as to the inheritance of the ability to taste PTC?

BIBLIOGRAPHY

Bateson, W.   1909   Mendel's Principles of Heredity. Cambridge University Press, London.

Fox, A. L.   1932   The relationship between chemical composition and taste. Proc. Nat. Acad. Sc. *18*: 115–20.

Hutt, F. B.   1949   The Genetics of the Fowl. McGraw-Hill, New York.

Landauer, W.   1942   Form and function in the Frizzle fowl: the interaction of hereditary potentialities and environmental temperature. Biol. Symp. *6*: 127–66.

Mendel, G.   1866   Versuche über Pflanzen Hybriden. In English translation *In* Classic Papers in Genetics, 1959, J. A. Peters, editor. Prentice-Hall, Englewood Cliffs, N. J.

Moore, R.   1961   The Coil of Life. The Story of the Great Discoveries in Life Sciences. A. A. Knopf, New York.

Sutton, W. S.   1902   The chromosomes in heredity. Biol. Bull. *4*: 231–51.

Chapter 6

Modification of Classical Genetic Ratios

Introduction

For a variety of reasons a classical genetic ratio such as the $3:1$ or the $9:3:3:1$ may not be observed even though predicted. Sometimes aberrant ratios may be the result of human errors in classification. For example, it is often noted in class experiments using eye color mutants of *Drosophila* that certain students cannot detect certain eye color changes and thus do not place each member of their fly population into the proper phenotypic class.

Aberrant ratios also may result when mutant individuals have lowered viability. Wingless mutant *Drosophila,* for example, tend to get mired in the culture medium more frequently than do normal flies. Surviving mutant individuals are therefore found in lower frequencies than predicted. Mendel was aware that lowered viability could lead to spurious results. In his experiment referred to on page 67, the dwarfed plants were carefully lifted and transferred to a special plot of ground. "This precaution was necessary, as otherwise they would have perished through being overgrown by their tall relatives."

Certain mutants prolong pre-adult stages or decrease adult longevity. The proportion of mutant adult individuals therefore varies with the age of the population. Other mutants may express themselves to different degrees depending upon the age of the individual or upon environmental variables such as light, temperature, humidity, and nutrition.

Finally, classic genetic ratios are often modified when genes which are independently transmitted affect the same characteristic and are therefore not independent in their expression.

Gene interaction

Let us consider a simple dihybrid cross $Aa\ Bb \times Aa\ Bb$ which produces offspring with the following genotypes and phenotypes.

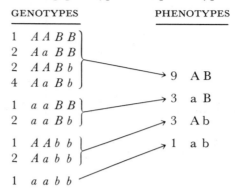

GENOTYPES		PHENOTYPES
1	*A A B B*	
2	*A a B B*	
2	*A A B b*	
4	*A a B b*	→ 9 A B
1	*a a B B*	→ 3 a B
2	*a a B b*	→ 3 A b
1	*A A b b*	→ 1 a b
2	*A a b b*	
1	*a a b b*	

Epistacy

The classical $9:3:3:1$ ratio shown above would be modified, however, if gene *A* masked the expression of gene *B*. For example, gene *A* might suppress eye formation (whereas the *a* allele is inactive in this respect), while gene *B* results in the production of a brown pigment which is laid down in the eye (and its recessive allele is also inactive). Under these circumstances the following ratios would be predicted:

P_1 $AAbb\ ♀ \times aaBB\ ♂ \longrightarrow F_1$ $AaBb\ ^♂_♀\ ^♂_♀ \longrightarrow F_2$ $\underline{9AB:\ 3Ab:\ 3aB:\ 1ab}$
      eyeless   brown-   eyeless   12 eyeless   3 brown- 1 colorless
                     eyed   eyed

Conversely, if *a* masked the expression of gene *B*

P_1 $AAbb\ ♀ \times aaBB\ ♂ \longrightarrow F_1$ $AaBb\ ^♂_♀\ ^♂_♀ \longrightarrow F_2$ $9AB:$ $3Ab:$ $\underline{3aB:\ 1ab}$
      colorless   eyeless   brown-   9 brown-   3 colorless   4 eyeless
                                                 eyed   eyed

In the above cases the expression of one gene conditions that of another, and the relationship is *nonreciprocal*. The phenomenon of nonreciprocal gene interaction is called *epistacy*. The first example is one of dominant epistacy, and the gene *A* is said to be *epistatic* to *B* which is *hypostatic* to *A*. The second example is of recessive epistacy. In both cases the F_2 generation has three instead of four phenotypic classes.

Complementary genes

Reciprocal or complementary types of gene interaction have also been observed by geneticists. In the case of dominant complementarity the dominant alleles of two or more genes are required for the expression of some trait. For example, the genes A and B might both be required for pigment formation. Under such circumstances the following ratios would be predicted:

P₁ here:

$$P_1 \quad \underset{\text{colorless}}{AAbb\ ♀} \times \underset{\text{colorless}}{aaBB\ ♂} \longrightarrow F_1 \quad \underset{\text{colored}}{AaBb\ \substack{♂ \\ ♀}\ \substack{♂ \\ ♀}} \longrightarrow F_2 \quad \underset{\text{9 colored}}{\underline{9AB:\ \underset{}{3Ab:\ 3aB:\ 1ab}}}_{\text{7 colorless}}$$

Conversely, in the case of recessive complementarity, the dominant alleles of two or more genes might suppress pigment formation with the following results:

$$P_1 \quad \underset{\text{colorless}}{AAbb\ ♀} \times \underset{\text{colorless}}{aaBB\ ♂} \longrightarrow F_1 \quad \underset{\text{colorless}}{AaBb\ \substack{♂ \\ ♀}\ \substack{♂ \\ ♀}} \longrightarrow F_2 \quad \underline{\underset{\text{15 colorless}}{9AB:\ 3Ab:\ 3aB:}\ \underset{\text{1 colored}}{1ab}}$$

Note that complementarity results in the F₂ generation's containing two instead of four phenotypic classes.

Genes affecting aleurone color in maize

A classical case of gene interaction is found in the inheritance of aleurone color in *Zea mays*. The genes involved are A (3), C (9), R (10), and P (5), and their recessive alleles a, c, r, and p. The number in parentheses gives the chromosome upon which the gene is located. In order for the corn kernel to possess colored aleurone at least one A and one C gene must be present. Given A and C in the heterozygous or homozygous condition and in addition R in the heterozygous or homozygous condition then a red pigment is produced. Purple pigment is synthesized if P is present in addition to A, C, and R.

Let us consider the results of the following cross. A plant of genotype *AACCRrPp* is self-pollinated. The offspring will contain the following phenotypic classes:

$$AC \underset{1r}{\overset{3R}{<}} \begin{matrix} 3P \longrightarrow 9\ ACRP\ \text{(purple)} \\ 1p \longrightarrow 3\ ACRp\ \text{(red)} \\ 3P \longrightarrow 3\ ACrP \\ 1p \longrightarrow 1\ ACrp \end{matrix} \Big\} \text{(white)}$$

The expected ratio, 9 purple: 3 red: 4 white, is a converted 9:3:3:1 ratio. Figure 6–1 shows an ear bearing purple, red, and white kernels in a 9:3:4 ratio. Similar conversions are demonstrated in Table 6–1.

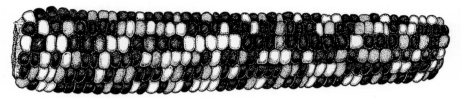

Figure 6–1   A corn ear bearing purple, red, and white kernels in a 9:3:4 ratio.

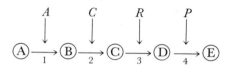

Figure 6–2

It is simple enough to devise a model to explain a situation like the inheritance of aleurone color (see Fig. 6–2). The circles represent a series of related compounds which are interconvertible. Thus A can be converted to B, B to C, and so on. Compounds A, B, and C are colorless, D is red, and E is purple. Genes *A, C, R,* and *P* allow these reactions to proceed by producing the necessary enzymes. The recessive alleles *a, c, r,* and *p* are inactive. Therefore, an individual which is *aa, cc,* or *rr* cannot produce pigment because the reaction chain is blocked at step 1, 2, or 3. An individual of genotype *AACCRRpp* is red, because D can be produced but cannot be converted to E. Thus the genes controlling the end reactions cannot express themselves if the dominant alleles of the genes controlling the early steps in the chain of chemical reactions are not functioning.

TABLE 6–1

GENOTYPE OF SELF-POLLINATED PLANT	F$_1$ RATIOS	CONVERTED RATIO
AACcRrPP or *AaCcRRPP*	9 purple: 7 white	9:3:3:1
AaCcRrPP	27 purple: 37 white	27:9:9:9:3:3:3:1
AACcRrPp or *AaCcRRPp*	28 white: 27 purple: 9 red	27:9:9:9:3:3:3:1

Fruit shape in squash

Two pairs of genes which affect fruit shape and are independently transmitted exist in the summer squash, *Cucurbita pepo*. The three fruit shapes and the genotypes which produce them are shown in Figure 6–3.

DISC	SPHERE	ELONGATE
A A B B*	*A A b b**	*a a b b**
A A B b	*A a b b*	
A a B B	*a a B B**	
A a B b	*a a B b*	

[handwritten notes to the right of figure:]

sphere
$Aa\,Bb \times aabb$

$AaBb$ 1
$AaBb$ ⎱ 2
$aa\,Bb$ ⎰
$aa\,bb$ 1

Figure 6–3

Races of the genotypes marked with an asterisk breed true. The shape of the fruit depends upon whether growth has been primarily in length or width. The homozygous double recessive grows primarily in length and produces as a consequence sausage-shaped, elongate fruit. The individual homozygous for but one set of recessive genes grows equally in length and width and produces spherical squash. The disc squash grows primarily in width. Thus the dominant alleles appear to favor growth in width. If a doubly heterozygous disc squash is test crossed to an elongate squash, we find that the normal 1:1:1:1 ratio expected for the phenotypic classes among the offspring is converted to 1 disc:2 sphere:1 elongate.

Comb shape in chickens

Two pairs of genes which interact to affect comb size and shape but are independently transmitted exist in chickens. The phenotypes and the genotypes which produce them are shown in Figure 6–4.

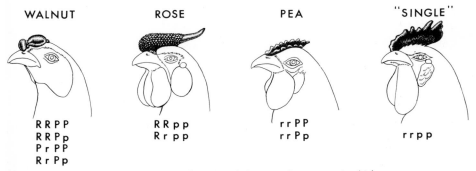

WALNUT	ROSE	PEA	"SINGLE"
R R P P	R R p p	r r P P	r r p p
R R P p	R r p p	r r P p	
P r P P			
R r P p			

Figure 6–4   The relation between comb size and shape and genotype in chickens.

The combs from birds lacking a P gene (Rose and Single) are relatively large. Combs from birds lacking an R gene (Pea and Single) are narrow and toothed, whereas those containing an R gene are lobate or papillate. If doubly heterozygous Walnut fowl interbreed, they will produce an F_1 containing Walnut, Rose, Pea, and Single individuals in a $9:3:3:1$ ratio. Here then is an example of gene interaction which does *not* disturb the classical genetic ratios.

Deviations from expected ratios and the use of the "chi-square" technique

Karl Pearson has developed a statistical technique which enables the investigator to determine how closely an experimentally determined set of ratios fits a given theoretical expectation. We will now see how this technique, the *chi-square method,* may be applied to a given set of data.

Drosophila males with dumpy wings are mated to virgin females with sepia-colored eyes. The offspring are all normal in phenotype, and these are interbred to produce an F_2 generation.

TABLE 6–2

wing shape	normal	dumpy	normal	dumpy
eye color	normal	normal	sepia	sepia
observed numbers	730	220	225	89
expected numbers on the basis of a 9:3:3:1 ratio.	711	237	237	79
deviations	+19	−17	−12	+10

$$\chi^2 = \sum \frac{d^2}{e} = \frac{19^2}{711} + \frac{17^2}{237} + \frac{12^2}{237} + \frac{10^2}{79} = \frac{2560}{711} = 3.6$$

n = number of classes = 4
D/F = number of degrees of freedom = n − 1 = 3.   P = 0.31

The first row of numbers in Table 6–2 gives the numbers of individuals found in each of four phenotypic classes in the F_2 generation. These data look like they fit a $9:3:3:1$ ratio, which is what one would expect, if the genes affecting wing shape and eye color were transmitted independently,

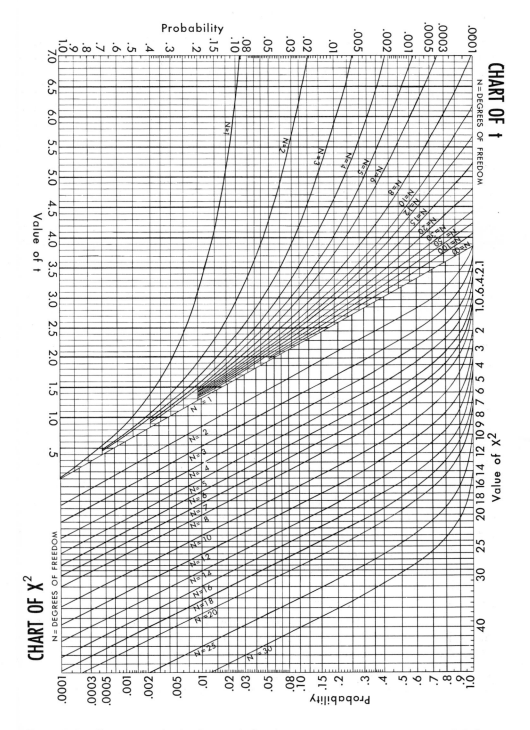

Figure 6–5 Charts giving the distribution of x^2 and t. (Redrawn from *Genetics Notes* by J. F. Crow, Burgess Publishing Co.)

and if the abnormal alleles were recessive to the normal ones. The total
number of flies is 1264. One-sixteenth of 1264 is 79; $\frac{3}{16}$ths of 1264 is 237;
$\frac{9}{16}$ths is 711. The deviations shown in the third row are obtained by subtract-
ing the expected numbers from the observed ones. The sum of the deviations
will be zero. To calculate chi-square (χ^2), square each deviation, and then
divide the squared deviation by the expected number in each class. Finally
all quotients are summed. The explanation can be expressed symbolically
by $\chi^2 = \sum \frac{d^2}{e}$. Here the Greek letter capital sigma (Σ) = the sum of, d =
deviation, and e = expected number. The value obtained for chi-square is
3.6. The value for chi-square must now be converted into a P value. This is
done by using the graph shown in Figure 6–5. There are 16 curves on the
graph and which one is used depends upon the "degrees of freedom,"
symbolized D/F. The number of degrees of freedom is one less than the
number of classes. Since there are four classes of offspring, D/F = 3.
Using the third curve from the right we find that a χ^2 of 3.6 corresponds
roughly to a P value of 0.31. A probability of 0.31 means that were the
experiment repeated independently many times, 31 per cent of the time
one would obtain chance deviations as large or larger than those just
observed. It is therefore reasonable to conclude that the data are an
example of a 9:3:3:1 ratio.

Let us suppose in another similar experiment we calculate a value for
chi-square of 8 which corresponds to a P value of 0.05 (see Fig. 6–5). In
such a case it would be unreasonable to assume our data fit a 9:3:3:1
ratio, since one would obtain chance deviations as large or larger than those
observed only once in 20 repetitions. It has been decided arbitrarily that
a P value equal to or less than 0.05 indicates that the observed and
expected values *are* significantly different. If the P values are equal to or
less than 0.05 but greater than 0.01 the results are said to be *significantly
different;* P values $\leq$ 0.01 > 0.001 are *highly significant;* and those $\leq$ 0.001
are called *very highly significant* by convention.

The chi-square method cannot be applied to percentages derived from
numerical values, and it should not be used in situations where the number in any class is less than five.

Occasions arise where a given set of data may approximate either of two
theoretical ratios (1:1 versus 9:7, for example). By simple arithmetic it will
be obvious that the data are closer to one ratio than to the other. However,
the question may be raised as to whether the second ratio can be excluded
from consideration. A chi square test will be useful in such a situation.

6–1. What genotypic ratios will be observed in the F_1 produced by crossing two individuals of genotype $AaBb$, if a and b cause death early in embryogenesis when homozygous?

6–2. In the mouse, pigment will not be produced in the hair unless the gene C is present. If the individual is CC or Cc, its coat coloration depends upon its genotype with respect to another gene A on a different chromosome. Aa or AA individuals are gray; aa individuals are black. Two gray mice produce a litter containing gray, albino, and black mice in a ratio of $9:4:3$. What was the genotype of the parents?

6–3. In the chicken, pigment will not be produced in the plumage unless the gene C is present. A second gene I which inhibits pigment formation is located on a different chromosome. The White Leghorn breed of chickens has the genotype $IICC$, whereas the White Plymouth Rock is $iicc$. F_1 individuals from a White Leghorn-White Plymouth Rock cross are bred together to produce an F_2. What are the expected phenotypic ratios in the F_2?

6–4. In maize a gene I inhibits pigment production in the kernel if heterozygous or homozygous. A corn plant is known to be of genotype $CCRRPP$, but its genotype with respect to A and I is unknown. Upon self-pollination it produces ears bearing 1491 white and 311 purple kernels. It is obvious that these data fit a $13:3$ ratio more closely than a $3:1$ ratio. What do you conclude was the genotype of the parent plant? Calculate χ^2 on the assumption that the above data are an example of a $3:1$ ratio. Can this assumption be rejected?

6–5. Pollen from a corn plant of genotype $AACCRRPP$ is placed upon the silks of a corn plant of genotype $AACCrrPP$. What are the genotypes of the pericarp, endosperm, and embryo of the kernels which result? What will be the color of the aleurone?

6–6. In *Drosophila* the dull red eye color is due to the presence of a bright red and a dark brown pigment. Individuals homozygous for the recessive, second chromosomal gene *brown* cannot synthesize the red pigment. Individuals homozygous for the recessive, third chromosomal gene *scarlet* cannot synthesize the brown pigment. Individuals heterozygous for *brown* and *scarlet* are crossed and produce 9008 offspring. 5177 are normal, 1777 are brown, 1710 are scarlet, and 344 white-eyed. Diagram the cross and explain the results. Perform a χ^2 to determine if the data represent a $9:3:3:1$ ratio. Independent experiments have shown that white-eyed flies are only 60 per cent as viable as flies with pigmented eyes. After making an appropriate correction for the lowered viability of white-eyed flies perform a second χ^2 analysis. Contrast your results.

6–7. How may a classical $9:3:3:1$ ratio be converted into a (1) $12:3:1$, (2) $9:3:4$, (3) $9:7$, (4) $15:1$, (5) $13:3$, or a (6) $9:6:1$ ratio?

6–8. Lang crossed snails of a red-shelled race with those of a yellow-shelled race and obtained offspring. These were bred together and produced an F_2. The ratio of red- to yellow-shelled individuals in the young F_2 population was $1:3$. However, as the individuals aged some of the yellow ones became red. After one year the ratio was 3 red : 1 yellow. Explain this "reversal of dominance."

6–9. Demonstrate with respect to the inheritance of aleurone pigmentation in maize that gene R interacts with C in a complementary fashion; whereas gene R interacts with gene P in an epistatic fashion.

BIBLIOGRAPHY

Babcock, E. B., and R. E. Clausen 1927 Genetics in Relation to Agriculture, Chap. 13. McGraw-Hill, New York.

Bateson, W., and R. C. Punnett 1906 Comb characters. Report to Evolution Committee of the Royal Society of London, II, pp. 11–16.

Emerson, R. A., G. W. Beadle, and A. C. Fraser 1935 A summary of linkage studies in maize. Cornell Univ. Agr. Exper. Sta. Mem. *180*.

Fisher, R. A. 1946 Statistical Methods for Research Workers, 10th ed. Oliver & Boyd, Edinburgh, Scotland.

Lang, A. 1908 Über die Bastarde von *Helix hortensis* Müller und *Helix nemoralis* L. (Mit Beiträgen von Bosshard, Hesse und Kleiner.) Festschrift d. Universität Jena.

Senders, V. L. 1958 Measurement and Statistics. Oxford University Press, New York.

Sinnott, E. W. 1927 A factorial analysis of certain shape characters in squash fruits. Am. Naturalist *61*: 333–44.

Smith, C. A. B. 1954 Biomathematics, Chap. 21: Simple statistical procedures. C. Griffin & Co., London.

Snedecor, G. W. 1946 Statistical Methods. Iowa State University Press, Ames.

Chapter 7

Quantitative Inheritance

Introduction

Quantitative inheritance refers to inheritance which depends upon the cumulative action of many genes, each of which produces a small effect. The inheritance of grain yield in various crops, beef and milk production in cattle, egg production in hens, and DDT resistance in *Drosophila* are examples of traits depending upon such multifactor inheritance. In man, multifactor inheritance is probably responsible for much of the significant variability which exists between the members of a population with respect to characteristics such as intelligence, the possession of special aptitudes, stature, weight, skin pigmentation, susceptibility to various pathological and infectious conditions, and so on. Of course, it is well established that environmental factors play an important role in modifying the expression of such inherited potentialities.

Since the study of quantitative inheritance requires a great deal of counting and measuring, it is essential that the student understand certain statistical methods which enable one to boil down large masses of data into a form which is more readily handled.

The statistical approach

Let us assume that we wish to study the distribution of heights in a population of individuals from an inbred strain of plants. We go to a plot of ground where thousands of plants are growing and measure the heights of 100 individuals. The data are assembled, and the heights are listed in

GENETICS

order ranging from tallest to shortest. To simplify matters the data are divided into a series of eleven height classes (which are presented in the first column of Table 7–1). Note that the intervals covered in all classes are equal

TABLE 7–1

Class Interval	x Class Midpoint	f No. of Individuals in Class Interval	fx	fx²
100.0–109.9 cm.	105 cm.	0	0	0
90.0– 99.9 cm.	95 cm.	1	95	9025
80.0– 89.9 cm.	85 cm.	3	225	21675
70.0– 79.9 cm.	75 cm.	7	525	39375
60.0– 69.9 cm.	65 cm.	18	1170	76050
50.0– 59.9 cm.	55 cm.	23	1265	69575
40.0– 49.9 cm.	45 cm.	21	945	42525
30.0– 39.9 cm.	35 cm.	17	595	20825
20.0– 29.9 cm.	25 cm.	9	225	5625
10.0– 19.9 cm.	15 cm.	1	15	225
0– 9.9 cm.	5 cm.	0	0	0
		100	5090	284,900
		Σf	Σfx	Σfx^2
				$\bar{x} = 50.90$

($\sim$10 cm.). Each class midpoint is given in the second column. We see that there were no plants shorter than 10 cm. or taller than 99.9 cm. Twenty-three plants were in the 55 cm. class (that is, their heights fell in the 50.0 through 59.9 cm. interval). This is the class which contains more individuals than any other, and it is called the *modal class*. Let us call each value in the second column a value of x, and each value in the third column a value of f. Multiply the value of x in one row by the value of f in the same row and put the product in column 4. Σf gives the total number of individuals examined, and Σfx gives the summation of the heights of the entire population. By convention the symbol $\bar{x}$ is used to denote the *mean* or *average*.

$$\bar{x} = \frac{\Sigma fx}{\Sigma f} = \frac{5090}{100} = 50.90 \text{ cm. per plant.}$$

Thus the average plant height is about 51 cm.

In Figure 7–1A the data in Table 7–1 have been plotted graphically. Figure 7–1B shows similar curves drawn for two hypothetical populations which have the same average but which differ in variability. Population A is obviously more uniform than population B. To distinguish population A from population B we need to be able to express the variability or "spread"

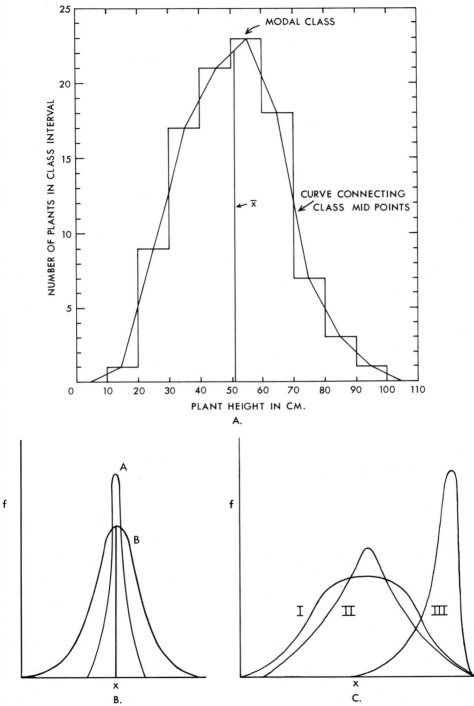

Figure 7-1

of values in each population. The term used to express such variability is the standard deviation which is symbolized by s.

$$s = \sqrt{\frac{\Sigma fx^2 - x^2\Sigma f}{(\Sigma f) - 1}} = \sqrt{\frac{284{,}900 - (50.90^2 \times 100)}{99}}$$

$$= \sqrt{\frac{25{,}819}{99}} = \sqrt{260.7980} = 16.15$$

Thus the data in Table 7–1 can be boiled down to two figures, the average ($\bar{x}$) and its standard deviation (s), and such data can be presented as follows $\bar{x} \pm$ s, or in this case 50.90 ± 16.15.

The arithmetic methods just presented apply to distributions of measured values which are *normal* (that is, they follow the shapes of curves such as those seen in Fig. 7–1A and 7–1B). Such methods cannot be used for frequency distributions that are flat-topped, as in Figure 7–1C (I); pointed, as in Figure 7–1C(II); or asymmetric, as in Figure 7–1C (III).

Table 7–2 gives data which show how much of the area under a normal frequency distribution curve is included by different multiples of s.

TABLE 7–2

$\bar{x} \pm 1s$	68%
$\bar{x} \pm 1.96s$	95%
$\bar{x} \pm 2s$	96%
$\bar{x} \pm 2.576s$	99%
$\bar{x} \pm 3s$	99.7%

Another useful term is the *coefficient of variation*, v, which expresses the standard deviation as a percentage of the mean.

$$v = \frac{100s}{\bar{x}} = 31.7\%$$

In the experiment just described we took a sample of 100 plants from a much larger population of plants. Let us assume the large population contained 10,000 plants. We are interested in determining what information the small sample gives about the larger population. If we repeated the previously described experiment 100 times, we would have (at great labor) examined the entire population, and we would have 100 values of $\bar{x} \pm$ s. If we were to make a plot of the frequency distribution of the 100 mean values, we would again get a bell-shaped curve similar to those shown in Figures 7–1A and B. The average value for the 100 means would correspond to the total population mean. The standard deviation of the distribution of all the means would express the spread of the averages.

Statisticians have shown by suitable mathematical analysis that the standard deviation of the distribution of all the means (which is called the *standard error* for short and symbolized by s_x) can be estimated from the standard deviation. In fact $s_{\bar{x}} = \dfrac{s}{\sqrt{\Sigma f}}$. In our example $s_{\bar{x}} = \dfrac{16.15}{\sqrt{100}} = 1.615$. The standard error is thus a measure of how much the means of other similar samples drawn from the same larger population will vary.

It is conventional in scientific publications to present data such as those presented in Table 7–1 in terms of the mean plus or minus the standard error rather than the standard deviation (that is: 50.90 ± 1.62).

It is often necessary to determine the significance of the difference between two means. This can be done by substituting the appropriate values in the following equation and calculating a value for t.

$$t = \frac{\bar{x}_a - \bar{x}_b}{\sqrt{s_c{}^2\left(\dfrac{1}{N_a} + \dfrac{1}{N_b}\right)}}; \text{ where } s_c{}^2 = \frac{(N_a - 1)s_a{}^2 + (N_b - 1)s_b{}^2}{N_a + N_b - 2};$$

and where $D/F = N_a + N_b - 2$

here $\bar{x}_a$ and $\bar{x}_b$ are the 2 means, s_a and s_b are the corresponding standard deviations and N_a and N_b are the numbers of individuals examined in each case (Σf in Table 7–1).

The use of this formula can be demonstrated by comparing two populations (a and b) which give two different values for average height (16.73 and 17.35 inches, respectively) and which differ considerably in their variability. In population a, 178 individuals are measured; in population b, 187 (see Table 7–3).

TABLE 7–3

Population	$\bar{x}$	s	v	N or Σf
a	16.73	0.99	5.9%	178
b	17.35	2.15	12.4%	187

$$t = \frac{17.35 - 16.73}{\sqrt{(2.846)\left(\dfrac{1}{178} + \dfrac{1}{187}\right)}} = \frac{0.62}{0.177} = 3.5$$

$$D/F = 178 + 187 - 2 = 363$$

The value of t when calculated turns out to be 3.5 for 363 degrees of freedom. The chart of the distribution of t given in Figure 6–5 enables us to convert the calculated value of t to a probability of roughly 0.0005. Therefore the means are very highly significantly different.

The multiple factor hypothesis

In the case of the inheritance of quantitative characters there is an absence of clear-cut segregation into readily recognizable classes showing typical Mendelian ratios. This phenomenon is well demonstrated by data on the inheritance of ear length in corn collected by Emerson and East (see Fig. 7–2). Two strains of corn differing very significantly in mean ear length were crossed and produced an F_1. The mean ear length of the F_1

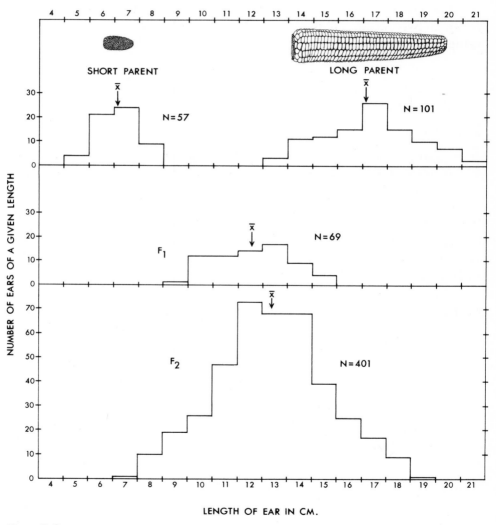

Figure 7–2

population was intermediate between the parental means. F_1 individuals upon self-pollination produced an F_2. The F_1 and F_2 means were not significantly different. The coefficient of variation, however, was much higher in the F_2 population than in the F_1 population. In fact, the spread is so great in the F_2 that the extreme values obtained overlap the values found in the two P_1 populations.

To explain situations like the one just described the multiple factor hypothesis was advanced by the Swedish geneticist Nilsson-Ehle in 1908 and extended by East, an American, in 1910. The hypothesis assumes that the trait in question results from the cumulative action of multiple sets of independently transmitted genes each of which produces only a small effect.

The following hypothetical model will illustrate the main points of the hypothesis. Let us suppose that the genotype of the strain of corn with long ears is *AABBCC* and that of the short-eared strain is *aabbcc*. With respect to all other genes the two strains are identical. Assume further that the environment affects all genotypes equally and therefore can be disregarded. Let all alleles represented by small letters produce one unit of X and those represented by large letters produce 3 units of X. Each unit of substance X in turn allows the ear to grow one centimeter in length. The cross is diagrammed in Figure 7–3. All the ears produced by the short P_1 race should be 6 cm. long, all those produced by the long P_1 race should be 18 cm. long, and the F_1 population should be intermediate with all ears 12 cm. long. The F_2 population contains individuals which result from 64 different classes of fertilizations and belong to 27 genotypic classes. The genotypic classes in turn give rise to seven phenotypic classes which produce ears which vary in length from 6 to 18 cm. The mean ear length of the F_2 is identical with that of the F_1, but the F_2 population shows great variability, whereas the F_1 population showed none. Furthermore $\frac{1}{64}$th of the F_2 plants has ears as short as those of the short P_1 parent and a similar proportion has ears as long as those of the long P_1 parent. The above model does fit the observed facts rather well, although it is obviously an oversimplification. Furthermore, the model suggests that the number of allelic pairs of genes involved in a given case of quantitative inheritance should be related to the proportion of F_2 individuals similar in phenotype to one of the P_1 parents. That proportion in fact should be $\frac{1}{4^n}$, where n is the number of allelic gene pairs. For example, in our model where n = 3; $1/(4)^3 = \frac{1}{64}$, the proportion of F_2 individuals with ears as long as those from the long P_1 parent.

According to this model, since the genes in question are additive in their effects, the F_1 population mean should fall halfway between the means of the two P_1 populations. This happens often, but frequently the F_1 mean

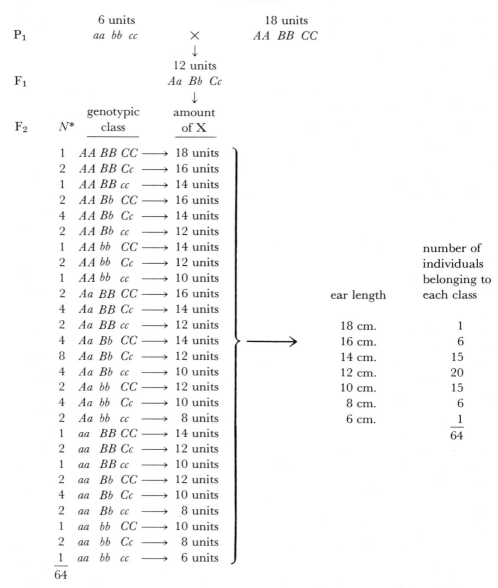

		6 units			18 units
P$_1$		*aa bb cc*	×		*AA BB CC*

↓

12 units
Aa Bb Cc

↓

F$_2$	N*	genotypic class	amount of X
	1	*AA BB CC* ⟶	18 units
	2	*AA BB Cc* ⟶	16 units
	1	*AA BB cc* ⟶	14 units
	2	*AA Bb CC* ⟶	16 units
	4	*AA Bb Cc* ⟶	14 units
	2	*AA Bb cc* ⟶	12 units
	1	*AA bb CC* ⟶	14 units
	2	*AA bb Cc* ⟶	12 units
	1	*AA bb cc* ⟶	10 units
	2	*Aa BB CC* ⟶	16 units
	4	*Aa BB Cc* ⟶	14 units
	2	*Aa BB cc* ⟶	12 units
	4	*Aa Bb CC* ⟶	14 units
	8	*Aa Bb Cc* ⟶	12 units
	4	*Aa Bb cc* ⟶	10 units
	2	*Aa bb CC* ⟶	12 units
	4	*Aa bb Cc* ⟶	10 units
	2	*Aa bb cc* ⟶	8 units
	1	*aa BB CC* ⟶	14 units
	2	*aa BB Cc* ⟶	12 units
	1	*aa BB cc* ⟶	10 units
	2	*aa Bb CC* ⟶	12 units
	4	*aa Bb Cc* ⟶	10 units
	2	*aa Bb cc* ⟶	8 units
	1	*aa bb CC* ⟶	10 units
	2	*aa bb Cc* ⟶	8 units
	1	*aa bb cc* ⟶	6 units

64

ear length	number of individuals belonging to each class
18 cm.	1
16 cm.	6
14 cm.	15
12 cm.	20
10 cm.	15
8 cm.	6
6 cm.	1
	64

* N = the number of individuals belonging to each class.

Figure 7–3

approximates the geometric[1] rather than the arithmetic mean between the parental values. This suggests that in some cases each set of multiple genes acts to multiply by some constant factor the effect of the residual genotype upon the trait.

---

[1] arithmetic mean = $\dfrac{x_a + x_b}{2}$; geometric mean = $\sqrt{x_a \cdot x_b}$

Selection for quantitative characters

Since most characteristics of practical significance in agriculture and animal husbandry depend upon multifactorial inheritance, animal and plant breeders are primarily concerned with selection for quantitative characters.

An example of the effect of selection can be taken from Figure 7–3. Let us assume that corn plants producing ears 16 cm. long are selected, and consequently that individuals of genotypes *AaBBCC, AABbCC,* or *AABBCc* serve as progenitors of the next generation. Any of these plants upon self-fertilization or upon cross-fertilization brings forth offspring, ¼th of which produces ears 14 cm. long, ½ of which produces ears 16 cm. long, and ¼th of which produces ears 18 cm. long. Selection has therefore produced a second generation whose mean equals that of the selected parents and whose variability is reduced over that of the population from which the parents were selected.

In most cases when actual breeding experiments are carried out one finds that the progeny, instead of showing a mean identical to their selected parents, shows one intermediate between the original population mean and the expected value. As a consequence selection is less efficient than predicted. The reason that our expectations are not fulfilled is that the true situation is far more complicated than the model. The model assumes that all the variability encountered results from the segregation of many genes, each of which has a simple additive effect. However, the total variability experienced by the breeder includes, in addition to this component, variability introduced by the environment and deviations from the additive scheme introduced by genes which interact or show dominance.

For example, a breeder might discard plants of the desired genotypes which had poor levels of performance because of suboptimal nutrition and include inferior genotypes that were environmentally fortunate. As a consequence some plants of genotypes such as *AAbbCC* or *AaBbCC* might be included in the selected sample, and they would be responsible for a shift of the mean toward lower values and for increased variation. It is of course possible to produce populations which are genetically homogeneous. Highly inbred lines, or the F_1 of a cross between two such lines, or a population of organisms propagated vegetatively, are, with the exception of individuals bearing spontaneous mutations, genetically homogeneous. Variability shown in such populations is due almost entirely to environmental inhomogeneities. An estimate of the relative contribution of the hereditary and environmental components to the variability of a genetically nonhomogeneous population (A) can be obtained by comparing the variance[2] of this

---

[2] The amount of variation is sometimes expressed as the variance. When all the values in the population are expressed as deviations from the population mean, the variance is the mean of the squared deviations. The standard deviation is the square root of the variance.

population to that of a genetically homogeneous population (B) grown under the same range of normal environmental conditions. The difference in variance between A and B is the genetic component. Thus, if population A had a variance of 0.5 and population B had a variance of 0.3, the genotypic variance would be 0.2. Thus the total variability would be made up of environmental and genetic components contributing 60 per cent and 40 per cent to the total, respectively.

Breeders experience an additional and quite different source of error when they attempt to select individuals of superior genotype on the basis of their phenotypic performance, in those situations where some of the genes involved in the production of the character under study show domi-nance or interact. Thus, if the phenotype produced by AA is undetectably different from that produced by Aa individuals, then individuals of both genotypes will be selected on the basis of their performance. As the unde-sirable gene a segregates out in later generations the population mean will be lowered and the variance raised. In the case of gene interaction, recom-bination will often separate advantageous gene constellations again with a resulting increase in variance and a mean performance below the ideal.

Thus the breeder through selection can only hope to improve those characteristics which primarily depend upon the additive effects of many genes. Consequently it is of great importance to have some measure as to what portion of the phenotypic variance is ascribable to genes with additive effects. If the phenotypic variance is symbolized by V_P, then $V_P = V_E + V_A + V_D + V_I$; where V_E is the variance component due to the environ-ment, V_A is the variance component due to genes with additive effects, V_D is the variance component due to genes showing dominance, and V_I is the variance component due to interacting genes. The estimate of importance to the breeder is the so-called *heritability* of a trait. Heritability, symbolized by H, is equal to $\dfrac{V_A}{V_P}$. The estimation of heritabilities has been made for

TABLE 7–4 Heritability Values for Various Characteristics in Domestic and Laboratory Animals (after Falconer).

Cows—per cent butterfat (0.6), milk yield (0.3)
Pigs—body length (0.5), weight at 180 days (0.3), litter size (0.15)
Sheep—length of wool (0.55), body weight (0.35)
Poultry—egg weight (0.6), age at laying first egg (0.5), body weight (0.1)
Rats—age at puberty in females (0.15)
Mice—tail length at 6 weeks (0.6), body weight at 6 weeks (0.35), size of first litter (0.15)

Drosophila melanogaster—number of abdominal bristles (0.5), thorax length (0.4), ovary size (0.3), egg production (0.2)

a great variety of characters, chiefly in domestic and laboratory animals (see Table 7–4). In fact such estimations form the major subject of research in this area. The precise techniques which involve making correlations between the performances of relatives of varying degrees of relationship can be found in Falconer's book. Once the heritability of a given trait is estimated it is possible for the breeder to predict the results of selection. The predicted offspring average equals the population mean plus the difference between this mean and the mean of the selected parents multiplied by the heritability. Take, for example, the case where the mean weight of a population of 180 day-old pigs is 110 lbs. and the selected parents weighed 120 and 140 lbs. According to Table 7–4 the heritability of weight in pigs is 0.3. Therefore the expected offspring average will be

$$110 + \left[\left(\frac{120 + 140}{2} - 110 \right) \times 0.3 \right] = 116 \text{ lbs.}$$

7–1. Consider a hypothetical case of quantitative inheritance of fruit weight in which each of the capital-letter genes acts to *multiply* by some constant factor the effect of the residual genotype upon the trait. Assume the residual genotype is respon- sible for a fruit weight of 10 gms. and that each capital-letter gene doubles the effect of the residual genotype as shown below.

Number of capital- letter genes	Weight (Gm.)
0	10
1	20
2	40
3	80
4	160
5	320
6	640

Therefore the inbred light parent, *aabbcc*, has a mean fruit weight of 10 gm. and the inbred heavy parent, *AABBCC*, has a mean fruit weight of 640 gm. Deter- mine $\bar{x}$ for the F_1 and F_2 populations. Graph the frequency distribution for the F_2 population. Do you obtain a bell-shaped curve?

7–2. The data used in plotting Figure 7–2 are shown below.
Calculate $\bar{x}$, v, and $s_{\bar{x}}$ in each case.

Ear Length in cm.

	5	6	7	8	9	10	11	12	13	14	15	16	17	18	19	20	21
Long Parent									3	11	12	15	26	15	10	7	2
Short Parent	4	21	24	8													
F_1					1	12	12	14	17	9	4						
F_2				1	10	19	26	47	73	68	68	39	25	15	9	1	

7–3. Consider a hypothetical case of quantitative inheritance involving the genes *A, B, C,* and *D*. Each capital-letter gene contributes 3 cm. to the height of the organism, whereas each small-letter gene contributes 1 cm. A cross is made between individuals of an inbred strain of genotype *AAbbCCdd* and of genotype *aaBBccDD*. F_1 individuals are crossed to give an F_2. Diagram the results and discuss the spread of phenotypes expected in the parental, F_1, and F_2 populations.

7–4. Hayes has reported the following results from a quantitative study of leaf number in two varieties of tobacco and the hybrids between them.

Number of Leaves per Plant

	14	15	16	17	18	19	20	21	22	23	24	25	26	27	28	29	30	31	32	33	T
Cuban					3	16	34	46	20	5											124
Havana				1	10	11	23	34	31	16	12	3	2								143
F_1 from $C \times H$			1	1	3	8	39	60	30	7		1									150
F_2 from $F_1 \times F_1$	3	4	8	8	20	18	30	24	25	17	16	5	4	3	1	1	1	1	2	1	192

T = total plants observed

Contrast the values for $\bar{x}$ and v for the four populations. What conclusions can you reach as to the inheritance of leaf number in the tobacco strains studied? Note that these distributions of values differ from the others described in that they are *discontinuous*. Since one is measuring leaf number, all the values recorded are *whole* numbers. In the other examples used which involved length, weight, etc., the measurements recorded were carried out several decimal places. As a consequence there was a continuous spectrum of values. Inferences based upon calculations assuming a normal distribution are sometimes unreliable, if the distribution is discontinuous.

7–5. Davenport has suggested that differences in pigmentation between Negroes and whites are due to two independent loci, each of which is represented by two alleles (A^1 and A^2 at one locus and B^1 and B^2 at the other). A^2 and B^2 genes produce dark pigmentation and are cumulative in their effects. Thus "whites" have no A^2 or B^2 alleles, "light browns" have 1; "medium browns" 2; "dark browns" 3; and "blacks" are $A^2A^2B^2B^2$. Can a "white-black" mating produce "white" or "black" offspring? Can a "white-medium brown" mating produce "black" offspring? What phenotypes should be found among the offspring of two "medium brown" individuals?

BIBLIOGRAPHY

Bailey, N. T. J.   1959   Statistical Methods in Biology. Wiley, New York.

Burton, E. W.   1951   Quantitative inheritance in Pearl Millet. Agr. J. *43*: 409–17.

Chai, C. K.   1956   Analysis of quantitative inheritance of body size in mice. Genetics *41*: 157–78.

Clark, C. E.   1953   An Introduction to Statistics, Wiley, New York.

Davenport, C. B.   1913   Heredity of Skin Color in Negro-White Crosses. Carnegie Inst. Wash. Pub. *188*. 106 pp.

East, E. N.   1910   A Mendelian interpretation of variation that is apparently continuous. Am. Nat. *44*: 65–82.

Emerson, R. A., and E. M. East   1913   The inheritance of quantitative characters in maize. Nebraska Agr. Exp. Sta. Res. Bull. *2*.

Falconer, D. S. 1960 Introduction to Quantitative Genetics. Ronald Press, New York.

Green, E. L. 1954 Quantitative genetics of skeletal variation in the mouse. J. Natl. Cancer Inst. *15*: 609–24.

Hayes, H. K. 1912 Correlation and inheritance in *Nicotiana tabacum.* Conn. Agr. Exp. Sta. Bull. *171*: 1–451.

Hoel, P. G. 1960 Elementary Statistics. Wiley, New York.

Hutt, F. B. 1958 Genetic resistance to disease in domestic animals. Comstock Pbl., Ithaca, New York.

Immer, F. R. 1952 Applied Statistics. Burgess Publ. Co., Minneapolis, Minn.

Kempthorne, O. 1957 An Introduction to Genetic Statistics. Wiley, New York.

King, J. C. 1955 Integration of the gene pool as demonstrated by resistance to DDT. Amer. Nat. *89*: 39–46.

Mather, K. 1949 Biometrical Genetics. Dover Publ., New York.

Mohamed, A. H. 1959 Inheritance of quantitative characters in *Zea mays.* I. Estimation of the number of genes controlling the time of maturity. Genetics *44*: 713–24.

Nilsson-Ehle, H. 1908 Einige Ergebnisse von Kreuzungen bei Hafer und Weizen. Dot Notiser.

Robertson, F. W. 1957 Studies in quantitative inheritance. XI. Genetic and environmental correlation between body size and egg production in *Drosophila melanogaster.* J. Genetics *55*: 428–43.

Smith, H. H. 1944 Recent studies on inheritance of quantitative characters in plants. Botan. Rev. *10*: 349–82.

Chapter 8

Linked Genes and Linkage Groups

Introduction

In Chapters 5 through 7 we dealt with the inheritance of traits which first involved one and then a number of gene pairs. In the latter instance the situation was sometimes relatively simple; but often complications arose which were due to interactions between genes with respect to their determination of phenotype. Up to now all the genes studied have been independent in their transmission because they resided on different physical entities. We must now study genes which reside on the same chromosome and which therefore show *linkage* rather than independent assortment during their transmission to gametes.

Before beginning a discussion of linked genes it will be useful to explain a superior method for symbolizing genetic crosses. Let us consider a third chromosomal mutation in *Drosophila melanogaster* which causes the body color to be darker than normal. The mutant is called *ebony body* and the mutant gene is symbolized by e. The normal gene is symbolized by $+^e$. Other independent mutations at the ebony locus are distinguished by giving them superscripts. For example, the mutant *ebony-sooty* is symbolized by e^s. Genes recessive to the normal or wild type allele are always given a symbol beginning with a small letter. Genes dominant to their wild type allele are given symbols beginning with a capital letter. Thus the dominant mutant *Curly wing* is symbolized by *Cy*.

The *ebony claret* cross

Let us consider a cross involving two genes which are on the same chromosome. We have already described *ebony*. The gene *claret* when

homozygous gives a brownish eye color which is easily distinguished from
the brick red, wild type eye color of *Drosophila melanogaster*. The cross is
diagrammed in Figure 8–1. The fact that the genes are on the same chromosome is shown by placing the gene symbols on top of a horizontal line. Thus,
the F_1 individual has one third chromosome containing *claret* and the wild
type allele of *ebony;* the other third chromosome has *ebony* and the wild type
allele of *claret*. Sometimes the symbolism is simplified by leaving out the
second horizontal line and by omitting the superscripts for the + alleles.
This is done in the case of the F_2 genotypes, since it is obvious what the +
refers to in each case.

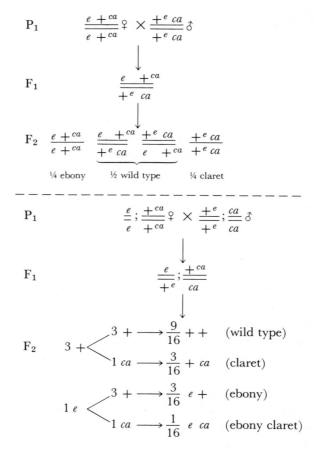

Figure 8–1

   Had *claret* and *ebony* been on different chromosomes the symbolism
followed would be that shown below the dashed horizontal line. Note that
the two different chromosome pairs are separated by semicolons. In this case
we get the classical $9:3:3:1$ ratio for the phenotypic classes shown in the
F_2 generation.

When the actual experiment was done the observed results were: 7411 wild type: 3724 claret: 3775 ebony. The calculated χ^2 was 0.86 which for 2 D/F gives a P of 0.7. Thus the data fit the expected $2:1:1$ ratio.

We see then that we have here a method for detecting whether or not two genes are on the same chromosome in *Drosophila*. Individuals homozygous for the one recessive gene are crossed to individuals homozygous for the other gene. F_1 individuals are crossed and the F_2 gives either a $2:2:1$ or a $9:3:3:1$ ratio.

Reciprocal test crosses

Let us now consider reciprocal test crosses between $F_1 + ca/e +$ individuals and *e ca* individuals. By reciprocal crosses one means that in one case the cross is between the F_1 ♂ and the *e ca* ♀; in the other F_1 ♀ and the *e ca* ♂.

I		II	
$P_1 \quad \dfrac{e\ +}{+\ ca}$ ♂ $\times$ $\dfrac{e\ ca}{e\ ca}$ ♀		$P_1 \quad \dfrac{e\ +}{+\ ca}$ ♀ $\times$ $\dfrac{e\ ca}{e\ ca}$ ♂	
↓		↓	
F_1	claret 4925	F_1	claret 3511
	ebony 5075		ebony 3480
			wild type 1516 ⎫
			ebony claret 1493 ⎭ 3009
			Total 10,000

Figure 8–2

It is seen in Figure 8–2 that the reciprocal crosses give *different* results. Had *e* and *ca* been on different chromosomes, we would expect claret, ebony, wild type, and ebony claret flies to be found among the offspring in a $1:1:1:1$ ratio. Had *e* and *ca* been on the same chromosome and had they shown *complete* linkage, we would expect claret and ebony flies to be found among the offspring in a $1:1$ ratio. This is what we observe when the P_1 male is the $e +/+ ca$ individual. However, when the P_1 female is the $e +/+ ca$ individual, we get an intermediate result as if *e* and *ca* were *incompletely* linked. You will recall (see p. 45) that in *Drosophila* exchanges occur between homologous chromosomes during oogenesis but not during spermatogenesis. The wild type and ebony claret individuals observed in Figure 8–2 result from such exchanges. They make up the *crossover classes* which in this example constitute 30 per cent of the offspring of the second cross. The frequency of such crossover classes is proportional to the distance which separates the two genes. In most diploid species crossing over occurs in *both* sexes, and as a result a cross of the type shown in Figure 8–1 would *not* produce an F_2 ratio of $2:1:1$.

In Figure 8–2 the heterozygous flies were of genotype $\frac{e\ +}{+\ ca}$. The other possible distribution of genes in heterozygotes would be $\frac{e\ ca}{+\ +}$. When both mutants are present on one homologue and the other homologous chromosome carries the plus alleles the genes are said to be in the *coupling* configuration. The *repulsion* configuration refers to the distribution exemplified by $\frac{e\ +}{+\ ca}$ flies.

Sex linkage

Most diploid organisms contain a pair of chromosomes which differ between the two sexes; these are the *sex chromosomes*. The other chromosomes are called *autosomes*. The so-called X- and Y-chromosomes of *Drosophila* are the sex chromosomes. Males are XY and females are XX; and in addition the somatic cells of both sexes contain three pairs of autosomes. The Y-chromosome is J-shaped, since its centromere is nearer one end than the other. In crosses, the Y-chromosome is symbolized by ➚. The Y is a heterochromosome (see p. 27) and is relatively inert genetically. Since it contains practically no + alleles,[1] it cannot mask the expression of recessive genes located upon its partner X-chromosome.

Sex linkage represents a special case of linkage, and it occurs when a gene which produces a certain phenotypic trait (often unrelated to secondary

I	II
white-eyed male × wild type female	white-eyed female × wild type male

P_1 $\frac{w}{\rightarrow} \times \frac{+}{+}$ P_1 $\frac{w}{w} \times \frac{+}{\rightarrow}$

$\downarrow$ $\downarrow$

F_1 $\frac{+}{w} \quad \frac{+}{\rightarrow}$ F_1 $\frac{w}{+} \quad \frac{w}{\rightarrow}$

Figure 8–3

---

[1] The Y-chromosome does carry the + allele of the X-chromosomal gene *bobbed*, which affects bristle morphology.

sexual characters) is located on a sex chromosome. The result of this situation is that in certain crosses the phenotypic trait in question may be observed only in individuals of one sex. Furthermore, one often observes differences between the results of reciprocal crosses.

These generalities can be demonstrated by making crosses between white-eyed and wild type *Drosophila*. In this case white eyes are found in individuals homozygous or *hemizygous*[2] for the recessive, X-chromosomal gene *w*. The results of such crosses are shown in Figure 8–3.

In the F_1 of cross I all flies are red-eyed, whereas in cross II the F_1 females are red-eyed and F_1 males are white-eyed. Note that, unlike the case with autosomal genes, reciprocal crosses give different results.

Deleterious sex-linked genes will affect males more frequently than females, since the gene can never be masked in the male. In man, certain diseases including Christmas disease, agammaglobulinemia, hemophilia, and red-green color-blindness are caused by sex-linked recessive genes.

Male *Drosophila* belong to the *heterogametic* sex, since they can produce two types of gametes (X-bearing and Y-bearing). Females can produce only X-bearing gametes and are therefore *homogametic*. In some organisms in which the male is the heterogametic sex, no Y-chromosome is present. Males simply produce X-bearing and X-deficient sperm. Grasshoppers and bugs such as *Protentor* (see Fig. 8–4) show this XX ♀, XO ♂ sex-chromosome mechanism. In birds, lepidoptera, reptiles, and in some fish and amphibians the male is the homogametic sex.

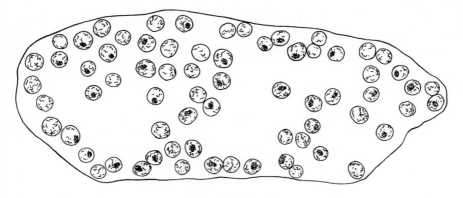

Figure 8–4   A population of spermatid nuclei seen in the testis of the hemipteran *Protentor*. The 36 X-bearing nuclei contain a densely staining chromosomal element which is missing from the 33-X-deficient nuclei.   (Redrawn from Wilson's *The Cell in Development and Heredity,* Macmillan.)

---

[2] A male *Drosophila* is hemizygous with respect to any X-chromosomal gene. Since the fly can have but a single dose of such a gene, the terms homozygous and heterozygous are meaningless.

Attached-X females

There exist strains of *Drosophila* which are characterized by having females whose X-chromosomes are joined together. These females also carry a Y-chromosome and are often represented symbolically as follows: $\widehat{X}XY$. They produce $\widehat{X}X$- and Y-bearing eggs which are normally fertilized by X or Y-bearing sperm. Four types of zygotes result: $\widehat{X}X$ Y, $\widehat{X}X$ X, Y Y, and Y X, of which only $\widehat{X}X$ Y and X Y individuals survive. Note that the male offspring are *patroclinous* (that is, they have received their X-chromosome from their *father*) and that the daughters receive *both* X's from their mother. Paternal sex-linked genes will be passed on from father to son and sex-linked genes will be passed on from mother to daughter, generation after generation. Thus, an attached-X female homozygous for the gene *w*, when crossed to a male hemizygous for the gene *f* (which produces forked bristles) will yield white-eyed daughters and forked-bristled sons. This bizarre type of sex linkage will persist generation after generation.

Assignment of mutants to linkage groups

Let us suppose that a study is made of large populations of *Drosophila* for the purpose of picking up a number of spontaneous mutations. Each time a fly which exhibits an abnormality is observed, it is bred to a normal individual. In many cases the offspring are wild type, but the F_2 contains individuals showing the abnormality. It follows that the abnormality is inherited as a recessive. Eventually a small group of mutant strains of flies is obtained, ten of which are shown in Table 8–1.

TABLE 8–1

STRAIN	PHENOTYPE	SYMBOL
1	brown eye color	*bw*
2	fused wing veins	*fu*
3	glassy eye texture	*gl*
4	hairy body	*h*
5	miniature wings	*m*
6	singed bristles	*sn*
7	scarlet eye color	*st*
8	straw body color	*stw*
9	shaven bristles	*sv*
10	vestigial wing	*vg*

The mutants *fu*, *m*, and *sn* can be placed on the X-chromosome, because they exhibit sex linkage. The results of reciprocal crosses are identical with respect to the seven other mutants. Now crosses are made between *bw* and the six other mutants, and F_1 individuals are inbred to produce an F_2. A 2:1:1 ratio is observed for crosses involving *stw* and *vg*. Therefore *bw*, *stw*, and *vg* are on the same chromosome, and these mutants are arbitrarily placed in linkage group 2. A 9:3:3:1 ratio is observed for crosses involving *gl*, *h*, *st*, and *sv*. Next crosses are made between *gl* and *h*, *st* and *sv*. A 2:1:1 ratio is observed for crosses involving *h* and *st*. Therefore *gl*, *h*, and *st* are placed in linkage group 3. Since a 9:3:3:1 ratio is observed in the F_2 of the *gl* × *sv* cross, *sv* must be placed in linkage group 4. In this way ten mutant genes have been sorted into four linkage groups. Note that the number of linkage groups is identical to the haploid number of chromosomes, a finding which has been repeated in all other organisms which have been subjected to a thorough genetic study. In the next chapter we shall see that by appropriate methods genes in a given linkage group may be placed in an orderly sequence which corresponds to their order on the chromosome.

8–1.   Sex-linked genes are often said to exhibit a "criss-cross" type of inheritance. What do you suppose is meant by this?

8–2.   A cross between a yellow tom cat and a black female results in four tortoise-shell female and three black male kittens. How is coat pigmentation inherited?

8–3.   A well-known pedigree for hemophilia is that Haldane assembled showing the descendants of Queen Victoria of England, who presumably was heterozygous for this sex-linked recessive gene.

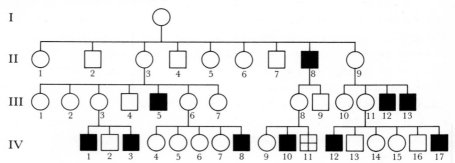

In the modified pedigree above the offspring of normal males and apparently $+/+$ females have been omitted. The husbands of Queen Victoria and of females II_3, II_9, III_3, III_6, III_8, and III_{11} and the wife of male II_8 are also deleted. Pick out the female descendants of Queen Victoria who are known transmitters of the gene. There is no record of hemophilia among the ancestors of Queen Victoria. What does this fact suggest?

8–4.   In poultry the inheritance of barred plumage (characteristic of the Barred Plymouth Rock breed) is sex linked. The barred pattern is dominant over unbarred plumage. Diagram the results of a cross between a barred female and a nonbarred male. Diagram the reciprocal cross.

8–5.   Hens contain a degenerate testis which may become functional if the ovary is destroyed. Cases of "sex reversal" have occurred in which hens are transformed into sperm-producing roosters. No change in the chromosome content of the tissues occurs, however. Such "roosters" may mate with normal hens and an F_1 may result. What would the predicted sex ratio be? (Assume X-deficient individuals die.)

8–6.   A sex-linked recessive gene in *Drosophila* symbolized by *l* causes death during embryogenesis when hemizygous. If a female heterozygous for *l* is crossed to a wild type male, what should be the sex ratio of the adult progeny?

8–7.   What would be the proportion of wild type, ebony, claret, and ebony claret F_2 individuals in the cross diagrammed in the upper portion of Figure 8–1, if crossing over also occurred in *Drosophila* males? Refer also to Figure 8–2 II. What would be the proportion of wild type, ebony, claret, and ebony claret individuals, if the P_1 individuals were *e ca*/$++$ in genotype and crossing over occurred only in females?

8–8.   A virgin female *Drosophila* upon being crossed to a *w* male produces 107 wild
       type female and 94 white-eyed male offspring. A virgin female of identical
       genotype to the P_1 female upon being crossed to a phenotypically wild type male
       produces 131 wild type males. What was the genotype of the P_1 flies in the
       second cross?

8–9.   N. W. Olsen (Science *120*: 545, 1954) has reported that eggs laid by virgin
       turkeys occasionally undergo a certain degree of embryonic development. Cyto-
       logical studies indicate that such embryos carry the diploid chromosome number.
       In instances in which the sex could be determined the embryo was found to be
       a male. How can these results be explained?

8–10. The nail-patella syndrome is a hereditary disease in man. Individuals afflicted
       with this disorder have misshapen fingernails and kneecaps which are small or
       absent. The disease is due to a dominant autosomal gene. Renwick and Lawler
       have compiled a pedigree for a mating between a husband of blood type AB
       suffering from the nail-patella syndrome and a wife of blood type O who was
       free from the disease.

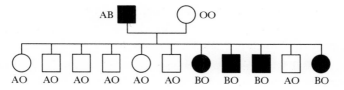

       Note that the children inheriting the father's B gene also suffer from the nail-
       patella syndrome. What conclusions can you draw from these data?

8–11. The relationship between genotype and phenotype is shown below for three
       inherited conditions: (1) white forelock in man, (2) baldness in man, and
       (3) the *fes* sterility factor in *Drosophila melanogaster*.

	(1)			(2)			(3)	
	♂	♀		♂	♀		♂	♀
f/f	white forelock	white forelock	*b/b*	bald	sparsity of hair	*fes/fes*	fertile	sterile
f/+	white forelock	normal	*b/+*	bald	normal	*fes/+*	fertile	fertile
+/+	normal	normal	*+/+*	normal	normal	*+/+*	fertile	fertile

       These conditions exemplify situations where gene expression is dependent upon
       the sex of the organism. Contrast these three conditions and then point out
       differences between this class of phenomena and sex linkage.

BIBLIOGRAPHY

Bell, J.   1926   Colour-Blindness. Eugenics Laboratory Memoirs 23. University of
       London. Cambridge University Press, Cambridge, England.

Biggs, R., and R. G. MacFarlane   1957   Human Blood Coagulation and Its
       Disorders, 2nd ed. C. C. Thomas, Springfield, Ill.

Bridges, C. B., and T. H. Morgan   1919   Contributions to the Genetics of *Drosophila melanogaster*. II. The second-chromosome group of mutant characters. Publ. Carnegie Instn. No. 278: 123–304. Washington, D. C.

Bridges, C. B., and T. H. Morgan   1923   The third-chromosome group of mutant characters of *Drosophila melanogaster*. Publ. Carnegie Instn. No. 327: 251. Washington, D. C.

Haldane, J. B. S.   1942   New Paths in Genetics. Harper, New York.

Harris, H.   1959   Human Biochemical Genetics. Cambridge University Press, Cambridge, England.

Israels, M. C. G., H. Lempert, and E. Gilbertson   1950   Haemophilia in the female. Lancet *260*: 1375–80.

Montague, A.   1959   Human Heredity. Mentor Book (MT 311), New York. (Gives complete pedigree of Queen Victoria.)

Morgan, T. H.   1919   The Physical Basis of Heredity. J. B. Lippincott, Philadelphia.

Morgan, T. H., A. H. Sturtevant, H. J. Muller, and C. B. Bridges   1923   The Mechanism of Mendelian Heredity. Holt, New York.

Morgan, T. H., and C. B. Bridges   1916   Sex-linked Inheritance in *Drosophila*. Publ. Carnegie Instn. No. 237: 1–88. Washington, D. C.

Morgan, T. H., C. B. Bridges, and A. H. Sturtevant   1925   The Genetics of *Drosophila*. Bibliographia Genetica *2*: 1–262.

Muller, H. J.   1914   A gene for the fourth chromosome of *Drosophila*. J. Exper. Zool. *17*: 325–36.

Nilsson, I. M., S. Bergman, J. Reitalu, and J. Waldenstrom   1959   Haemophilia A in a "girl" with male sex-chromatin pattern. The Lancet, Vol. 2 (Sept. 5), pp. 264–6.

Renwick, J. H., and S. D. Lawler   1955   Linkage between the ABO and nail-patella loci. Annals of Human Genetics *19*: 312–31.

Walls, G. L.   A branched-pathway schema for the color vision system and some of the evidence for it. Amer. J. Ophtal. *39* (Part II): 8–23.

Chapter 9

Crossing Over and Genetic Mapping

Introduction

Crossing over occurs during early meiotic prophase and is preceded by synapsis of homologous chromosomes. It results from an exchange between the nonsister chromatids of a tetrad and leads genetically to *incomplete linkage* (see p. 105 and Fig. 8–2) and cytologically to the formation of a *chiasma* (see p. 36). How crossing over takes place remains an enigma. Whatever the mechanism, it must be extremely precise, since the two points of exchange are at identical places on the two chromatids.

It is assumed that in situations in which the linear chromosomal distance between two genes is relatively great, the possibility that a chromatid exchange will occur in the intervening region is higher than in situations in which the genes in question are separated by a smaller physical distance. In the case of the genes *e* and *ca* on the third chromosome of *Drosophila melanogaster* such an exchange occurs in about 60 per cent of the tetrads. This results (see Fig. 9–1) in an e +/+ ca female producing eggs 30 per cent of which belong to crossover classes (+ + and e ca). Thus the chromatid exchange frequency (0.6) is twice the frequency of crossover classes (0.3). Complete linkage will be shown when two genes are so close together that an exchange never occurs in the intervening region. When two genes are so far apart that an exchange always occurs in the intervening region, an upper limit of 50 per cent will be reached for the frequency of the resulting crossover classes. Since crossover and noncrossover chromatids now each make up 50 per cent of the total population, a situation indistinguishable from independent assortment will be produced.

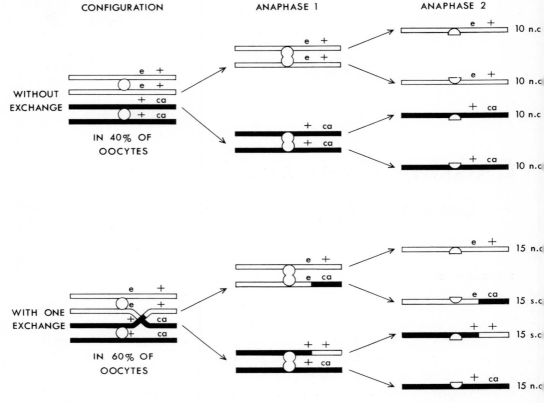

Figure 9-1   An illustration that the chromatid exchange frequency is twice the frequency of cross-over classes. The situation is oversimplified by neglecting the results of double crossing over, n.c.c. (noncrossover chromatid); s.c.c. (single crossover chromatid).

The three-point cross and map construction

If the chromatids are marked at three points by suitable genes, then double chromatid exchanges can be detected. On page 109 it is shown that the genes *m, fu,* and *sn* are located in linkage group I of *Drosophila*. A cross utilizing these genes to mark the chromosome at three points is shown in Figure 9-2. The P_1 female has the *m, fu,* and *sn* genes on one homologue and the + alleles on the other. The order of the genes is unknown, and *fu* is arbitrarily placed as the central locus. The F_1 population contains 11,056 flies belonging to eight different phenotypic classes. These in turn can be grouped into four pairs of complementary classes. The noncrossover classes (m fu sn and + + +) contain the most flies (7333). The complementary classes containing the fewest flies should represent the double crossover

$$P_1 \quad \frac{m \quad fu \quad sn}{+ \ + \ +}\,♀ \times \underrightarrow{m \quad fu \quad sn}\,♂$$

$$\downarrow$$

$$F_1 \; ♂ \, ♂ \; \& \; ♀ \, ♀$$

phenotype	number		
A { m fu sn	3661	} 7333	(66.3%)
{ + + +	3672		
B { m fu +	676	} 1341	(12.1%)
{ + + sn	665		
C { + fu sn	165	} 338	(3.1%)
{ m + +	173		
D { + fu +	1003	} 2044	(18.5%)
{ m + sn	1041		

$$\Sigma \ 11{,}056$$

Figure 9–2

classes. Inspection of the data reveals that the + fu sn and m + + classes together contain the smallest number of individuals. The double crossover classes (enclosed in Fig. 9–2 by a dashed rectangle) can be converted to the parental configuration by inverting m and its + allele. It follows that m must lie between fu and sn.

In Figure 9–3 the maternal tetrad configuration is shown with m now occupying the central locus. Region I is defined as the region which intervenes between the fu and m loci, and region II lies between m and sn. Note that a double exchange converts $fu \ m \ sn/ + + +$ to $fu + sn/ + m +$. An exchange in region I produces $fu + +$ and $+ m \ sn$ chromatids, and these gave rise to 2044 offspring. An exchange in region II produces fu m + and + + sn individuals totaling 1341. Some 338 individuals belong to double crossover classes, and these flies result from exchanges in regions I *and* II.

It follows that 21.54 per cent of the offspring $(100 \times \dfrac{2044 + 338}{11056})$ represent exchanges in region I and 15.19 per cent represent exchanges in region II. Since when making a crossover map one assumes the probability of an exchange occurring is a function of the linear distance between the

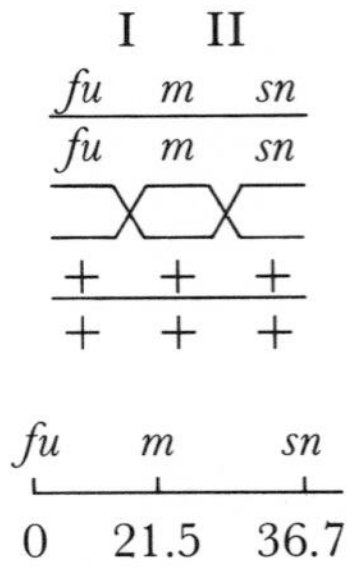

GENETICS

I   II

fu   m   sn
fu   m   sn

+   +   +
+   +   +

fu   m   sn

0   21.5   36.7

$$I = \frac{2044 + 338}{11056} = 0.2154$$

$$II = \frac{1341 + 338}{11056} = 0.1519$$

$$I + II = 0.2154 \times 0.1519 = 0.0327$$

$$C = \frac{O}{E} = \frac{0.0306}{0.0327} = 0.936$$

Figure 9–3

two genes, *fu* and *m* must be separated by a greater distance than *m* and *sn*. It is customary to express these distances in *crossover units*. The number of crossover units separating two genes is identical to the percentage of the offspring which results from an exchange between the two genes. Thus *fu* and *m* are 21.5 crossover units apart, while *m* and *sn* are separated by 15.2 crossover units. We can now make a linkage map for the X-chromosome (see Fig. 9–3) with the *fu* at 0, *m* at 21.5, and *sn* at 36.7. It is impossible at this stage to decide where the centromere is located with respect to the three loci.

Interference

It is a well-known law of probability that if an event *a* occurs with a probability of 0.1 (that is, it occurs once in every 10 occasions) and an independent event *b* occurs with a probability of 0.2, then the chances of both events occurring simultaneously is the product of their independent probabilities or in this example 0.02 (0.1 × 0.2). Now the map distance between two genes is a function of the probability that a chromatid exchange will occur in the intervening region. In the case of the *fu m sn* chromatid the chance that *m* will be separated from *fu* and *sn* by a double exchange is the product of the probabilities of two separate events (0.215 × 0.152 = 0.0327). The observed frequency of double crossover classes is 0.0306 or 93.6 per cent of the expected value.

It is often noted that the observed frequency of double crossover classes is far less than expected, and this implies that crossing over in region I suppresses or interferes with crossing over in region II, and *vice versa*. This phenomenon was given the name *interference* by Muller, who discovered it, and the degree of interference is expressed by the *coefficient of coincidence*. This coefficient (C) is defined as the observed number of double crossovers (O) divided by the expected number (E). In our example (see Fig. 9–3) C = 0.936.

TABLE 9–1 A Selected List of Useful Mutants of *Drosophila melanogaster*

LOCUS	SYMBOL	NAME AND DESCRIPTION
1–0.0	*y*	*yellow*—yellow body color
1–0+	*ac*	*achaete*—certain bristles absent
1–0+	*Hw*	*Hairy-wing*—extra bristles on wing veins, head, and thorax
1–0++	*sc*	*scute*—absence of certain bristles, especially scutellars
1–0.1	*svr*	*silver*—silver body color
1–0.6	*br*	*broad*—wing broad
1–0.8	*pn*	*prune*—eye color mutant
1–1.5	*w*	*white*—white compound eyes and ocelli
1–3±	*N*	*Notch*—wings notched, lethal when hemizygous
1–3±	*fa*	*facet*—eye rough textured
1–4.6	*dm*	*diminutive*—small, slender bristles; female sterile
1–5.5	*ec*	*echinus*—eyes large and rough textured
1–6.9	*bi*	*bifid*—proximal fusion of longitudinal wing veins
1–7.5	*rb*	*ruby*—eye color mutant
1–13.7	*cv*	*crossveinless*—crossveins of wings absent
1–15.0	*rux*	*roughex*—eye small and rough
1–16.3	*vs*	*vesiculated*—wings blistered
1–17.0	*dx*	*deltex*—longitudinal wing veins form deltas at edge
1–17.9	*shf*	*shifted*—abnormal wing venation
1–18.9	*cm*	*carmine*—eye color mutant
1–19.3	*scp*	*scooped*—wings curl up
1–20.0	*ct*	*cut*—wing edges scalloped; eyes kidney-shaped
1–21.0	*sn*	*singed*—bristles and hairs curled and twisted; some alleles female sterile
1–23.1	*oc*	*ocelliless*—ocelli absent; female sterile
1–27.5	*t*	*tan*—tan body color
1–27.7	*lz*	*lozenge*—eye ovoid and glossy; some alleles female sterile
1–32.8	*ras*	*raspberry*—eye color mutant; some alleles female sterile
1–33.0	*v*	*vermilion*—eye color mutant
1–36.1	*m*	*miniature*—small wings
1–38.3	*fw*	*furrowed*—eyes furrowed; bristles gnarled
1–40.7	*wy*	*wavy*—wings transversely waved
1–43.0	*s*	*sable*—dark body color
1–44.4	*g*	*garnet*—eye color mutant
1–44.5	*ty*	*tiny*—small bristles; female sterile
1–51.5	*sd*	*scalloped*—wing edges scalloped
1–51.6	*Bg*	*Bag*—wing blistered; hemizygous lethal
1–54.5	*r*	*rudimentary*—wings obliquely truncated; some alleles female sterile
1–56.7	*f*	*forked*—bristles curled and twisted
1–57.0	*B*	*Bar*—eye size reduced
1–59.5	*fu*	*fused*—fusion of certain longitudinal wing veins; female sterile
1–62.5	*car*	*carnation*—eye color mutant
1–66.0	*bb*	*bobbed*—bristles short

TABLE 9–1 *Continued*

LOCUS	SYMBOL	NAME AND DESCRIPTION
2–0	*al*	*aristaless*—aristae of antennae reduced in size
2–0.3	*ds*	*dachsous*—wings short
2–1.3	*S*	*Star*—eye small and rough; homozygous lethal
2–4.0	*ho*	*held out*—wings extended
2–5±	*fes*	*female-sterile*—homozygous female sterile
2–8.5±	*Cy*	*Curly*—wings curled up; homozygous lethal
2–11.0	*ed*	*echinoid*—eyes large and rough
2–12.0	*G*	*Gull*—wings curved down, divergent; homozygous lethal
2–13.0	*dp*	*dumpy*—wings obliquely truncated
2–16.5	*cl*	*clot*—eye color mutant
2–22.0	*Sp*	*Sternopleural*—sternopleural bristles increased in number; homozygous lethal
2–31.0	*d*	*dachs*—tarsi four instead of fivejointed
2–41.0	*J*	*Jammed*—wings crumpled
2–44.0	*ab*	*abrupt*—fifth longitudinal vein stops before reaching wing edge
2–48.5	*b*	*black*—dark body color
2–51.0	*rd*	*reduced*—small bristles; some alleles female sterile
2–53.9	*hk*	*hook*—bristles hooked at tip
2–54.5	*pr*	*purple*—eye color mutant
2–55.0	*lt*	*light*—eye color mutant
2–55.1	*stw*	*straw*—body color mutant
2–55.3	*tk*	*thick*—wings short and broad
2–55.4	*ap*	*apterous*—wings missing; some alleles female sterile
2–55.7	*bur*	*burgundy*—eye color mutant
2–56.1	*ltd*	*lightoid*—eye color mutant
2–57.5	*cn*	*cinnabar*—eye color mutant
2–57.6	*fs 2.1*	*female sterile 2.1*—homozygous female sterile
2–58.5	*blo*	*bloated*—wings blistered
2–60.8	*chl*	*chaetelle*—extra wing veins
2–62.0	*en*	*engrailed*—cleft scutellum
2–67.0	*vg*	*vestigal*—wings reduced in size
2–71.1	*cg*	*comb-gap*—sex combs large; gap in fourth longitudinal wing vein; female sterile
2–72.0	*L*	*Lobe*—eye reduced
2–72.3	*kn*	*knot*—wing venation aberrant
2–74±	*gp*	*gap*—fourth longitudinal vein has a section missing
2–75.5	*c*	*curved*—wings curved down
2–81.0	*fj*	*four-jointed*—tarsi four instead of five jointed
2–83±	*nw*	*narrow*—wings narrow; males and females sterile
2–91.5	*sm*	*smooth*—abdomen denuded of bristles
2–93.3	*hy*	*humpy*—thorax ridged; males and females sterile
2–99.2	*a*	*arc*—wings bent down
2–100.5	*px*	*plexus*—wing shows extra network of veins
2–104.5	*bw*	*brown*—eye color mutant
2–104.7	*mi*	*minus*—small bristles; females sterile

TABLE 9–1 *Continued*

LOCUS	SYMBOL	NAME AND DESCRIPTION
2–106.7	*ll*	*lanceolate*—narrow, divergent wings
2–107.0	*sp*	*speck*—black speck in axil of wing
2–107.3	*bs*	*blistered*—wings blistered
3–0	*ru*	*roughoid*—eyes small and rough
3–0.2	*ve*	*veinlet*—the third, fourth, and fifth longitudinal wing veins have terminal gaps
3–19.2	*jv*	*javelin*—bristles cylindrical
3–20.0	*dv*	*divergent*—wings held outstretched; venation disturbed
3–23.0	*Hn*	*Henna*—eye color mutant; homozygous lethal
3–26.0	*se*	*sepia*—eye color mutant
3–26.5	*h*	*hairy*—extra hairs
3–35.0	*rs*	*rose*—eye color mutant
3–37±	*rt*	*rotated*—abdomen twisted
3–40.4	*D*	*Dichaete*—wings held outstretched, alulae missing, dorsocentral bristles reduced in number, homozygous lethal
3–40.5	*Ly*	*Lyra*—wings scalloped, narrow; homozygous lethal
3–41.4	*Gl*	*Glued*—eye oblong, smooth in texture; homozygous lethal
3–43.2	*th*	*thread*—aristae of antennae threadlike
3–44.0	*st*	*scarlet*—eye color mutant
3–45±	*tra*	*transformed*—females transformed to sterile males
3–45.3	*cp*	*clipped*—wing margins clipped
3–46.0	*W*	*Wrinkled*—wing wrinkled
3–47.0	*in*	*inturned*—thoracic bristles directed toward midline
3–47.1	*ri*	*radius incompletus*—gap in second longitudinal vein
3–47.3	*eg*	*eagle*—wings extended
3–47.5	*Dfd*	*Deformed*—eyes small; homozygous lethal
3–47.7	*pb*	*proboscipedia*—mouth parts transformed into leglike structures
3–48.0	*p*	*pink*—eye color mutant
3–48.5	*tet*	*tetraltera*—wings transformed to halteres
3–48.7	*by*	*blistery*—wing blistered
3–49.7	*ma*	*maroon*—eye color mutant
3–50.0	*cu*	*curled*—wings curved up and divergent
3–51.3	*ttr*	*tetrapter*—halteres winglike
3–52.0	*kar*	*karmoisin*—eye color mutant
3–52.4	*ry*	*rosy*—eye color mutant
3–56.7	*jvl*	*javelinlike*—bristles cylindrical
3–58.2	*Sb*	*Stubble*—bristles short and thick; homozygous lethal
3–58.5	*ss*[a]	*spineless-aristapedia*—antenna and arista tarsuslike
3–58.8	*bx*	*bithorax*—metathoracic segment resembles mesothorax
3–62.0	*sr*	*stripe*—dorsal stripe on thorax
3–63.1	*gl*	*glass*—eye texture glassy
3–66.2	*Dl*	*Delta*—longitudinal wing veins form deltas at edge; homozygous lethal
3–69.5	*H*	*Hairless*—many bristles missing; homozygous lethal

TABLE 9–1 *Continued*

LOCUS	SYMBOL	NAME AND DESCRIPTION
3–70.7	*e*	*ebony*—dark body color
3–75.7	*cd*	*cardinal*—eye color mutant
3–90.0	*Pk*	*Prickly*—bristles shortened; homozygous semilethal
3–91.1	*ro*	*rough*—eye small and rough textured
3–93.8	*Bd*	*Beaded*—wing excised; homozygous lethal
3–94.1	*Pw*	*Pointed-wing*—wings pointed at the tip; homozygous lethal
3–100.7	*ca*	*claret*—eye color mutant
3–104.3	*bv*	*brevis*—bristles short
4–0	*ar*	*abdomen rotatum*—abdomen twisted clockwise
4–0	*ci*	*cubitus-interruptus*—gaps in fourth longitudinal wing vein
4–0	*gvl*	*grooveless*—scutellar groove diminished
4–0	*Scn*	*Scutenick*—scutellum shortened with nick in rear edge; homozygous lethal
4–0+	*bt*	*bent*—wings bent
4–0+	*ey*	*eyeless*—eyes small or absent
4–0+	*Mal*	*Malformed*—eye malformed
4–0++	*sv*	*shaven*—small bristles
4–0++	*spa*	*sparkling*—eye rough, bulging
4–?	*Ce*	*Cell*—wing veins fused, homozygous lethal

Within a chromosome arm of *Drosophila melanogaster,* interference is complete (that is, C = O and no double crossovers occur) within a map interval $\leq$ 10 units. It thus appears that there is a certain minimal length of chromatin within which double crossing over does not occur. This finding is in harmony with the cytological observation that chiasmata are evenly spaced along the length of a bivalent. When the map interval is greater than 40 units, C = 1. In chromosomes with centrally placed centromeres there appears to be no interference across the centromere.

Recently situations have been encountered (particularly in microbial genetics) in which the coefficient of coincidence is greater than 1. This phenomenon, which is called *negative interference,* is not understood and, although well established, is the exception rather than the rule.

Mapping over long distances

Let us now attempt to add the sex-linked genes *y* (yellow body color) and *cv* (crossveinless wings) to the genetic map of the X-chromosome. By suitable crosses we find that *y* and *sn* are 20 units apart and that *y* and *fu* are 50 units apart. For reasons which will be explained later (p. 132) we know that the X-chromosome has its centromere very near one end and that *y* is located on the end of the X-chromosome farthest away from the centromere. A three-point cross involving *y*, *cv*, and *sn* places *cv* between *y* and *sn* (13.7 units from *y* and 7.3 units from *sn*) To fit all the facts the gene order must be *y cv sn m fu* (see Fig. 9–4), and therefore *fu* must lie nearest

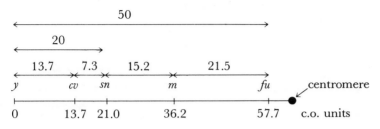

Figure 9–4

the centromere-bearing end of the X-chromosome. If *y* is arbitrarily given a map value of 0, then a genetic or crossover map can be built up by adding up the crossover distances between genes which are close enough together so that there is almost complete interference. When this is done the *fu* locus is placed at 57.7 units even though only 50 per cent crossing over is observed between *y* and *fu*. Since genetic maps are constructed in this fashion, they are often more than 50 units long.

The best genetic map in existence is that for *Drosophila melanogaster* (see Table 9–1). Such a map represents the combined labors of generations of geneticists.

Multiple strand exchanges

In Figure 9–3 a double exchange is diagrammed which involves the two inner chromatids of a tetrad. Of course, a double exchange can also involve three or four chromatids with the results shown in Figure 9–5. The four types of double exchange diagrammed at A, B, C, and D are found to occur at equal frequencies. In type A, two chromatids (one of maternal and one of paternal origin) are not involved in exchanges. In types B and C, one chromatid (of maternal or of paternal origin) is not involved in an exchange. In type D all chromatids are involved in exchanges. Note that only one-quarter of the chromatids which result from double exchanges are double crossover chromatids. Thus the frequency of double chromatid exchanges is four times the observed frequency of the double crossover chromatids.

Weinstein has shown that for the X-chromosome of *Drosophila* over 90 per cent of the chromatids one recovers originate from single and double exchanges, and thus that most X-chromosome tetrads have one or two chromatid exchanges.

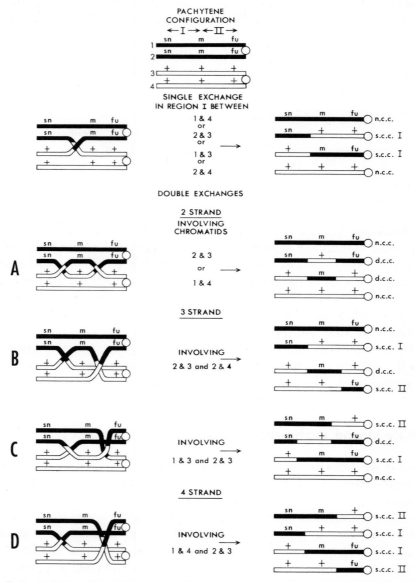

Figure 9–5   Multiple strand exchanges involving the four chromatids numbered as shown in the uppermost figure. When the total number of chromatids resulting from double exchanges is added up, four are found to be n.c.c., four are s.c.c. I, four are s.c.c. II, and four are d.c.c.; n.c.c. (noncrossover chromatids); d.c.c. (double crossover chromatids); s.c.c. I (single crossover chromatids involving an exchange in region I); s.c.c. II (single crossover chromatids involving an exchange in region II).

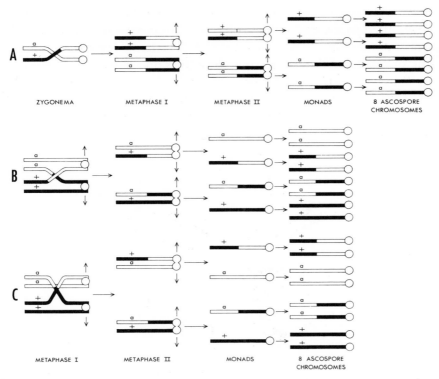

ZYGONEMA   METAPHASE I   METAPHASE II   MONADS   8 ASCOSPORE CHROMOSOMES

METAPHASE I   METAPHASE II   MONADS   8 ASCOSPORE CHROMOSOMES

Figure 9–6   Proof through ascospore analysis in *Neurospora* that crossing over occurs during the tetrad stage. (A) Crossing over during the two-strand stage can produce only the + + + + aaaa segregation pattern. (B) and (C) Crossing over at the four-strand stage produces aa + + aa + + or + + aaaa + + segregation patterns. Such patterns are observed (see Fig. 9–7).

Proof that crossing over occurs during the tetrad stage

In most organisms it is impossible to recover the four monads which are produced by a single primary gametocyte. In animal eggs, for example, three of the products of meiosis are eliminated as polar bodies, while in the male the four sperm which result from a single primary spermatocyte are hopelessly lost among the billions of other sperm in the testis. In *Neurospora,* however, all the products of a meiotic division are confined in a thin-walled ascus sac (see p. 53) which holds them in a definite order which is established by the direction of the nuclear segregations during meiosis.

Let us consider the outcome of meiosis in a zygote, fusion nucleus of genotype *a* / +. Assume that the + gene produces a pigment in the ascospore wall and that the *a* gene is inactive. We have here a means of determining whether crossing over occurs in the two- or in the four-strand stage. As Figure 9–6 demonstrates, if crossing over occurs between *a* and the centromere during the two-strand stage, asci will be produced containing four pigmented ascospores followed by four nonpigmented ascospores. If an exchange did *not* occur one would still get the 4-4 pattern. However, crossing over during the tetrad stage produces one of two patterns: 2 light-2 dark-2 light-2 dark or 2 dark-4 light-2 dark (or its equivalent 2 light-4 dark-2 light). The fact that in asci one observes 4-4, 2-4-2 and 2-2-2-2 patterns (see Fig. 9–7) proves that crossing over occurs during the four-strand stage.

Figure 9–7   Segregation patterns for alleles controlling pigmentation of the ascospore wall of *Neurospora*. Each ascospore is approximately 30 micra long.

Factors affecting crossing over

Crossing over is a phenomenon which undergoes variation depending upon genetic and environmental conditions. Thus in certain species, crossing over may be abolished or depressed in one sex (see Table 9–2). Bridges has shown that as *Drosophila* females age, crossing over is depressed particularly between genes which lie close to the centromere. That the frequency of crossing over is also affected by temperature was shown by Plough. Here again the effect is most pronounced in chromosome regions near the centro-

TABLE 9–2   Sexual Differences in Crossing Over in Different Species

REPRESENTATIVE SPECIES	♂	♀
fruit fly	absent	present
silk worm	present	absent
garden pea	present	equal to ♂
mouse	present	higher than ♂
pigeon	higher than ♀	present

mere. At temperatures between 17°C and 29°C, crossing over is fairly constant. It *increases,* however, at *lower* or *higher* temperatures. The presence of heterozygous autosomal inversions (see p. 138) is also known to greatly increase the amount of crossing over in the X-chromosome.

Somatic crossing over

That crossing over occurs in somatic tissues of *Drosophila* under certain circumstances has been demonstrated by Stern (see Fig. 9–8), and Ponte-

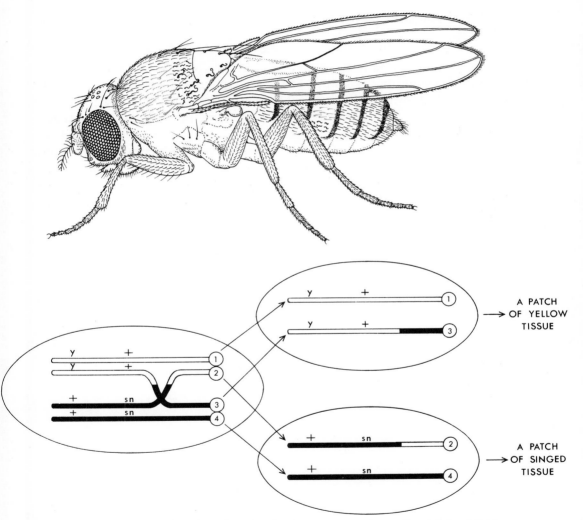

Figure 9–8   (A) A *Drosophila melanogaster* female of genotype *y + / + sn*. Most bristles show the dominant traits and are consequently long and black. However, adjacent patches of yellow (drawn to appear pale) and singed tissue are seen on the thorax and abdomen. (B) The mechanism of origin of the twin spots through crossing over in somatic cells is diagrammed above.   (After Hannah-Alava.)

corvo has shown that somatic crossing over may occur in artificially produced diploid nuclei in mycelia of various species belonging to the mold
genus *Aspergillus*. Somatic crossing over may be widespread in its occurrence, but it probably occurs at a frequency thousands of times lower than
is the case for germinal crossing over. The fact that somatic crossing over
is relatively common in *Drosophila* is no doubt due to the occurrence of
somatic pairing (see p. 45) in these insects and the absence of this phenomenon in most other organisms.

Sister chromatid exchanges

In the previous discussion we have considered only those crossover
chromatids which arise as the result of exchanges between nonsister chromatids. It should not be implied that exchanges never occur between sister
chromatids. However, in the case of rod-shaped chromosomes (take those
shown in Fig. 9–5 as an example) a sister chromatid exchange is not detectable genetically. That sister chromatid exchanges occur in mitotic cells has
been shown by Taylor and his associates using autoradiographic techniques,
and Schwartz has produced cytological evidence that sister-strand crossing
over occurs in the meiotic cells of maize heterozygous for a ring and a rod
chromosome. In *Drosophila* the available evidence indicates that sister-
strand exchanges do not occur.

9-1. How can you demonstrate in *Drosophila* that two genes are on the same chromosome when they are so widely separated that a chromatid exchange always
occurs in the intervening region? Now answer the same question for an organism
where crossing over occurs in both sexes.

9-2. Assume a female of genotype *a b c/* + + + produces 100 tetrads of which 34 have
no exchanges between *a* and *c;* 22 have an exchange between *a* and *b;* 36 have
an exchange between *b* and *c;* and 8 have an exchange between *a* and *b* and
another between *b* and *c.* Calculate the number of chromatids belonging to each
of the following eight classes: a b c, + + +, a + +, + b c, a b +, + + c,
a + c, and + b +. Map *a, b,* and *c,* giving *a* the value of 0 crossover units.

9-3. In building genetic maps why is it essential to work with regions so short that
no double exchanges occur?

9-4. Given: In *Neurospora* 100 zygote fusion nuclei of genotype *a/* +. If the *a* locus is
so close to the centromere that an exchange never occurs in the intervening
region, all the 100 asci which are produced will contain 4 *a* followed by 4 +
ascospores. If the *a* locus is so far from the centromere that an exchange always
occurs in the intervening region, all the 100 asci will show either of the two
following arrangements of ascospores: *a a* + + *a a* + + or *a a* + + + + *a a.*
(or its equivalent + + *a a a a* + +). Does the above discussion suggest how one
might construct linkage maps for *Neurospora?* In order to compare the map distances between a gene and the centromere in *Drosophila* and *Neurospora,* the
Neurospora value must be halved. Why? From the data presented in Figure 9-7
determine the distance between the gene that produces ascospore pigmentation
and the centromere.

9-5. In maize the genes *bm* (brown midrib), *v* (virescent seedling), and *pr* (red
aleurone) reside on chromosome 5. A test cross to an individual of genotype
+ + +/*v pr bm* produces the following progeny according to Emerson, Beadle,
and Fraser: + + +, 232; bm + v, 46; + pr v, 84; + + v, 201; bm pr v, 235;
+ pr +, 40; bm + +, 77; and bm pr +, 194. Determine the sequence of the
genes on the chromosome and calculate the map distances between the genes and
the coefficient of coincidence.

9-6. Stern, in his study of somatic crossing over, observed the twin spots described in
Figure 9-7. Less frequently he noted only *yellow* spots, and still less frequently
only *singed* spots. How did these patches of tissue arise? Why were they infrequent?

9-7. What is the probability of drawing two aces simultaneously from a deck of cards?

BIBLIOGRAPHY

Barratt, R. W., D. Newmeyer, D. D. Perkins, and L. Garnjobst   1954   Map construction in *Neurospora crassa.* Advances Genet. *6:* 1–93.

Bridges, C. B.   1927   The relation of the age of the female to crossing over in the third
chromosome of *Drosophila melanogaster.* J. Gen. Physiol. *8:* 698–700.

Emerson, R. A., G. W. Beadle, and A. C. Fraser   1935   A summary of linkage studies in maize. Cornell Univ. Agr. Sta. Mem. *180*.

Hannah-Alava, A.   1960   Genetic mosaics. Scientific American (May), pp. 118–33.

Janssens, F. A.   1909   La théorie de la chiasmatypie. La Cellule *25*: 389–411. (The classic paper in which the suggestion was first made that exchanges between nonsister chromatids produce chiasmata.)

Plough, H. H.   1917   The effect of temperature on crossing over. J. Exper. Zool. *24*: 147–209.

Pontecorvo, G., and E. Käfer   1958   Genetic analysis based on mitotic recombination. Advances Genet. *9*: 71–104.

Redfield, H.   1955   Recombination increase due to heterologous inversions and the relation to cytological length. Proc. Nat. Acad. Sc. *41*: 1084–91.

Schwartz, D.   1953   The behavior of an X-ray induced ring chromosome in maize. Am. Naturalist *87*: 19–28.

Stern, C.   1936   Somatic crossing over and segregation in *Drosophila melanogaster*. Genetics *21*: 625–730.

Sturtevant, A. H.   1913   The linear arrangement of 6 sex-linked factors in *Drosophila,* as shown by their mode of association. J. Exper. Zool. *14*: 43–59. (The classic paper in which genetic mapping was first accomplished.)

Sturtevant, A. H.   1915   The behavior of chromosomes as studied through linkage. Ztschr. ind. Abstamms- u. Vererbungsl. *13*: 234–87.

Taylor, J. H.   1958   Sister chromatid exchanges in tritum-labeled chromosomes. Genetics *43*: 515–29.

Weinstein, A.   1936   The theory of multiple strand crossing over. Genetics *21*: 155–99.

Chapter **10**

Chromosomal Aberrations

Introduction

Chromosomes which are aberrant because of the loss, duplication, or rearrangement of their genetic material are often observed in living cells. Some types of chromosomal aberrations are the result of spontaneous or induced chromosome breakage. The ruptured ends of broken chromosomes often remain "sticky," and as a result chromosome fragments subsequently may rejoin by twos. The rejoining of broken chromosomes naturally involves the synthesis of chemical bonds, and this in turn requires both time and energy. The work of Wolff and others implicates ATP as the energy source for this process.

Intrachromosomal aberrations

In any discussion of aberrations it is best to start with simpler types involving changes which occur in but one chromosome. Such *intrachromosomal* or *homosomal* aberrations fall into two general subdivisions: (1) changes such as *deficiencies* and *duplications* which involve the number of loci on a chromosome, and (2) *inversions* and *shifts* which involve changes in the arrangement of loci.

Deficiencies

The sex-linked mutation *Notch* of *Drosophila melanogaster* described in 1917 by C. B. Bridges is an excellent example of a deficiency. Females

129

Figure 10–1   Photomicrograph of a wing from a *Notch* female.

heterozygous for N show notches in the trailing edge of the wing (see Fig. 10–1). Males hemizygous for N die during embryogenesis. The mutant is therefore lethal when hemizygous, but when in combination with its $+$ allele it produces a wing abnormality. *Notch* mutants have been recovered from many independent experiments, and each independent *Notch* has been given a different superscript to distinguish it from the others. If a female heterozygous for *Notch*[4] or *Notch*[8] is crossed to a *white* male, the results shown in Figure 10–2 are obtained.

$$P_1 \qquad \frac{N^4}{+} ♀ \times \frac{w}{⇒} ♂$$

$$\downarrow$$

$$F_1 \qquad \frac{N^4}{w} \quad \frac{N^4}{⇒} \quad \frac{+}{w} \quad \frac{+}{⇒}$$

$$(w\,N\,♀) \ (\text{dies}) \ (+\ ♀) \ (+\ ♂)$$

Figure 10–2

That is, white Notch females, wild type females, and wild type males are found in a $1:1:1$ ratio. Thus the recessive gene *white* expresses itself in the heterozygous *Notch*[4] female as if the + allele of *white* were missing from the N^4 chromosome contributed by its mother. The X-chromosome of the salivary gland cells of female larvae heterozygous for any one of the various *Notch* mutants often show a peculiar type of aberration (see Fig. 10–3). The

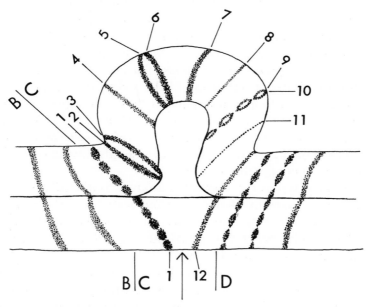

Figure 10–3   A deficiency loop in the paired X-chromosomes from a salivary gland cell of a larva heterozygous for *Notch*. Only a short section of the chromosome pair is shown. The chromosomes have been divided into 102 main sections, each of which is divided into six subsections (A to F). Within each subsection a variable number of individual bands are labeled 1, 2, etc. In this figure, subsection C of section 3 is presented. Note that bands 3C2 through 3C11 are missing from the lower chromosome.   (Redrawn from *Principles of Human Genetics*, 2nd edition, by Curt Stern. San Francisco: W. H. Freeman and Co., 1960.

maternal and paternal homologous chromosomes pair throughout their length except at one point, where a loop is formed by one homologue. This *deficiency loop* arises because the chromosome section present in the loop is missing in the homologous chromosome. The four salivary gland chromosomes of + type *Drosophila melanogaster* have been mapped by C. B. Bridges, P. N. Bridges, and B. M. Slizynski, and each of the 5149 bands which are visible under the light microscope have been recorded and given a specific code number. The 10 bands present in the above deficiency loop (bands

$3C_2$ through $3C_{11}$) represent a euchromatic segment near the tip of the X-chromosome. It is obvious that the $+$ alleles of both N and w must reside somewhere in this region. In time other N mutants were analyzed both cytologically and genetically and most were shown to be deficiencies of varying length. The N^8 deletion, for example, includes the loci of a cluster of genes (*w, rst, fa,* and *dm*), while the N^5 deletion fails to include the loci of *w, rst,* or *dm.* All chromosomes which behaved as though they were deficient for the *white* locus had one thing in common: they lacked the doublet band $3C_{2-3}$ and all *Notch* chromosomes were deficient for band $3C_7$. Thus this cytogenetic study of a series of overlapping deficiencies made possible the localization of two genes to specific bands of the salivary chromosomes. In a few cases it has been demonstrated that a single band contains a number of closely linked genes. The fact that a single band which is just within the limits of resolution of the light microscope may contain a minimum of three or four genes indicates that genes themselves are below the resolving power of the light microscope ($0.2\ \mu$). Note that if each band contained two genes the genetic machinery of *Drosophila* would contain 1×10^4 genes. This figure is certainly a reasonable estimate for the minimum number of genes for this species.

The laborious type of cytogenetic analysis outlined above has been carried out many times in *Drosophila melanogaster* with the result that the cytological loci of more genes are known for this species than all others put together. The total length of all four salivary chromosomes according to the 1937 estimate of C. B. Bridges is roughly 1200 microns. The total length of the genetic map is about 280 crossover units. Thus, if one map unit is made equal to 4.3 microns of salivary chromosome, the genetic and cytological maps may be drawn side by side. Once this is done lines can be drawn connecting the gene on the genetic map with its cytological locus whenever the necessary information is available. Figure 10–4 shows a reference map to the chromosome of *Drosophila melanogaster* prepared in this fashion. It represents decades of laborious work by dozens of the world's leading geneticists.

Although the various genes are found to lie in the same order in both the salivary chromosome map and the genetic map, great discrepancies often exist in the relative distances between two genes on the two maps. This fact indicates that crossing over is more frequent in some chromosomal regions than others. In general, crossing over seems to be lower per unit of chromosome length in the vicinity of the centromeres and telomeres. The student should keep in mind when comparing crossover and cytological maps that we have no cytological maps of the chromosomes undergoing crossing over; i.e. the chromosomes of the primary oocytes.

Duplications

The *Bar* "mutant" of *Drosophila,* which reduces the size of the compound eye, is a classic example of a duplication. De Marinis has provided evidence that *Bar* produces its effect by postponing the time of the onset of cell division in the eye primordium. *Bar* is due to the duplication of a euchromatic segment located toward the right end of the X-chromosome. This segment (16A) contains five bands, two of which are doublets. As shown in Figure 10–5 improper synapsis in the *Bar* region may occur during pachynema in females homozygous for *Bar.* This may result in *unequal crossing over* and the production of two chromatids, one of which contains one 16A segment and one of which has three. Thus unequal crossing over results in one chromatid which has "reverted to wild type," and a double *Bar* chromatid. Sturtevant first demonstrated this phenomenon in the progeny of females whose X-chromosome was marked in the region to the left and right of the *Bar* locus with the genes *forked bristle* (*f*) and *fused wing veins* (*fu*).

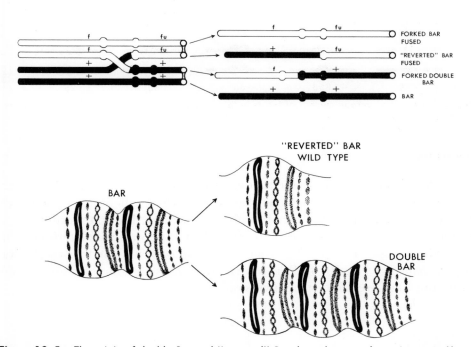

Figure 10–5 The origin of double *Bar* and "reverted" *Bar* through unequal crossing over. Upper diagram: representation of unequal crossing over between two nonsister strands in a tetrad of a heterozygous *Bar* female carrying the marker genes *forked* and *fused* in the coupling configuration. Lower drawing: the 16A region in the salivary X-chromosomes of wild type, *Bar,* and double *Bar* flies.

(After M. J. D. White.)

Given chromosomes with the 16A segment present, once, twice, or three times, six diploid genotypes can be constructed. Five of these are presented in Figure 10–6. Note that as the number of 16A segments per nucleus increases from two to six the number of facets in the compound eye of the adult female decreases by 30 times. Note also that heterozygous double *Bar* females have fewer facets in their eye than homozygous *Bar* females, even though in both instances the number of 16A segments per nucleus is four. It is obvious that not just the number of segments is important, but their position as well. Evidently a nucleus containing a chromosome with three 16A segments in tandem and the fourth on its homologue is more effective in reducing facet number than one containing two chromosomes each with two segments in tandem. The term *position effect* was originally applied by Sturtevant to this type of phenomenon. Position effects tell us that the way a gene expresses itself often depends upon its adjacent chromosomal environment. This phenomenon will be discussed further in Chapter 14 under the topic of pseudoallelism.

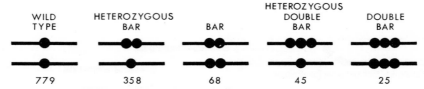

Figure 10–6   The average number of facets in the compound eyes of female *Drosophila melanogaster* of varying genotypes with respect to the *Bar* locus.

Inversions

Inversions are chromosome segments which have been turned through 180° with the result that the gene sequence for the segment is reversed with respect to that of the rest of the chromosome (see Fig. 10–7). Inversions may include or exclude the centromere. The first type are called *pericentric* or *heterobrachial* (see Fig. 10–7), whereas the second is called *paracentric* or *homobrachial* (see Fig. 10–8). Paracentric inversions are found far more often in nature than are pericentric inversions.

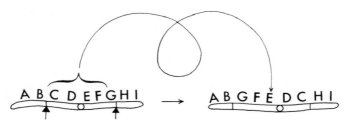

Figure 10–7   The production of a pericentric inversion.

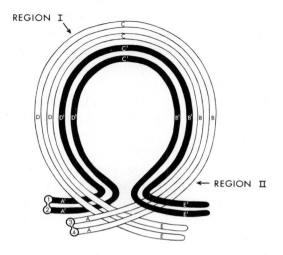

SINGLE EXCHANGE (REGION I, STRANDS 2 & 3)

TWO STRAND DOUBLE EXCHANGE (REGION I, STRANDS 2&3; REGION II, STRANDS 2&3)

THREE STRAND DOUBLE EXCHANGE (REGION I, STRANDS 2&3; REGION II, STRANDS 2&4)

THREE STRAND DOUBLE EXCHANGE (REGION I, STRANDS 1&3; REGION II, STRANDS 2&3)

FOUR STRAND DOUBLE EXCHANGE (REGION I, STRANDS 1&4; REGION II, STRANDS 2&3)

Figure 10–8 Upper: the pairing configuration during pachynema in a paracentric inversion hetero-zygote. Lower: the results of various types of exchanges. Note that no monocentric single crossover chromatids are produced.

In Figure 10–8 the pairing configuration during pachynema in a paracentric inversion heterozygote is diagrammed. Note that a single exchange
anywhere within the inversion loop results in the production of two noncross
over chromatids and one dicentric and one acentric chromatid which are
eliminated. Double exchanges within the inverted segment produce noncrossover, double crossover, acentric, and dicentric chromatids in a
1:1:1:1 ratio. Note that no single crossover chromatids are recovered.
Inversions are therefore *crossover suppressors,* and in fact it was their action
on crossing over that led to their discovery.

Let us assume that a *Drosophila* female is heterozygous for a long inversion of the X-chromosome, but that the autosomes have the normal gene
sequence. As shown in Figure 10–9A the dicentric and acentric chromosomes which result from single exchanges or three-strand double exchanges
within the inversion loop usually are not included in the egg nucleus. In
the case of four-strand double exchanges, two dicentrics and two acentrics
are produced (see Fig. 10–8) with the result that the oocyte nucleus receives
no X-chromosome (see Fig. 10–9B). If such an egg nucleus is fertilized by
an X-bearing sperm, a patroclinous Y-deficient male will be formed. Since
such males are perfectly viable but sterile, it follows that the Y-chromosome
is required for male fertility in *Drosophila.* Fertilization of an X-deficient egg
by a Y-bearing sperm will produce a nullo-X zygote nucleus. Under such
circumstances death occurs early in embryogenesis. A four-strand double
exchange between relatively inverted segments in a large autosome will

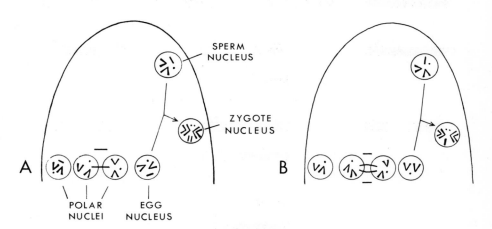

Figure 10–9   A diagram illustrating the orientation and fate of the four ootid nuclei in the *Drosophila* egg following the second meiotic division. Here it is assumed that exchanges have occurred
between relatively inverted segments in X-chromosomes. The V-shaped second and third and the dot-
shaped fourth chromosomes are normal. (A) A dicentric bridge following a single exchange or
a three-strand double exchange. (B) A double dicentric bridge following a four-strand double
exchange. Note that the zygote nucleus has only one rod-shaped X-chromosome.

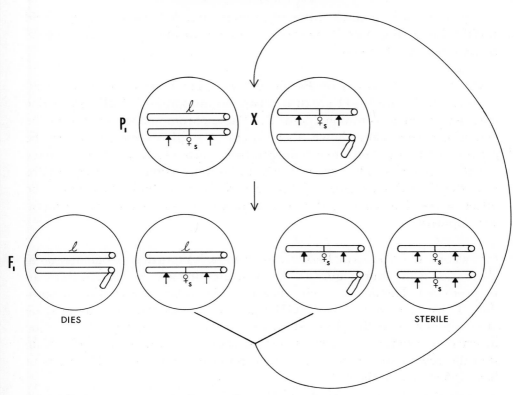

Figure 10–10 A symbolic representation of a balanced stock which can be maintained generation after generation without selection.

result in the production of an egg nucleus deficient for that chromosome. Following fertilization the embryo will die because of chromosome imbalance.

"BALANCING" CHROMOSOMES. Many cases arise in genetic research in which one wishes to maintain in the heterozygous state a recessive mutation which when homozygous produces sterility or lethality. For this purpose a number of "balancing chromosomes" has been synthesized by Muller and others. The way the method works is shown in Figure 10–10. Here a lethal gene, *l,* is kept over a balancer chromosome containing a long inversion (its breakage points are represented by arrows) in which resides a gene which causes female sterility when homozygous, but does not affect male fertility when hemizygous. The balanced stock can be maintained generation after generation without selection, since the only viable, fertile individuals among the offspring are those which one desires to perpetuate the cross. Note that for this breeding scheme to function indefinitely the + alleles of the *l* and

♀ *s* genes must remain on different homologues. A single crossover would nullify this prerequisite. However, the inversion prevents the recovery of single crossover chromosomes.

INVERSIONS AS A MEANS OF PRODUCING SPECIFIC DUPLICATIONS OR DEFICIENCIES. In Figure 10–11 are drawn two chromosomes (I & II) having one breakage point in common (point 3). These chromosomes arose from the ancestral chromosome shown above them. A single exchange (×) in the region common to both inversions produces chromatids which either have lost the segment which is not common to both inversions (B in this case) or have duplicated this segment. This method is very useful in the study of the effect of the deficiency or duplication of specific chromosomal loci upon development.

INVERSIONS AS A MEANS OF PRODUCING "SHIFTS." A fourth type of homosomal aberration is the shift. Figure 10–12 illustrates one way in which a shift can be produced. The ancestral chromosome (I) can be converted to chromosome II by a rotation of the EFGH segment. Chromosome II may at some later time break at the points shown by arrows, and this segment may be inverted to produce the gene sequence shown in chromosome III. Note that the genes now are present in the right order, but that the DE segment has been shifted to the right.

INTERCHROMOSOMAL EFFECTS OF INVERSIONS. The fact that the presence of an inversion in one chromosome increases the frequency of crossing over in non-homologous chromosomes was first demonstrated by Sturtevant in 1919. The degree to which crossing over is enhanced appears to be a function of the inversion used. T. Oksala has brought forward a hypothesis to explain this phenomenon. He has suggested that during meiosis in the *Drosophila* female that the distal ends of the chromosome arms are all attached at a circumscribed area of the nuclear envelope to produce a typical bouquet configuration. It is from these associated distal chromosomal regions that pairing begins. The proximal, centromeric parts of the chromosomes with their heterochromatic blocks lie at the top of the bouquet. If one ignores chromosome IV, there are six heterochromatic blocks present at zygonema (those belonging to the homologous X, second and third chromosomes). It will be recalled that heterochromatin appears to adhere indiscriminately with all other heterochromatin. The six heterochromatic blocks in question pair at random, and consequently either two homologous or two non-homologous ones may join. On the other hand the pairing of euchromatic regions involves only homologues. Nonhomologous pairing of the hetero-chromatic blocks therefore results in a change of pairing partner at each

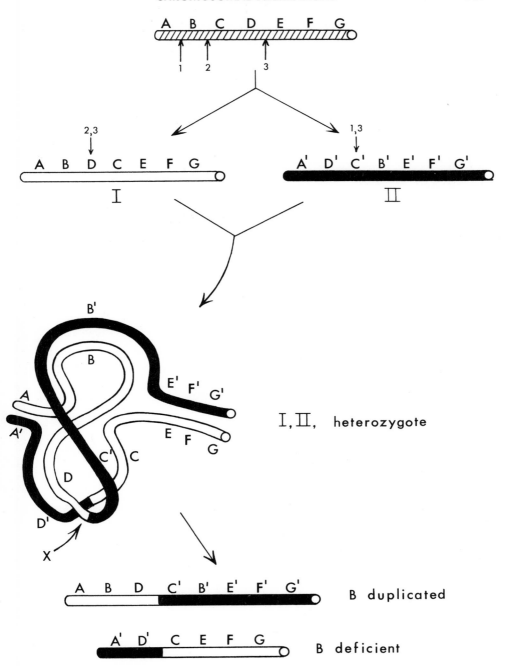

Figure 10–11 The production of chromatids bearing deficiencies or duplications resulting from an exchange (X) between different inversion-bearing chromatids. The shaded chromosome has the ancestral gene sequence. From it arise the black and white chromosomes as the result of independent inversions. Both inversions have one breakage point in common. In the heterozygous configuration only two of the four chromatids are shown.

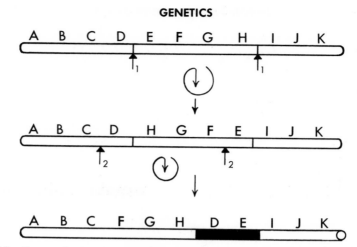

Figure 10–12   Consecutive inversions resulting in the shift of a chromosomal segment.

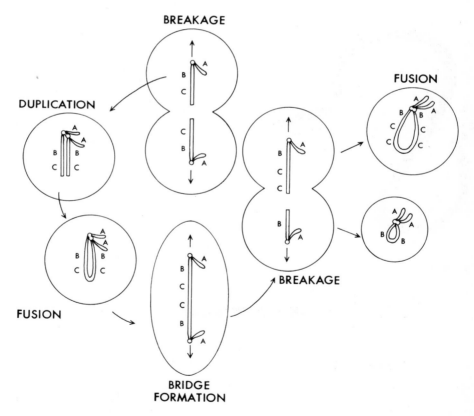

Figure 10–13   A diagrammatic representation of a breakage-fusion-bridge cycle such as that described in maize by McClintock.

euchromatin/heterochromatin interface. The results of this altered synaptic configuration are short, unpaired, euchromatic, chromosomal regions near heterochromatin, and in such unpaired regions crossing over cannot occur. As a consequence the frequency of crossing over per unit of chromosome length is reduced in regions near heterochromatin. That such is the case is evident from consulting Figures 2–9 and 10–4. Under Oksala's hypothesis crossing over would be enhanced if pairing of nonhomologous heterochromatic blocks could be prevented. This is presumably what happens when one or two chromosomes are heterozygous with respect to one or more inversions. Thus when chromosomes II and III contain inversion loops their heterochromatic blocks cannot pair with heterochromatin belonging to the X-chromatin, and consequently crossing over is increased in the sex chromosome.

BREAKAGE-FUSION-BRIDGE CYCLES. It will be recalled that an exchange within a paracentric inversion will produce a dicentric chromosome. Such a dicentric will be pulled toward both poles at once during meiotic anaphase and will eventually be torn apart. McClintock has shown in maize that broken chromosomes formed in this and other ways fail to heal. Instead their ends remain sticky and subsequent to duplication the sticky ends of sister chromatids fuse. The result (see Fig. 10–13) is a dicentric which undergoes breakage at anaphase, and so the cycle continues, with the chromosome being broken anew at every mitosis. Since each subsequent break is likely to be at a different place than previous ones, the genotype of the cells which result will become increasingly abnormal. In the endosperm of the developing kernel the breakage-fusion-bridge cycle persists, producing patches of tissue of varying genotypes. In the embryo, however, the broken ends heal and the cycle ceases. Why broken ends behave differently in different tissues is a mystery.

Interchromosomal aberrations

Interchromosomal or heterosomal aberrations arise from situations where nonhomologous chromosomes are broken, and interchange occurs between the resulting fragments.

Eucentric reciprocal translocations

Of the various representative types of heterosomal aberrations shown in Figure 10–14 the eucentric reciprocal translocation is the most important.

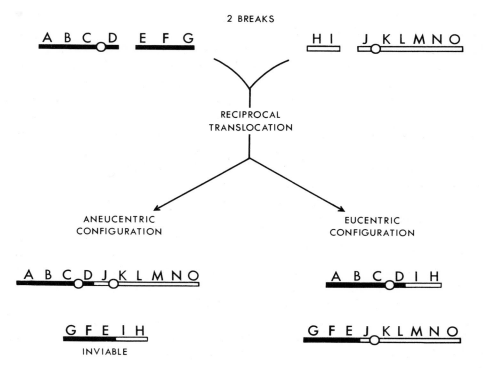

Figure 10-14 Representative types of interchromosomal aberrations.

A technique for detecting translocations between the large autosomes of *Drosophila* is shown in Figure 10–15. Let us assume that under certain experimental conditions a translocation occurs between chromosomes 2 and 3 in 1 per cent of the sperm produced by a wild type male. Such males are mated to *bw; st* females (females homozygous for *bw* and *st* cannot form colored pigment in their eyes). Each F_1 male is test crossed in a separate culture. If an F_1 male arises from an egg fertilized by sperm carrying normal second and third chromosomes, then that male will not be a translocation heterozygote, and it will produce four types of gametes in equal frequencies (+ +, *bw* +, + *st*, and *bw st*). Since a test cross is made, the X_2 culture will contain wild type, brown-eyed, scarlet-eyed, and white-eyed flies in a 1:1:1:1 ratio.

The situation is different in the case of an F_1 male translocation heterozygote. Synapsis in a translocation heterozygote results in a cross-shaped double tetrad such as that shown in Figure 10–15. At first meiotic anaphase the bivalents separate with 1 and 4 going to one pole and 2 and 3 to the other or 1 and 3 going to one pole and 2 and 4 to the other. The latter type

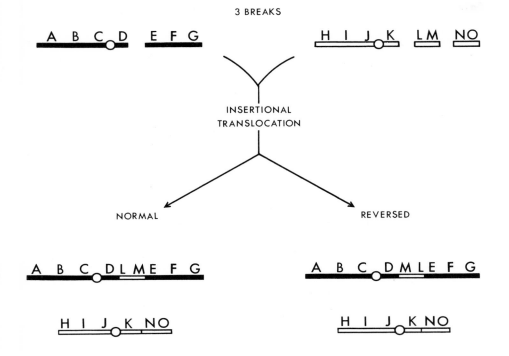

of segregation produces *aneuploid* gametes with certain chromosomal regions missing and others in duplicate. Eggs fertilized by such sperm die during embryogenesis. Therefore the viable offspring produced from a test cross to such a translocation heterozygote are wild type and white-eyed flies. If 1 per cent of the sperm from the P_1 male contains translocations between chromosomes 2 and 3, then 1 per cent of the X_2 cultures will show only + and white flies in it, while 99 per cent will show flies belonging to all four phenotypes.

Wild type males and females from any one of the F_2 cultures containing only white-eyed and wild type flies can be mated together. Such flies are translocation heterozygotes and will produce four types of gametes. We can refer to each gamete type by the constitution of the centromeres. Thus a 1, 4 gamete contains both translocated chromosomes (see Fig. 10–15). The 16 types of fertilizations which can occur are shown in Figure 10–16. Only six of these give zygotes with balanced genotypes. The rest die, since they have certain chromosome regions duplicated and others deficient. Thus one effect of a translocation is to make individuals heterozygous for it semisterile. Note that the 1144 zygote is homozygous for the translocation. From such individuals a homozygous translocation stock can be derived.

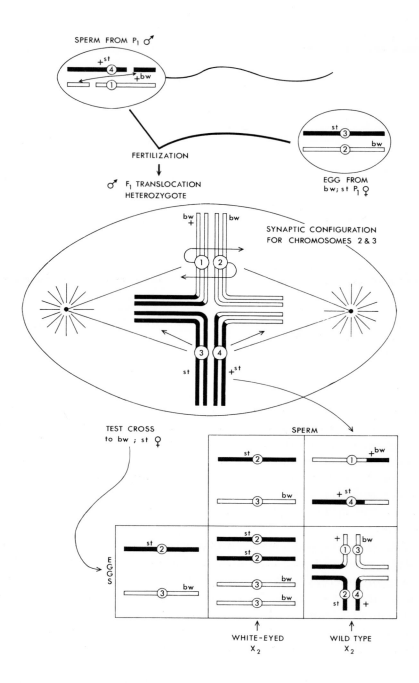

SPERM FROM P₁ ♂

FERTILIZATION

♂ F₁ TRANSLOCATION HETEROZYGOTE

EGG FROM bw; st P₁ ♀

SYNAPTIC CONFIGURATION FOR CHROMOSOMES 2 & 3

TEST CROSS to bw ; st ♀

SPERM

EGGS

WHITE-EYED X₂

WILD TYPE X₂

Figure 10–15 Diagram of a technique for detecting translocations between the large autosomes of *Drosophila melanogaster*. X₂ refers to the offspring of the F₁ test cross.

EGGS

	1, 3	2, 4	1, 4	2, 3
1, 3	X 1133	TH 1234	X 1134	X 1233
2, 4	TH 1234	X 2244	X 1244	X 2234
1, 4	X 1134	X 1244	HT 1144	TH 1234
2, 3	X 1233	X 2234	TH 1234	S 2233

(The left side column "SPERM" runs vertically.)

$\frac{1}{16}$ S   = Standard
$\frac{10}{16}$ X   = Duplication-Deficiency
$\frac{4}{16}$ TH = Translocation Heterozygote
$\frac{1}{16}$ HT = Homozygous Translocation

Figure 10–16

Patterson and his associates have studied the viability and fertility of a large number of homozygous, radiation-induced translocations of *Drosophila*. It is interesting to note (see Table 10–1) that many are homozygous lethals. For example, only 19 of 120 translocations between chromosomes 2 and 3 were viable in the homozygous condition. However, these were all fertile. Of 71 translocations between chromosomes 1 and 3 only 30 were viable when homozygous, and three of these were sterile. Findings like these lead one to suspect that inactivation of genetic material adjacent to the points of breakage in the translocated chromosomes may often occur. In other cases the deleterious effect of translocations when homozygous upon viability and fertility may be due to position effects. In the eucentric translocation configuration shown in Figure 10–14 for example, we see that gene D now lies adjacent to gene I instead of its normal neighbor, gene E. Now it might happen that genes D and E function together in the production of some vital substance (see p. 236). Their separation would therefore result in lethality although neither gene was itself damaged.

We have already referred to an example of a stable type of position effect in the case of *Bar*. Chromosome aberrations often bring genes located in the euchromatin into contact with heterochromatin. In many instances a wild type gene from the euchromatin when placed adjacent to heterochromatin

TABLE 10–1

CHROMOSOMES INVOLVED IN TRANSLOCATIONS	NUMBER TESTED	PER CENT VIABLE	NUMBER TESTED	PER CENT FERTILE
1 and 2	57	52.6	23	91.3
1 and 3	71	42.2	30	90.0
1 and 4	14	100.0	13	100.0
2 and 3	120	15.8	19	100.0
2 and 4	33	69.6	17	88.2
3 and 4	37	48.6	18	88.8

$$\Sigma\ 332 \qquad\qquad \Sigma\ 120$$

by a chromosome aberration will function in an unstable fashion in certain tissues. The result will be *variegation,* that is, the production of patches of tissue which differ phenotypically from surrounding cells. In such variegated position effects it is often observed that neighboring genes as well as the one directly in contact with heterochromatin are modified. Some heterochromatic regions are much more effective than others in influencing the extent of variegation.

Translocation homozygotes have the normal number of linkage groups and normal tetrads are observed at pachynema. However, the genetic map of the translocated chromosomes will be modified. In the case of the eucentric translocation shown in Figure 10–14, for example, genes A and I will now show linkage, whereas they once segregated independently. The ancestrally linked genes D and E now segregate independently. It will be recalled that individuals heterozygous for a single reciprocal translocation have one less than the normal number of linkage groups and show a cross-shaped double tetrad at pachynema. Genetic mapping of the aberrant chromosomes of a translocation heterozygote will produce one four-armed linkage map.

BALANCED LETHALS AND TRANSLOCATION COMPLEXES. Let us consider a monoecious plant which is heterozygous for a translocation and for two recessive lethal genes, l^1 and l^2. In Figure 10–17 we see the diplotene configuration for the double tetrad produced in such an individual. Note the loci of l^1 and l^2. As chiasmata terminalize during diplonema and diakinesis, the bivalents disengage (but remain attached at their tips) and so form either of two

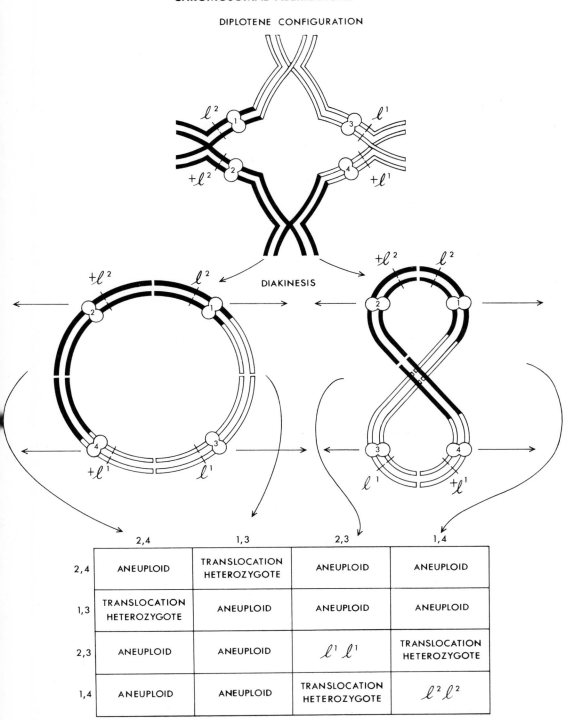

Figure 10-17 A balanced lethal system operating in a translocation heterozygote. Note that only offspring heterozygous for the reciprocal translocations are viable.

equally probable configurations: a ring of four bivalents or a chromosome chain shaped like a figure 8. In the first case adjacent bivalents are included in the secondary gametocytes, and these will be aneuploid; in the second case alternate bivalents enter secondary gametocytes and such gametocytes will be euploid, that is, they will contain a complete chromosomal complement. Upon self-fertilization an F_1 population will be produced. This will contain only individuals genotypically identical to the parent, because the individuals homozygous for the standard chromosomes (2233) will be homozygous for the lethal gene l^1, and those homozygous for the reciprocal translocations (1144) will be homozygous for the lethal gene l^2. Such a situation in which only heterozygotes survive because both homozygotes are lethal is called a *balanced lethal system*. In the above case we would have the paradoxical phenomenon of an organism with a haploid chromosome number of 2 (but with one linkage group) which bred true (but was heterozygous). Note that the balanced lethal system would break down if a lethal gene and its + allele exchanged places through crossing over. The plant will be semisterile, since only one-fourth of the zygotes it produces will

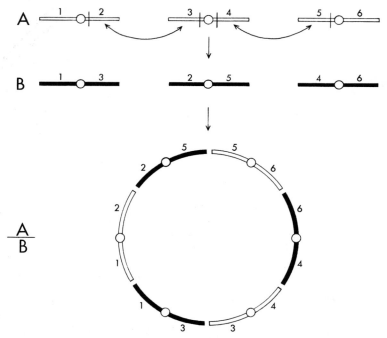

Figure 10–18 A diagram illustrating the mode of origin of a ring of six chromosomes at diakinesis. A = the haploid chromosome complement of the ancestral race. B = the haploid chromosome complement of a derived race resulting from two interchanges between three nonhomologous chromosomes. A/B = the diploid hybrid between A and B.

be viable. The fertility of the plant would be doubled if only alternate bivalents were allowed to enter secondary gametocytes.

We have discussed first the simplest situation, in which the translocations involved only two nonhomologous chromosomes. In Figure 10–18 a situation is shown where two interchanges involving three nonhomologous chromosomes produce a ring of six chromosomes during late diplonema and diakinesis. Three interchanges involving four nonhomologous chromosomes would produce a ring of eight chromosomes, and so on. The process might go on until all the chromosomes in the nucleus were involved in one translocation complex. Translocation complexes are found in plant species such as *Paeonia californica, Rhoeo discolor,* and *Oenothera grandiflora* (where we find rings of 10, 12, and 14 chromosomes, respectively).

Oenothera lamarckiana, the species of evening primrose which has been studied in the greatest detail, has two linkage groups, but a haploid chromosome number of 7. At first meiotic metaphase a ring of 12 bivalents and a lone tetrad are observed. In the majority of cases, for unknown reasons, alternate bivalents go to each pole with the result that euploid gametes are formed. A balanced lethal system allows survival of only zygotes heterozygous for the complex. Crossing over is suppressed in the species, and as a result the balanced lethal system is maintained.

It is a well-known fact that individuals heterozygous at a large number of loci show *hybrid vigor* or *heterosis*. Such hybrids generally have a growth rate, reproductive capacity, longevity, and general viability superior to individuals from inbred lines. Reeve and Robertson have suggested that the hybrid has greater biochemical versatility, since it has more kinds of genes and presumably, as a consequence, more different kinds of enzyme systems. The hybrid is therefore more efficient metabolically and more adaptable. The complicated genetic mechanism described above which has evolved in plants like *Oenothera lamarckiana* ensures that such species will remain heterozygous at a large number of loci. *Oenothera lamarckiana* presumably evolved from a species similar to *Oenothera hookeri* which is free of translocations and shows seven tetrads at meiotic metaphase.

The cytological proof of crossing over

A complex set of translocations in *Drosophila melanogaster* provided Stern with the material he needed for a most ingenious experiment. The strain used by Stern had a normal set of second and third chromosomes. However, the X-chromosome was J-shaped, because it had a fragment of a Y-chromosome translocated to a position near its centromere. The second X was broken in two, and the acentric fragment was translocated to one of the fourth chromosomes. The centric fragment contained the genes *Bar* and *carnation* eye color.

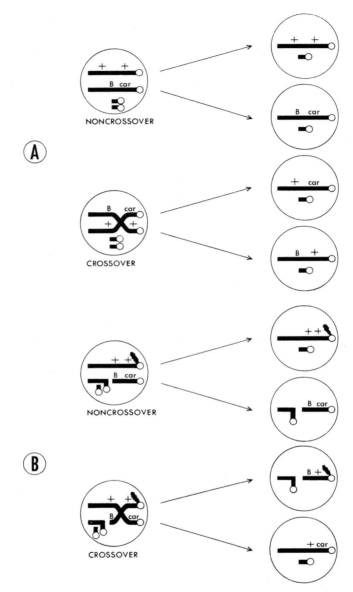

Figure 10-19   The results of crossing over between *Bar* and *carnation* in a normal strain (A) and a translocation strain (B). The X- and fourth chromosomes are shown. Note that crossing over in A results in no cytological change, whereas crossing over in B results in chromosomes which are morphologically different from noncrossover chromosomes.

In a normal strain (see Fig. 10–19 A), crossing over between B and *car* will produce $B +$ and $+ car$ chromatids which cannot be distinguished cytologically. However, crossing over between B and *car* in the transloca-

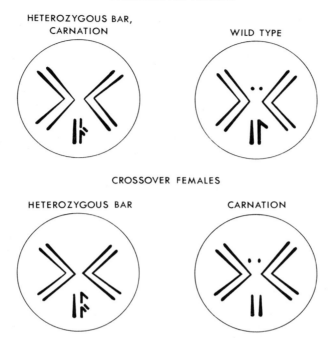

NONCROSSOVER FEMALES

HETEROZYGOUS BAR, CARNATION

WILD TYPE

CROSSOVER FEMALES

HETEROZYGOUS BAR

CARNATION

Figure 10–20   The expected chromosomal complements of *Drosophila* females of various phenotypes from Stern's experiment.

tion strain will place the Y fragment on the broken X-chromosome (see Fig. 10–19 B).

Stern crossed aberrant *B car*/+ + females to + *car* males. He then picked out female offspring belonging to both the noncrossover and the crossover classes and made a cytological study of the chromosomes in dividing oogonia of the flies belonging to each class. The expected results are diagrammed in Figure 10–20. The expectations were fulfilled, and as a result genetics and cytology were decisively united. In the same year (1931) Creighton and McClintock performed an analogous experiment in maize and again obtained the expected results.

10–1. Why is it so fortunate for Genetics that somatic pairing occurs in *Drosophila?*

10–2. Show that a female heterozygous for a long inversion of the X-chromosome should produce three times as many offspring containing a double crossover chromosome as patroclinous males.

10–3. Virgin homozygous *w m f* females are mated to A or to B males (both types are phenotypically wild type). F_1 males and females interbred to produce an F_2. The F_2 results are shown below. Determine the distance between *w* and *m* and *m* and *f* and the coefficient of coincidence. Determine the distances between *w* and *m*, *m* and *f*, and *f* and the centromere from your reference map of the X-chromosome of *Drosophila*. The $+$ m f, w $+^{^{\cdot}}$ $+$, w m $+$, and $+$ $+$ f classes are single crossovers in Experiment A. What are they in experiment B? Do you find support for your answer in the experimental data? How do A and B males differ? How could you substantiate your conclusions?

Exp.	+ + +	w m f	+ m f	w + +	w m +	+ + f	w + f	+ m +	total
A	1491	884	555	654	498	385	146	237	4850
B	1791	1716	51	55	78	47	98	50	3886

10–4. Demonstrate that a pericentric inversion can convert a metacentric to a sub-telocentric chromosome.

10–5. Does a single exchange in the inversion loop of a pericentric inversion produce acentric and dicentric chromatids? Would a *Drosophila* female heterozygous for a pericentric inversion be less fertile than one heterozygous for a paracentric inversion? Why? In view of your answer, can you think of any reason why a pericentric inversion would be retained in a population of *Drosophila robusta* as Levitan has shown?

10–6. In higher plants like corn very few of the translocations which have been recovered are lethal when homozygous. In animals like *Drosophila* a great many are lethal when homozygous. What is the reason for this difference? Remember the occurrence of the gametophyte generation in plants.

10–7. Starting with a normal chromosome complement such as that found in *Oenothera hookeri*, what is the minimum number of reciprocal translocations required to get a ring of 14 chromosomes at meiosis such as is found in *O. grandiflora?*

10–8. Assume a plant species exists with a haploid set of seven chromosomes which may be represented as follows: 1.2, 3.4, 5.6, 7.8, 9.10, 11.12, 13.14. The species becomes subdivided into three isolated races. Race A retains the ancestral arrangement. Race B as the result of three translocations shows the following haploid arrangement of chromosome arms: 1.4, 2.3, 5.6, 7.12, 8.11, 9.13, 10.14. Race C as the result of four translocations becomes: 1.7, 3.6, 4.5, 2.10, 8.9, 11.13, 12.14. What will be the configuration as to rings of bivalents and tetrads in the race hybrids A/B, A/C, and B/C?

10–9. Assume you have four homozygous strains of corn. Number 1 is normal, 2 is a reciprocal translocation for chromosomes 1 and 2, 3 is a 2-3 translocation, and 4 is a 2-4 translocation. A fifth homozygous strain (y) also is suspected of being a translocation. Individuals from the unknown strain are crossed to the four tester strains, and the chromosome configuration at meioses is determined. The results are as follows:

(1) X (y) ⟶ ring of 4   (3) X (y) ⟶ 2 rings of 4
(2) X (y) ⟶ ring of 6   (4) X (y) ⟶ ring of 6

What chromosomes are translocated in the unknown strain?

10–10. Of the various chromosomal aberrations which is of the greatest evolutionary importance?

BIBLIOGRAPHY

Bridges, C. B.   1936   The Bar "gene" a duplication. Science *83*: 210–11.

Bridges, C. B.   1937   Correspondences between linkage maps and salivary chromosome structure, as illustrated in the tip of chromosome 2R of *Drosophila melanogaster*. Cytologia Fujii Jubilee Volume: 745–55.

Bridges, C. B.   1938   A revised map of the salivary gland X-chromosome of *Drosophila melanogaster*. J. Hered. *29*: 11–13.

Bridges, C. B., and P. N. Bridges   1939   A revised map of the right limb of the second chromosome of *Drosophila melanogaster*. J. Hered. *30*: 475–6.

Bridges, P. N.   1941   A revised map of the left limb of the third chromosome of *Drosophila melanogaster*. J. Hered. *32*: 64–5.

Bridges, P. N.   1941   A revision of the salivary gland IIIR chromosome map of *Drosophila melanogaster*. J. Hered. *32*: 299–300.

Bridges, P. N.   1942   A new map of the salivary gland IIL chromosome of *Drosophila melanogaster*. J. Hered. *33*: 403–8.

Cleland, R. E.   1936   Some aspects of the cytogenetics of *Oenothera*. Botan. Rev. *2*: 316–48.

Creighton, H. B., and B. McClintock   1931   A correlation of cytological and genetical crossing-over in *Zea mays*. Proc. Nat. Acad. Sc. *17*: 492–7.

De Marinis, F.   1952   Action of the *Bar* series in relation to temperature studied by means of the Minute-n mosaic technique. Genetics *37*: 75–89.

Dobzhansky, Th.   1936   Induced chromosome aberrations in animals. *In* Biological Effects of Radiation, Chap. 38, B. Duggar, editor. McGraw-Hill, New York.

Green, M. M.   1960   A new heterochromatin effect in *Drosophila melanogaster*. Proc. Nat. Acad. Sc. *46*: 524–8.

Levitan, M.   1950   Retention of a pericentric inversion in populations of *Drosophila robusta*. Genetics *35*: 674.

Lewis, E. B.   1950   The phenomenon of position effect. Advances Genet. *3*: 73–116.

McClintock, B.   1938   The fusion of broken ends of sister half-chromatids following chromatid breakage at meiotic anaphases. Missouri Agr. Exper. Sta. Res. Bull. *290*: 48.

Muller, H. J., and A. A. Prokofyeva   1935   The individual gene in relation to the chromomere and the chromosome. Proc. Nat. Acad. Sc. *21*: 16–26.

Muller, H. J., A. A. Prokofieva-Belgovskaya, and K. V. Kossikov   1936   Unequal crossing over in the Bar mutant as a result of duplication of a minute chromosome section. Compt. rend. (Dokl.) Acad. sc. URSS, N. S., *1(10)*: 87–8.

Oksala, T.   1953   Chromosome pairing, crossing over, and segregation in meiosis in *Drosophila melanogaster* females. Cold Spring Harbor Symposia Quant. Biol. *23*: 197–210.

Patterson, J. T., W. Stone, S. Bedichek, and M. Suche   1934   The production of translocations in *Drosophila*. Am. Naturalist *68*: 359–69.

Reeve, E. C. R., and F. W. Robertson   1952   Heterozygosity, environmental variation and heterosis. Nature *170*: 296.

Slizynska, H.   1938   Salivary gland analysis of the *white-facet* region of *Drosophila melanogaster*. Genetics *23*: 291–9.

Slizynski, B. M.   1944   A revised map of salivary gland chromosome IV. J. Hered. *35*: 322–4.

Stern, C.   1931   Zytologisch-genetische Untersuchungen als Beweise für die Morgansche Theorie de Faktorenaustauchs. Biol. Zentralbl. *51*: 547–87.

Stern, C., and M. Kodani   1955   Studies on the position effect at the *cubitus interruptus* locus of *Drosophila melanogaster*. Genetics *40*: 343–73.

Sturtevant, A. H.   1919   Contributions to the genetics of *Drosophila melanogaster*. III. Inherited linkage variations in the second chromosome. Carnegie Trust, Publ. No. 278: 305–41. Washington, D. C.

Sturtevant, A. H.   1925   The effects of unequal crossing over at the *Bar* locus in *Drosophila*. Genetics *10*: 117–47.

Wolff, S., and H. E. Luippold.   1955   Metabolism and chromosome-break rejoining. Science *122*: 231–2.

Chapter 11

Variation in the Number
of Chromosomes

Introduction

Variations in chromosome number may occur through the duplication or loss of complete chromosome sets or of single chromosomes. The term *aneuploid* is used to refer to nuclei characterized by incomplete genomes. Conversely, *euploid* nuclei contain a complete basic set of chromosomes or a multiple of that basic number. Euploid nuclei may constitute a *polyploid* series with 1, 2, 3, 4, or more complete sets of chromosomes. Let us assume that the basic chromosome number (N) for a given species is 3. If the non-homologous chromosomes are designated as A, B, and C, the monoploid (1N), diploid (2N), triploid (3N), and tetraploid (4N) chromosomal complements would be ABC, AABBCC, AAABBBCCC, and AAAABBBBCCCC, respectively. A diploid organism will at times have tetraploid nuclei in some of its tissues, and its gametes are always monoploid. The gametic chromosome number is defined as the *haploid* number. In diploids the haploid chromosome number is the same as the monoploid number, but the haploid number for a tetraploid would be the diploid number of chromosomes.

Ploidy

Chromosome doubling may be induced experimentally by treating cells during division with a spindle poison such as the alkaloid colchicine. In the case of plants, seeds may be soaked in weak colchicine solutions, or the solution may be sprayed on buds or applied in a lanolin paste. Through such treatments monoploid nuclei can be converted to diploid, diploid nuclei to tetraploid, and so on. Colchicine is often useful in converting a sterile species hybrid into a fertile "double diploid." Thus a cross between species I (AABBCC) and species II (TTUUVV) will produce a sterile hybrid of genotype ABCTUV. Such a hybrid will have six nonhomologous chromosomes and cannot produce gametes with complete chromosome complements. Doubling the chromosome number with colchicine produces the following complement AABBCCTTUUVV. In the "double diploid" so formed each chromosome has a synaptic mate, and as a result gametes with balanced chromosome sets will be produced. Therefore the hybrid will be fertile and will breed true. Furthermore it will be reproductively isolated from its ancestors, since a back cross will result in progeny which are aneuploid. The terms *allotetraploid* and *amphidiploid* are synonymous with double diploid. The allotetraploid should not be confused with the auto-tetraploid referred to previously (AAAABBBBCCCC).

Polyploidy in plants

It is often noted that there occur different multiples of a basic chromosome number among related species of higher plants. The commercial wheats form a striking example of such a polyploid series (see Table 11–1). It appears that the species belonging to group B were derived from the wild emmer wheat of Syria. This species in turn arose from amphidiploid hybrids of *Triticum monococcum* and its relatives on one hand and various diploids similar to the present-day *Aegilops speltoides,* a wild grass with a haploid chromosome number of 7. The hexaploid species have (in addition to genomes A and B) a third genome C. The chromosomes of genome C

TABLE 11–1 Species of *Triticum*

GROUP A (Einkorn wheats), diploids (N = 7), genome A
  T. monococcum (einkorn)
  T. aegilopoides (wild einkorn)

GROUP B (Emmer wheats), tetraploids (N = 14), genomes A,B
  T. dicoccum (emmer)
  T. durum (durum)
  T. turgidum (poulard)
  T. polonicum (Polish)
  T. dicoccoides (wild emmer)

GROUP C (Vulgare wheats), hexaploids (N = 21), genomes A,B,C
  T. spelta (spelt)
  T. vulgare (*aestivum*) (common)
  T. compactum (club)

cannot pair with those belonging to genomes A or B. The C genome is homologous with the genome of a small, useless weed, *Aegilops squarrosa*. The original hybridization and spontaneous doubling of chromosome number presumably took place at the time of the Neolithic Lake cultures in Europe, between cultivated wheat plants of the emmer type and the weed species growing at the borders of fields. In addition to wheat many other of our most valuable crop plants are polyploids (see Table 11–2).

TABLE 11–2   Polyploid genera among crop plants

GENUS	COMMON NAME OF REPRESENTATIVE SPECIES
Arachis	peanut
Avena	oats
Coffea	coffee
Fragaria	strawberry
Gossypium	cotton
Hordeum	barley
Ipomoea	sweet potato
Medicago	alfalfa
Musa	banana
Nicotiana	tobacco
Prunus	plum
Pyrus	apple
Saccharum	sugar cane
Solanum	potato
Sorghum	sorghum
Trifolium	clover

The transfer of beneficial genes from one plant species to another

Common wheat, *Triticum vulgare*, is susceptible to leaf rust, a serious disease caused by the fungus, *Puccinia triticina*. A wild grass of the Mediterranean region, *Aegilops umbellulata*, is completely resistant to this disease. Unfortunately, crosses between *T. vulgare* and *A. umbellulata* yield inviable seeds. E. R. Sears recently managed to introduce the *Aegilops* gene for rust resistance into the *Triticum* genome, taking the following circuitous route. *A. umbellulata* was crossed to *T. dicoccoides*. A sterile hybrid was produced which by treatment with colchicine was transformed to a rust-resistant, fertile allotetraploid having 21 pairs of chromosomes (the A and B *Triticum* genomes and the U genome from *A. umbellulata*). The allotetraploid was crossed to *T. vulgare,* and a fertile, rust-resistant hybrid was produced which showed upon cytological analysis 14 pairs of chromosomes plus 14 chromosomes which failed to pair (the diploid A and B genomes plus the haploid C and U genomes). Such hybrids produce gametes containing the haploid A and B genomes, but varying numbers of C and U chromosomes. Sears wished to retain only the one U chromosome which contained the gene for rust resistance. The hybrid was therefore subjected to successive back crosses to replace U with C chromosomes. The offspring were always inoculated with rust spores, and those plants which were resistant (and therefore contained the U chromosome of interest) were analyzed cytologically. Eventually a plant was found which contained but one U chromosome and 21 pairs of *Triticum* chromosomes (a trisomic—see p. 162). However, this plant had poor qualities with respect to grain yield, and it transmitted the U chromosome to only 1 per cent of its pollen. Obviously the rust-resistant gene had to be transferred to a wheat chromosome. Rust-resistant offspring from the above plant were therefore irradiated with X-rays to induce chromosome breaks and were subsequently back crossed. Of 6091 F_2 offspring, 132 proved to be rust resistant. Cytological analysis showed 17 of these to contain translocations. One was an insertional translocation in which a small segment of the U chromosome (including the gene for rust resistance) was inserted into a wheat chromosome. This plant gave rise to a strain of wheat indistinguishable from normal wheat except that it was immune to the 22 known varieties of leaf rust disease. This series of experiments provides an illustration of the redesigning of the genome of agriculturally important species; something which will be of increasingly great practical importance.

Segregation in autotetraploids

In an autotetraploid nucleus each gene is present in quadruplicate, and as a consequence the genetics of tetraploids is more complicated than is the case for diploids. If a given gene exists in two allelic forms A and a, then five genotypic combinations can be formed $AAAA$ (quadruplex), $AAAa$ (triplex), $AAaa$ (duplex), $Aaaa$ (simplex), and $aaaa$ (nulliplex). If A is dominant to a, a will be manifest only in the nulliplex condition.

Let us consider the types of gametes produced by a duplex autotetraploid. If the gene in question is so close to the centromere that chiasmata rarely occur in the intervening region, then the assortment of genes into gametes can be predicted by considering all the possible ways four chromosomes can separate into twos. If the chromosomes are numbered as shown in Figure 11–1A the possibilities are 1–2 (aa), 1–3 (aA), 1–4 (aA), 2–3 (aA), 3–4 (AA), and 2–4 (aA). Thus aa, Aa, and AA gametes are produced in a

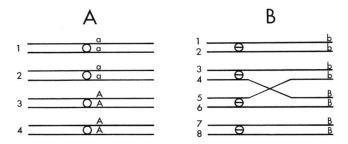

Figure 11–1   A duplex autotetraploid in which the locus under consideration is close to the centro-mere (A) or distant from the centromere (B). In the first case the gamete types can be predicted by considering the possible ways the four *chromosomes* (here shown with their constituent chromatids) can separate by twos. In the second case the gamete types can be predicted by considering all pos-sible ways eight *chromatids* can separate by twos.

1:4:1 ratio. As is demonstrated in Figure 11–2 the progeny resulting from the self-fertilization of a duplex autotetraploid will be present in the follow-ing genotypic ratios, 1 quadruplex:8 triplex:18 duplex:8 simplex:1 nulli-plex. The phenotypic ratios will be 1 recessive:35 dominant.

On the other hand, if the gene in question is so far from the centromere that chiasmata always occur in the intervening region, then the assortment of genes into gametes can be predicted by considering all the possible ways eight chromatids can separate in twos. If the chromatids are numbered as shown in Figure 11–1B, the possibilities are 1–2 (*bb*), 1–3 (*bb*), 1–4 (*bB*), 1–5 (*bb*), 1–6 (*bB*), 1–7 (*bB*), 1–8 (*bB*), 2–3 (*bb*), 2–4 (*bB*), 2–5 (*bb*), 2–6 (*bB*), 2–7 (*bB*), 2–8 (*bB*), 3–4 (*bB*), 3–5 (*bb*), 3–6 (*bB*), 3–7 (*bB*), 3–8 (*bB*), 4–5 (*bB*), 4–6 (*BB*), 4–7 (*BB*), 4–8 (*BB*), 5–6 (*bB*), 5–7 (*bB*), 5–8 (*bB*),

female gametes

	AA	4 Aa	aa
AA	AAAA 1	AAAa 4	AAaa 1
4 Aa	AAAa 4	AAaa 16	Aaaa 4
aa	AAaa 1	Aaaa 4	aaaa 1

male gametes

Figure 11–2

6–7 (*BB*), 6–8 (*BB*), and 7–8 (*BB*). Thus *bb*, *Bb*, and *BB* gametes are produced in a 6:16:6 or a 3:8:3 ratio. The progeny resulting from the self-fertilization of such a duplex autotetraploid will be present in the following phenotypic ratio 187 dominant:9 recessive, or 21:1 (see Fig. 11–3).

female gametes

	3 *BB*	8 *Bb*	3 *bb*
3 *BB*	*BBBB* 9	*BBBb* 24	*BBbb* 9
8 *Bb*	*BBBb* 24	*BBbb* 64	*Bbbb* 24
3 *bb*	*BBbb* 9	*Bbbb* 24	*bbbb* 9

(male gametes label on left)

Figure 11–3

Thus it is obvious that the recessive phenotype appears much less frequently in autotetraploid crosses (see Table 11–4). Since this is the case, working with the genetics of tetraploids is more laborious because larger populations of offspring must be examined. This fact can be brought out by contrasting the phenotypic ratios in the F_2 of diploid dihybrid and tetraploid dihybrid crosses (see Fig. 11–4). We see the 9:3:3:1 ratio converted to a 1225:35:35:1 ratio.

TABLE 11–4

PARENTAL GENOTYPE	SELFED	TEST CROSSED	SELFED	TEST CROSSED
quadruplex	all *A*	all *A*	all *B*	all *B*
triplex	all *A*	all *A*	783*B*:1*b*	27*B*:1*b*
duplex	35*A*:1*a*	5*A*:1*a*	20.8*B*:1*b*	3.7*B*:1*b*
simplex	3*A*:1*a*	1*A*:1*a*	2.48*B*:1*b*	13*B*:15*b*
nulliplex	all *a*	all *a*	all *b*	all *b*

A near centromere — *B* far from centromere

Expected F_1 phenotypic ratios after self-fertilizing autotetraploids or test crossing them to nulliplex individuals.

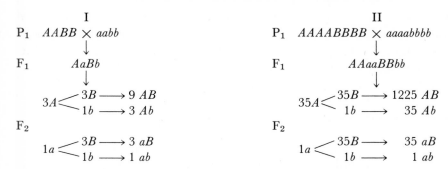

In tetraploid cross shown under II it is assumed that genes A and B are close to the centromere.

Figure 11–4

Meiotic behavior of polyploids

Autotetraploids form quadrivalents during zygonema. At any particular point, however, the homologues are associated by twos (see Fig. 11–5). It appears from these observations that the mysterious synaptic attraction homologous chromosomes have for one another is neutralized once they congregate by twos.

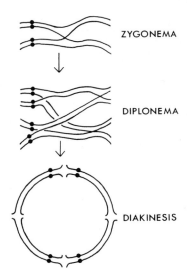

ZYGONEMA

DIPLONEMA

DIAKINESIS

Figure 11–5

In theory it should be very easy to distinguish autotetraploids from allotetraploids, since the latter form bivalents at zygonema, but in practice it is often not possible. For example, some species may result from the redoubling of an allotetraploid, and therefore may show characteristics of both allo- and autopolyploidy. Autotetraploids may also undergo "diploidization" through the accumulation of aberrations which slowly reduce the homology between the sets of chromosomes present. Thus after many generations each quadrivalent may be converted to a pair of bivalents.

Rapid evolution through polyploidy

The production of an autotetraploid adds no new alleles to the genome and generally results only in exaggerations of traits already present in the diploid. Allotetraploids on the other hand offer great opportunities for the production of new adaptive gene combinations, and since allopolyploids have accumulated diverse genomes, they would be expected to thrive in a wide variety of habitats. Biogeographical studies have shown that polyploids often occupy different habitats than their related diploids and that these habitats are ones more recently open to colonization. Furthermore, the production of allopolyploid species can take place very rapidly as the result of a succession of rare accidents. It appears that evolution through allopolyploidy has been very widespread among monoecious plants. However, once an allopolyploid species is formed its further evolution is retarded. This is because natural selection operates upon new phenotypes, but new genes find difficulty expressing themselves in polyploids. Thus if a gene is found in both genomes of an allopolyploid then that gene will be in the quadriplex condition. If a beneficial mutant of that gene arises which can affect the phenotype only when in the nulliplex condition, the opportunities for this gene to be selected are rare indeed.

Aneuploidy

Types of aneuploidy are demonstrated in Table 11–5. You will recall that in *Drosophila* nullosomic (nullo-X) and trisomic (triplo-X) individuals are

TABLE 11–5   Examples of types of aneuploidy

NOMENCLATURE	FORMULA	CHROMOSOME COMPLEMENT
Monosomic diploid	$2N - 1$	AABBCCD
Trisomic diploid	$2N + 1$	AABBCCDDD
Tetrasomic diploid	$2N + 2$	AABBCCDDDD
Double trisomic diploid	$2N + 1 + 1$	AAABBCCDDD
Pentasomic tetraploid	$4N + 1$	AAAABBBBCCCCDDDDD

A normal diploid nucleus would contain chromosomes A, B, C, and D in duplicate.

produced by inseminated, attached-X females (see p. 108). The fertilization of an X-deficient egg by an X-bearing sperm produces a monosomic embryo. In this case it develops into a sterile male, demonstrating that the Y-chromosome is essential for male fertility. Monosomics and trisomics are also known for the small fourth chromosome of *Drosophila*. Trisomics or monosomics for chromosomes 2 and 3 are inviable.

Polysomics in plants

The many varieties of polysomics synthesized by Blakeslee and his collaborators in the Jimson weed, *Datura stramonium,* provide excellent material for the study of the effects of chromosome balance. In *Datura* trisomics are available for each of its 12 chromosomes, and from the phenotypes shown by each trisomic one can determine the developmental effect of each chromosome on the plant as a whole. In addition there exists a series of tetrasomic diploids with more and pentasomic tetraploids with less exaggerated phenotypes than those of the trisomic diploids (see Fig. 11–6).

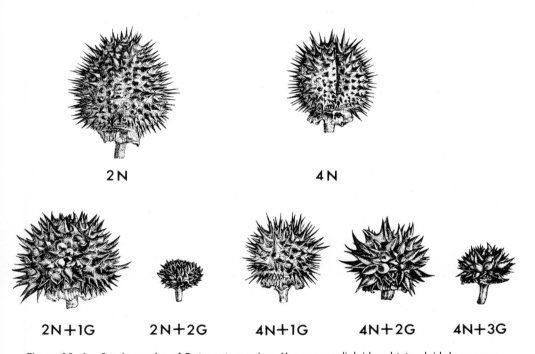

| 2N | 4N |

| 2N+1G | 2N+2G | 4N+1G | 4N+2G | 4N+3G |

Figure 11–6   Seed capsules of *Datura stramonium*. Upper row: diploid and tetraploid. Lower row: trisomic diploid, tetrasomic diploid, pentasomic tetraploid, hexasomic tetraploid, and heptasomic tetraploid. Extra doses of chromosome G appear to broaden and to reduce the capsule and to increase the size of the spines.   (After Blakeslee.)

Trisomic diploids are expected to give two types of gametes: N and N + 1. However, in plants it is often found that N +1 gametes fail to reach a theoretical transmission frequency of 50 per cent. Remember that in Sears's study (see p. 157) the U chromosome was transmitted to only 1 per cent of the progeny of the trisomic. This failure is sometimes due to poor viability of the gamete. For example, N + 1 pollen grains may be slow to germinate or may produce pollen tubes which grow slowly relative to euploid tubes. Sometimes N + 1 gametes fail to form because the extra chromosome lags at meiosis and as a consequence fails to get incorporated into a daughter nucleus at telophase.

In plant species such as *Datura stramonium* where a complete set of trisomics exists it is possible to determine the linkage group to which each new recessive mutant belongs as it arises by the so-called *trisomic method*. The mutant is simply crossed individually to each of the available trisomics. The F_1 trisomic is then test crossed to the mutant homozygote. If in the X_2 a ratio of 1 mutant : 1 wild type is observed among the progeny, then the mutant does not reside upon the chromosome which is present in triplicate in the trisomic tester stock. If the mutant is on this chromosome a ratio of 5 wild type : 1 mutant will be obtained, provided N + 1 gametes are formed and transmitted in the expected frequencies. If the transmission frequency is low for any of the reasons mentioned in the last paragraph, the F_2 ratio approaches 2 wild type : 1 mutant.

Trisomy and triploidy in man

Recently techniques have been introduced which make possible the routine determination of the chromosome number in man and the identification of individual chromosomes. Studies utilizing these techniques have shown that the presence of two sex chromosomes and 22 pairs of autosomes is necessary for normal development. At least three types of autosomal trisomics have been discovered in man, all of which result in congenital malformation and mental retardation. The presence of the smallest autosome in triplicate results in mongolism. Mongoloid children are characterized by extreme mental retardation. They also possess smallish heads, fissured tongues, and sometimes have a fold of skin over the inner angle of the eye (the epicanthic fold which characterizes members of the Mongolian race). One out of every 400 births occurring in the United States is a mongoloid. Such trisomics are the result of a type of mitotic malfunction which results in the failure of chromosomes to disjoin properly at anaphase. The result of this failure (termed nondisjunction) during meiosis is that both members of a particular chromosome pair are included in one daughter gamete nucleus, leaving no representative of this pair in the sister nucleus.

Thus $N - 1$ and $N + 1$ gametes are formed which upon fertilization yield $2N + 1$ and $2N - 1$ zygotes (trisomics and monosomics). It is suggested that in the human female the frequency of meiotic nondisjunction increases with age, since the risk of giving birth to a mongolian idiot rises sharply with advancing age. Any woman who becomes pregnant after age 40 years runs a statistical chance of from 1 to 6 per cent of having such a child.

As recently as February 1960 a year-old boy brought to a pediatric clinic at Orebro, Sweden, was found to have 69 chromosomes in the nuclei of his skin cells. His karyotype is presumably $3A + XXY$.

11–1. Monoploid races of many plant species exist. Plant breeders often convert these to diploids through colchicine treatment. Can you see any advantage to this procedure?

11–2. In 1928 Karpechenko described a classical cross between two different genera of plants, the radish (*Raphanus sativa*) and the cabbage (*Brassica oleracea*). Both species show 9 bivalents at zygonema. The semisterile hybrid (which shows 18 univalents at zygonema) produced a few seeds from which a second generation hybrid was obtained. This hybrid (called *Raphanobrassica*) was vigorous and fertile and showed 18 bivalents at zygonema. How can you explain these data?

11–3. Stebbins defines an autopolyploid as a polyploid of which the corresponding diploid is a fertile species, whereas the allopolyploid contains the doubled genome of a sterile or semisterile hybrid. What is the argument upon which this definition is based?

11–4. How is it possible to maintain triploid races of some agriculturally important plants? *asexual reproduction*

11–5. In emmer wheat what would be the number of chromosomes found in the nuclei of root tip cells in a (1) trisomic, (2) monoploid, (3) triploid, (4) autotetraploid, and (5) a monosomic? *29*   *14*   *42*   *56*   *27*

11–6. Demonstrate by the checkerboard technique that the phenotypic ratios shown in Table 11–4 are correct.

11–7. The evolution of plants that have evolved through allopolyploidy is often said to be reticulate in contrast to the dendritic evolution of most animals. What do you think is meant by this statement?

BIBLIOGRAPHY

Avery, A. G., S. Satina, and J. Rietsema   1959   Blakeslee: the Genus *Datura*. Ronald Press, New York.

Blakeslee, A. F.   1934   New Jimson weeds from old chromosomes. J. Hered. *25*: 80–108.

Böök, J. A., and B. Santesson   1960   Malformation syndrome in man associated with triploidy (69 chromosomes). Lancet No. 7129: 858–9.

Clausen, J., D. D. Keck, and W. M. Hiesey   1945   Experimental studies on the nature of species. II. Plant evolution through amphiploidy and autoploidy, with examples from the Madiinae. Carnegie Inst. Wash. Publ. No. 564. Washington, D. C.

Haldane, J. B. S.   1930   The theoretical genetics of autopolyploids. J. Genetics *32*: 359–72.

Karpechenko, G. D.   1928   Polyploid hybrids of *Raphanus sativa* L. × *Brassica oleracea* L. Ztschr. ind. Abstamm- u. Vererbungsl. *39*: 1–7.

Little, T. M.   1945   Gene segregation in autotetraploids. Botan. Rev. *11*: 60–85.

McFadden, E. S., and E. R. Sears   1946   The origin of *Triticum spelta* and its free-threshing hexaploid relatives. J. Hered. *37*: 81-9.

Patau, K., E. Therman, D. W. Smith, and R. I. De Mars   1961   Trisomy for Chromosome 18 in man. Chromosoma *12*: 280–85.

Sansome, F. W., and J. Philip   1939   Recent Advances in Plant Genetics. Churchill, London.

Sarkar, P., and G. L. Stebbins   1956   Morphological evidence concerning the origin of the B genome in wheat. Am. J. Bot. *43*: 297–304.

Sears, E. R.   1948   The cytology and genetics of the wheats and their relatives. Advances Genet. *2*: 239-70.

Sears, E. R.   1956   The transfer of leaf-rust resistance from *Aegilops umbellulata* to wheat. Brookhaven Symposia in Biology *9*: 1–22.

Stebbins, S. G.   1950   Variation and Evolution in Plants, Chapters 8, 9. Columbia University Press, New York.

Chapter 12

Sex Determination

Introduction

The realization of the relationship between chromosomal balance and sex determination resulted from a study by C. B. Bridges in 1920 of the aneuploid offspring produced by triploid *Drosophila* females. Since then the subject of the genetic control of sex has grown to such proportions that it deserves a separate chapter.

The offspring of triploids

Triploid females of *Drosophila melanogaster* produce a variety of eggs. Haploid and diploid eggs each make up one-sixteenth of the total, and various types of aneuploid eggs make up the remainder (see Table 12–1). These eggs may be fertilized by X- or Y-bearing sperm to produce 32 classes of zygotes. Among these are inviable zygotes, which are trisomic for chromosomes 2 and/or 3, and viable triplo-IV embryos. Additional classes of individuals are observed (see Table 12–2) which include *supersexes* and *intersexes*. Superfemales are diploid females which are trisomic with respect to the X-chromosome. Supermales have an X and a Y plus three sets of autosomes.

Supermales and superfemales resemble males and females respectively, but have lowered viability, notched wings, disturbed wing vein and bristle patterns, and they are sterile. Intersexes are triploids with one X-chromosome missing; a Y-chromosome may or may not be present. Intersexes show both male and female characteristics. For example, an intersex may

TABLE 12–1   The classes of eggs produced by a 3N ♀

CHROMOSOMAL CONSTITUTION

TYPE	X	II	III	IV
1	1	1	1	1
2	1	1	1	2
3	1	1	2	1
4	1	1	2	2
5	1	2	1	1
6	1	2	1	2
7	1	2	2	1
8	1	2	2	2
9	2	1	1	1
10	2	1	1	2
11	2	1	2	1
12	2	1	2	2
13	2	2	1	1
14	2	2	1	2
15	2	2	2	1
16	2	2	2	2

TABLE 12–2   The ratio of X-chromosomes to major autosomes among the viable offspring of triploid *Drosophila* ♀ ♀

SEXUAL TYPE	FORMULA	X/A
superfemale	XXX AA	1.5
triploid female	XXX AAA	1.0
diploid female	XX AA	1.0
Y-bearing diploid female	XXY AA	1.0
intersex	XX AAA	.67
male	XY AA	.5
supermale	XY AAA	.33

possess sex combs, genitalia which show a mixture of male and female parts, and one ovary and one testis. Various grades of intersexes are found, some of which are more malelike and others more femalelike. When reared at low temperatures male type intersexes predominate; at high temperatures intersexes of the female type are most common.

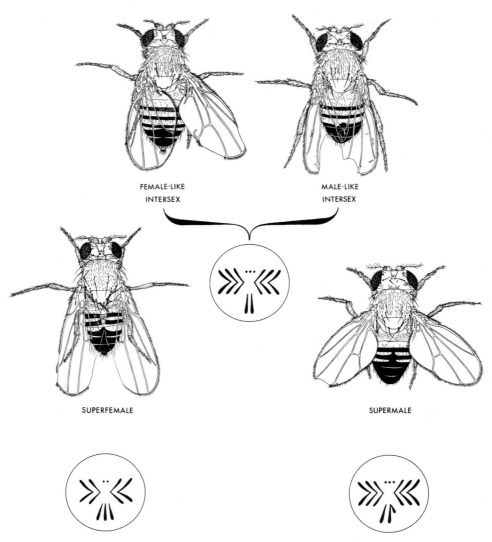

Figure 12-1 Supersexes and intersexes of *Drosophila melanogaster*. These individuals are characterized by the chromosomal complements shown below each fly. Supersexes and intersexes are
sterile and generally show disturbed bristle patterns and wing venation and a scalloping of the wing
margins. Male type intersexes and supermales possess sex combs, and sex combs are often found
on the forelegs of female type intersexes. However, in female type intersexes the sex comb may be
absent from one tarsus or reduced in size. The viability of the supersexes is very low.

(After Bridges.)

It appears in *Drosophila* that sex is determined polygenetically. The sex-
determining genes are so distributed that the net effect results in the autosomes determining maleness and the X-chromosomes femaleness. The Y
can be disregarded. Sex then depends upon the ratio of X-chromosomes to

autosomes. When the ratio is 1.0 or above, females result. When it is 0.5 or less, males are produced, and at the intermediate value 0.67, intersexes are formed (see Table 12–2).

Sturtevant's transformer gene

Sturtevant reported in 1945 the discovery of a recessive gene, *transformer* (*tra*), which when homozygous converts females into sterile males. Such males seem perfect in every respect, except that their testes are rudimentary and contain no sperm. Superfemales which are homozygous for *tra* are converted into "males" which have only half the number of teeth in their sex combs (see page 48). Thus superfemales are more resistant to the "masculinizing" effect of *tra* than are normal females.

To explain the action of *tra* on the sexual phenotype one may assume that the + allele of *tra* (which is normally in double dose in all flies) directly or indirectly leads to an enhanced activity of the female-determining substances produced by X-chromosomal genes, or suppresses the masculinizing action of substances produced by autosomal genes. The *tra* gene would be inactive in this respect. Thus in normal females the masculinizing action of the autosomes would be overcome by the feminizing action of the X-chromosomes only in the presence of a + allele at the *transformer* locus.

Sex determination in man

The situation in man seems to be different from *Drosophila*, since in man the Y-chromosome contains potent male-determining genes which can almost completely overcome the feminizing action of the rest of the genotype. In *Drosophila*, XXY embryos develop into fertile females and XO embryos into sterile males. XXY embryos in man develop into sterile males which show a condition called seminiferous tubule dysgenesis (or Klinefelter's syndrome). Such individuals show a masculine phenotype, but the testes are small and sperms are lacking in the semen. The condition is sometimes associated with mental retardation. XO individuals develop into sterile females. These females show a condition called female gonadal dysgenesis (or Turner's syndrome). Such women fail to menstruate upon reaching puberty, and their gonads are missing or rudimentary. Since XO individuals reach adulthood, it is obvious that in man (given a normal autosomal complement) only one X-chromosome is required for survival. XXY:3A individuals are phenotypically male. XXX:2A individuals are sterile females of average intelligence; whereas XXXY:2A individuals are mentally retarded, sterile males.

Sex determination in Melandrium

The mechanism of sex determination in man seems to be more like that found in the dioecious plant *Melandrium album* than that in *Drosophila*. Cytological studies have shown that the X- and Y-chromosomes can be readily distinguished on the basis of size (the Y being much smaller). Plants develop into females regardless of the ratio between the numbers of X-chromosomes and autosomes, provided no Y-chromosome is present. If a Y-chromosome is present, the plant develops into a male, provided the ratio between X- and Y-chromosomes does not exceed 3:2. At values of 2:1 or 3:1 (see Table 12–3) the plants are male with occasional hermaphroditic flowers. XXXXY plants are monoecious.

TABLE 12–3 Sexual type as a function of chromosomal constitution in *Melandrium*

SEXUAL TYPE		CHROMOSOMAL CONSTITUTION	X/Y
female		2A XX	0.0
male		2A XYY	0.5
male		2A XY	1.0
male		3A XY	1.0
male		4A XY	1.0
male		4A XXYY	1.0
male		4A XXXYY	1.5
male	with an	2A XXY	2.0
male	occasional	3A XXY	2.0
male	hermaphroditic	4A XXY	2.0
male	flower	4A XXXXYY	2.0
male		3A XXXY	3.0
male		4A XXXY	3.0
hermaphrodite		4A XXXXY	4.0

Evolution of the distinctiveness between X- and Y-chromosomes

It is assumed that the ancestral mechanism for sex determination involved a single sex-differentiating gene, and that subsequently other genes on the same chromosome became involved in sex determination. Genes governing the development of the homogametic sex accumulated upon the X, while those governing the development of the heterogametic sex accumulated upon the Y and the autosomes. At the same time (presumably through the occurrence of aberrations) the homology between X- and Y-chromosomes was reduced, and crossing over became restricted to only a portion of both chromosomes (the so-called pairing segments). The reduction in crossing over in the chromosomal regions carrying the sex-differentiating genes (the differential segments) resulted in the stability of the gene combinations preserving bisexuality. Under these circumstances there would be little or no natural selection to prevent within the differential segment the loss through mutation of the activity of those genes having alleles on the X-chromosome. A Y-chromosome which is relatively inert genetically would be expected to result from such a sequence of events.

Sex mosaics

As mentioned above, XX *Drosophila* develop into females and XO individuals into sterile males. Occasionally during embryogenesis of diploid females an X-chromosome will fail to be incorporated into a daughter nucleus at telophase. The resultant cell and its progeny will have the male XO genotype, and a predominantly female individual will result which has patches of male tissue. When the loss of one X-chromosome occurs at the first division after syngamy an individual will be produced which is half male and half female—a bilateral gynandromorph (see Fig. 12–2).

The restriction of polyploidy by bisexuality

Among parthenogenetic animals polyploidy is well documented. However, in nonparthenogenetic, bisexual species polyploidy is never found. Muller was the first to point out that in bisexual organisms polyploidy would upset the sex chromosome mechanism, since tetraploidy, hexaploidy, etc., would abolish the production of X- and Y-bearing gametes. If, for example, a tetraploid was formed by doubling the chromosome number of the heterogametic sex, the resulting individual would be XXYY AAAA. The gametes produced by this individual would be XYAA, since the two Xs and the two Ys would form bivalents at meiosis. If a tetraploid male fertilized a tetraploid female, the offspring produced would be XXXY AAAA, and consequently a viable, self-perpetuating, tetraploid, bisexual strain could never arise.

In some related species of bisexual animals situations arise which are reminiscent of polyploidy. For example, the Chinese hamster (*Cricetulus*

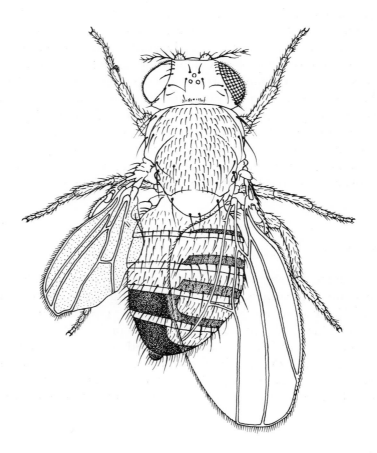

Figure 12–2 A bilateral gynandromorph of *Drosophila melanogaster*. The zygote was $+ +/w$ m. Loss of the X-chromosome containing $+^w$ and $+^m$ occurred at the first nuclear division. The cell containing but one X-chromosome gave rise to the tissues on the left side of the fly. Note the right side is female; the left male. The left eye is white and the left wing is miniature. Note the male pigmentation and sex comb on the left side.

griseus) has a haploid chromosome number of 11, whereas the Syrian hamster (*Mesocricetus auratus*) has a haploid number of 22. However, Moses and Yerganian have shown the DNA content per nucleus to be equivalent in both species, and consequently it appears that the doubling in the number of chromosomes resulted from chromosomal fragmentation. Therefore it is impossible to arrive at any conclusions as to the roles played by polyploidy, polyteny, or chromosomal fusion or fragmentation in the production of related species with divergent chromosomal complements unless one knows not just the chromosome number, but also the total length of all chromosome arms and the DNA content of the nuclei of the species under study.

Dosage compensation

A study of the expression of mutant genes which as a consequence of their location on the X-chromosome of *Drosophila* exist in two doses in the female and one in the male led Muller to postulate that special genetic mechanisms have been evolved to compensate for these dosage differences. According to his theory the mechanism involves the presence of other sex-linked *compensator genes* which when present in the female (in double dose) reduce the activity of her two doses of the "primary gene" so as to make the effect like that of one dose of the primary gene and one of the compensator gene in the male. These compensatory mechanisms have slowly evolved for the function of equalizing the effects of the nonmutant genes in the two sexes. One of the few sex-linked genes in *D. melanogaster* which shows no dosage compensation is *bobbed*. However, you will recall (p. 106) that *bobbed*, unlike most sex-linked genes, has an allele in the Y-chromosome.

The sex chromosome of *Drosophila pseudoobscura* is metacentric. The left arm is for the most part descended from the original rod-shaped X-chromosome which has remained as the X in *Drosophila melanogaster*. The right arm is relatively new and is homologous to the left arm of chromosome 3 of *melanogaster*. Muller and Lamy have shown that the mutants on the right arm of the *pseudoobscura* X are incompletely compensated in contrast to those on the older left arm. That is, the genes on the left arm look alike in both sexes; whereas those on the right arm are unlike. As would be expected in the latter case, the female mutant is closer in phenotype to wild type than is the male.

Muller and Lieb also demonstrated that transformed males (XX; *tra/tra*) have compensated in accordance with their genotype and not with their sexual phenotype.

Sexuality among unicellular organisms

In many unicellular organisms individual cells which normally lead an independent existence will under certain conditions come together and unite in pairs. Subsequently their bodies will fuse, and their nuclei do likewise. In many cases the cells which behave in this fashion are so similar in morphology and metabolism that neither of them can be regarded as male or female, and therefore one is arbitrarily referred to as + and the other as −. Brock has reported that in the yeast *Hansenula wingei* one mating type possesses a specific protein on its cell surface which is complementary to a specific polysaccharide on the cell surface of the opposite mating type. The initial phase of mating in which cells of opposite types combine is therefore analogous to the reaction between proteinaceous antibodies and a poly-saccharide antigen (see p. 225).

Conjugation in *Paramecium aurelia* has already been described in Chapter 4. The related species, *Paramecium bursaria,* exists in a series of varieties each reproductively isolated from the rest. Some of these varieties contain systems of *multiple* interbreeding mating types. Variety II, for example, contains eight mating types (E to M) each of which can mate with every other mating type of the variety, but not with itself. This phenomenon of multiple sexuality which has been observed in other protozoa and in fungi and algae apparently serves to increase the probability that each member of a mating pair will be genetically different. Under such circumstances the progeny produced will contain a wide spectrum of recombinant geno-types, some of which may confer advantages upon their possessor superior to those of the parental combinations.

In Chapter 4 the sexual cycle was described for *Neurospora.* Here hetero-caryon formation also occurs as a substitute for sexuality. You will recall that heterocaryons contain multiple haploid nuclei of differing genotypes and that these nuclei never unite. However, in another mold, *Aspergillus nidulans,* haploid nuclei in a multinucleate heterocaryon do unite to pro-duce unstable, heterozygous, diploid nuclei. The frequency of this event is very rare (1×10^{-7}). During the diploid stage mitotic crossing over occurs followed by a mitotic division at which the chromosomes are distributed randomly. Occasionally euploid, recombinant, viable, monoploid nuclei are produced. Pontecorvo has named this phenomenon *parasexuality.*

Environmental determination of sex

In the situations mentioned earlier in this chapter, sex is determined genetically at the time of fertilization. Furthermore the genetic sex of the organism cannot be reversed, although the sexual phenotype may sometimes be overridden by hormonal influences. However, in many lower organisms differentiation into either of the two sexes is under environmental rather than genetic control.

An excellent example of environmental determination of sexual pheno-type is afforded by *Bonellia viridis,* a marine Echiuroid worm studied exten-sively by F. Baltzer (see Fig. 12–3). The adult develops from a sexually neutral, free-swimming larva which may attach itself to the sea floor. In this case it develops into an adult female. On the other hand, the larva may land upon the proboscis of an adult female, in which case it migrates to the uterus where it differentiates into an adult male of minute size and parasitic habit.

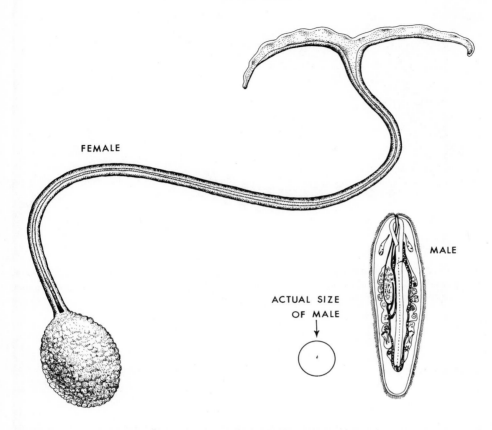

FEMALE

MALE

ACTUAL SIZE
OF MALE

Figure 12–3   The female and male of the echiuroid *Bonellia viridis*. The female is shown slightly enlarged; whereas the male is greatly magnified.   (Redrawn from T. Dobzhansky, *Evolution, Genetics
and Man*, 1955, John Wiley & Sons, Inc.)

Coe has shown that species belonging to the mollusc genus *Crepidula*
show consecutive sexuality with most individuals experiencing a functional
'male phase when young and later changing by a transitional stage to a
female phase (Fig. 12–4). The female phase continues for the remainder of
the animal's lifetime. There are also examples of molluscs which usually
behave in the above fashion, but in which a small proportion of the population is strictly unisexual.

Finally, we find many invertebrates and higher plants to be hermaphrodites. In these cases the sexually mature organism carries both male and
female sex organs; and as a consequence the question as to the relative roles
played by heredity and environment in sex determination becomes
meaningless.

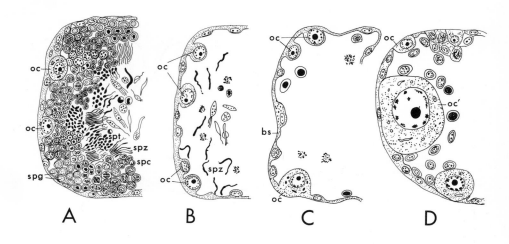

A   B   C   D

Figure 12–4   Changes in the gonad of the mollusc *Crepidula* experiencing consecutive sexuality. A. male phase; B.,C. transitional phases; D. female phase. Oc-immature oocyte, spg-spermatogonia, spt-spermatids, spz-spermatozoa, spc-spermatocytes, oc'-mature oocyte.   (After Coe.)

Arrhenotoky

As was mentioned in Chapter 3, arrhenotokous parthenogenesis (haplodiploidy) is particularly common in the hymenopterous insects such as ants, bees, and wasps. Since fertilized eggs develop into diploid females and unfertilized ones into haploid males, arrhenotoky is both a form of reproduction and a means of sex determination. Meiosis is normal in females, but crossing over and reduction in chromosome number fail to occur during spermatogenesis.

That males are not invariably haploid in all Hymenoptera was shown by the studies of P. W. Whiting on *Habrobracon juglandis* (see Fig. 12–5), a wasp which parasitizes the Mediterranean flour moth and other cereal-infesting caterpillars. Unmated females of *Habrobracon* produce haploid eggs which develop into males. Mated females produce both fertilized and un-fertilized eggs. The majority of the fertilized eggs yield diploid females; but diploid semisterile male also occur. Whiting's analysis led to the conclusion that a variety of sex alleles (X_a, X_b, X_c, etc.) exist in this species. Wasps heterozygous for any two alleles (i.e. X_a/X_b, X_a/X_c, X_b/X_c, etc.) develop into females. Haploid males are, of course, hemizygous for a given allele, whereas diploid males are homozygous (X_a/X_a, X_b/X_b, etc.).

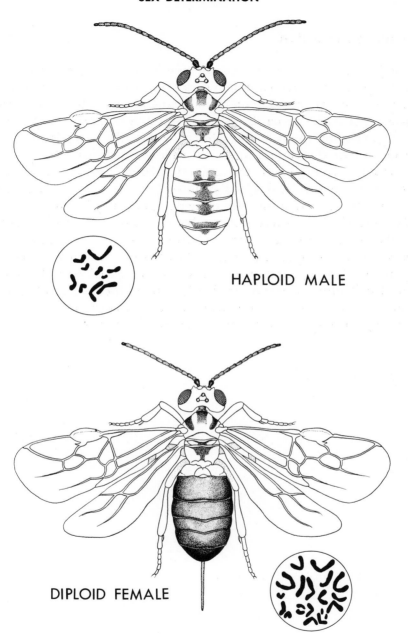

HAPLOID MALE

DIPLOID FEMALE

Figure 12–5 Dorsal views of *Habrobracon juglandis* (*Bracon brevicornis*) adults. Below are seen highly magnified gonial metaphase chromosomes (ten for the male and 20 for the female). The wasps are about 2.5 mm. long (measuring from the tip of the head to the end of the abdomen). Note the needle-shaped ovipositor of the female with which she stings and paralyzes the caterpillars which serve to nourish her offspring.   (After D. S. Grosch.)

Asexual reproduction

The importance of sexual reproduction is that it engenders an immense variety of genotypes which are then presented as phenotypes to the environment where they are acted upon by natural selection. The union of gametes of diverse genotypes generally occurs even among hermaphrodites, since cross fertilization is the rule and self-fertilization the exception.

Asexual reproduction (or apomixis, as it is sometimes called) is encountered among various plant and animal species. Asexual forms are very prolific, since life can be devoted exclusively to feeding and reproduction. However, very few organisms are obligate apomicts. The usual situation is for the species to have alternating cycles of sexual and apomictic behavior. The balance struck by a given species between sexual and asexual behavior appears to be a delicate one determined by both environmental and genetic components. Among haploid microorganisms asexual reproduction is the rule and sexuality the exception. Within the immense microbial populations found in nature spontaneous mutation plays the major role in providing new phenotypes upon which selection can operate.

12–1. L. Powers has shown that three pairs of genes determine the breeding behavior of the guayule plant, *Parthenium argentatum*. The recessive gene *a* when homozygous leads to the formation of unreduced eggs; gene *b* when homozygous prevents fertilization; and gene *c* causes unfertilized eggs to undergo embryogenesis. Thus plants of genotypes *AABBCC* or *AABBcc* reproduce sexually to form diploids; whereas those of genotypes *aaBBCC* or *aaBBcc* reproduce sexually to form polyploid offspring. *AAbbCC* and *aabbCC* individuals are sterile; whereas *aabbcc* individuals are obligatory apomicts. What phenotypic ratios are to be expected among the offspring resulting from a cross between two individuals of genotype *AaBbCc*?

12–2. In corn the recessive gene *ba* (barren stalk) when homozygous eliminates the ears; whereas the recessive gene *ts* (tassel seed) when homozygous converts the tassel into a functional pistillate inflorescence. Devise a manner of manipulating these genes so as to convert corn from a hermaphroditic to a bisexual species.

12–3. When cows give birth to twin calfs of unlike sex the female twin is often sexually abnormal. Such females (called *freemartins*) are sterile and are characterized by masculinized reproductive organs. Lillie demonstrated that this condition occurs when the twin fetuses share a common placenta and circulation. Does this finding suggest the reason for abnormal sexual development of the female twin? How could one test this hypothesis? Keep in mind the fact that pregnant female rats and mice when injected with large amounts of androgens produce fetuses whose reproductive systems are masculinized.

12–4. A male *Drosophila* hemizygous for the gene *white* is crossed to an attached-X female homozygous for the gene *singed*. Both flies are heterozygous for *tra*. What phenotypic ratios are expected among the offspring?

12–5. Some of the results of a study by Hughes-Schrader of the interspecific relationships in the mantid genus *Liturgosa* are presented below:

SPECIES	MALE DIPLOID CHROMOSOME NUMBER	RELATIVE TOTAL LENGTH OF CHROMOSOMES	RELATIVE DNA PER NUCLEUS
L. maya	17	1.0	1.00
L. cursor	33	0.9	0.94

Would you conclude that *L. cursor* arose from *L. maya* by autotetraploidy?

12–6. Assume a *Habrobracon* female of genotype X_aX_b is crossed to a haploid male of genotype X_b. What would be the sex ratio of the progeny provided 25 per cent of the eggs laid were unfertilized?

12–7. According to Pipkin (*Drosophila* Information Service *33*: 154) the percentages of the different sexual types developing at 22°C as progeny of triploid females are as follows: diploid females, 38.54; diploid males, 18.96; triploid females, 12.84; intersexes, 28.66; superfemales, 0.50; and supermales, 0.42. What conclusions can one draw as to the relative viability of each abnormal sexual type? (See Table 12–1.)

12–8. Recently Frost (*Proc. Nat. Acad. Sc. 46*: 47–51, 1960) has demonstrated in

Drosophila melanogaster the occurrence of females of chromosomal genotype XXXX AAA which have a much higher viability than diploid superfemales and are partially fertile. Do such females fit appropriately in the sequence shown in Table 12–1?

12–9. Speculate as to the mechanism by which individuals suffering from Klinefelter's syndrome or Turner's syndrome originate.

12–10. The single X-chromosome in the salivary gland nuclei of male larvae of *Drosophila melanogaster* has a diameter which is nearly as great as that of the two paired X-chromosomes of female larvae, yet the DNA content of the single X-chromosome of male gland cells is one-half that of the paired X-chromosomes in the salivary glands of females. Discuss these findings in view of your knowledge of dosage compensation.

12–11. You will recall that question 8–2 dealt with the sex-linked alleles responsible for the determination of coat color in cats. *Bb* females showing black and orange patches in their coat are called tortoiseshell or calico cats. The occurence of rare tortoiseshell males has long puzzled geneticists. Such males are sterile and show 39 instead of the normal 38 chromosomes. Advance a hypothesis to explain these findings.

BIBLIOGRAPHY

Allen, E. 1939 Sex and Internal Secretions. Williams & Wilkins, Baltimore, Md.

Baltzer, F. 1925 Untersuchungen über die Entwicklung und Geschlechtsbestimmung der *Bonellia*. Pubbl. staz. Zool. Napoli, Vol. *6*.

Baltzer, F. 1937 Analyze des Goldschmitschen Zeitgesetzes der Intersexualität auf Grund eines Vergleiches der Entwicklung der *Bonellia*—und *Lymantria*—Intersexe. W. Roux. Archiv. Entwicklungsmechenik *136*: 218–24.

Barr, M. L. 1959 Sex chromatin and phenotype in man. Science *130*: 679–85.

Bridges, C. B. 1925 Sex in relation to chromosomes and genes. Am. Naturalist *59*: 127–37.

Brock, T. D. 1959 Biochemical basis of mating type in yeast. Science *129*: 960–61.

Brown, E. H., and R. C. King 1961 Studies on the expression of the *transformer* gene of *Drosophila melanogaster*. Genetics *46*: 143–56.

Caullery, M. 1951 Organisme et Sexualité, 2nd ed. G. Doin, Paris.

Clausen, J. 1954 Partial apomixis as an equilibrium system in evolution. Caryologia *1*: 469–79.

Coe, W. R. 1943 Sexual differentiation in molluscs, I, Pelecypods. Quart. Rev. Biol. *18*: 154–64.

Coe, W. R. 1944 Sexual differentiation in molluscs, II, Gastropods, amphineurans, scaphopods, and cephalopods. Quart. Rev. Biol. *19*: 85–97.

Crow, J. F. 1946 The absence of a primary sex factor on the X-chromosome of *Drosophila*. Am. Naturalist *80*: 663–5.

Dobzhansky, T., and J. Schultz 1934 The distribution of sex factors in the X-chromosome of *Drosophila melanogaster*. J. Genetics *28*: 349–86.

Flanders, S. E. 1946 Control of sex and sex-limited polymorphism in the Hymenoptera. Quart. Rev. Biol. *21*: 135–43.

Gallien, L. 1959 Sex Determination. *The Cell 1*: 399–436. Academic Press, New York.

Hughes-Schrader, S. 1953 The nuclear content of DNA and interspecific relationships in the mantid genus *Liturgousa*. Chromosoma *5*: 544–54.

Krivshenko, J. 1959 New evidence for the homology of the short euchromatic elements of the X and Y chromosomes of *Drosophila busckii* with the microchromosome of *Drosophila melanogaster*. Genetics *44*: 1027–40.

Lillie, F. R. 1917 The free-martin: a study of the action of sex hormones in the foetal life of cattle. J. Exp. Zool. *23*: 371–452.

Morgan, T. H., C. B. Bridges, and A. H. Sturtevant 1925 The genetics of *Drosophila*. Bibliographia genetica *2*: 60–231.

Moses, M. J., and G. Yerganian 1952 DNA content and cytotaxonomy of several Cricetinae (hamsters). Records Genet. Soc. America *21*: 51–2.

Muller, H. J. 1925 Why polyploidy is rarer in animals than in plants. Am. Naturalist *59*: 346–53.

Muller, H. J. 1950 Evidence for the precision of genetic adaptation. Harvey Lectures (1947–48) Ser. *43*: 165–229. C. C. Thomas, Springfield, Ill.

Muller, H. J., and T. S. Painter 1932 The differentiation of the sex chromosomes of *Drosophila* into genetically active and inert regions. Ztschr. ind. Abstamms-u. Vererbungsl. *62*: 316–65.

Pipkin, S. B. 1940 Multiple sex genes in the X-chromosome of *Drosophila melanogaster*. U. Texas Publ. No. 4032: 126–56.

Pontecorvo, G. 1956 The parasexual cycle in fungi. Ann. Rev. Microbiol. *10*: 393–400.

Powers, L. 1945 Fertilization without reduction in guayule (*Parthenium argentatum* Gray), and a hypothesis as to the evolution of apomixis and polyploidy. Genetics *30*: 323–46.

Russell, L. B. 1961 Genetics of mammalian sex chromosomes. Science *133*: 1795–1803.

Siegel, R. W., and L. L. Larison 1960 The genetic control of mating types in *Paramecium bursaria*. Proc. Nat. Acad. Sc. *46*: 344–9.

Sonneborn, T. M. 1947 Recent advances in the genetics of *Paramecium* and *Euplotes*. Advances Genet. *1*: 262–358.

Stern, C. 1960 Dosage compensation-development of a concept and new facts. Canadian J. Genet .and Cytol. *2*: 105–18.

Sturtevant, A. H. 1945 A gene in *Drosophila melanogaster* that transforms females into males. Genetics *30*: 297–9.

Tanner, J. M., A. Prader, H. Habick, and M. A. Ferguson-Smith   1959   Genes on the Y chromosome influencing the rate of maturation in man. The Lancet Vol. 2. (Aug. 22), pp. 141–4.

Thuline, H. C., and D. E. Norby   1961   Spontaneous occurrence of chromosome abnormality in cats. Science *134*: 554–5.

Warmke, H. E.   1946   Sex determination and sex balance in *Melandrium*. Am. J. Botany *33*: 648–60.

Watterson, R., editor   1959   Endocrines in Development, Chap. 4. University of Chicago Press, Chicago.

Wenrich, D. H., editor   1954   Sex in Microorganisms. American Association for the Advancement of Science, Washington, D. C.

Whiting, P. W.   1943   Multiple alleles in complementary sex determination of *Habrobracon*. Genetics *28*: 365–82.

Chapter 13

Mutation

Introduction

A unique property of living things is the ability to reproduce. This faculty stems from the capability of genes to produce copies of themselves. In addition the gene often reproduces faithfully any innovations made in its structure. It is the capacity to replicate not only the original structure but the changes (which we call mutations) which over the course of millions of years and under the directing influence of natural selection have generated the countless species which live today or have existed in the past on our planet. Thus the capacity to evolve stems from the ability to mutate.

Spontaneous mutations

Spontaneous mutation rates have been determined for a number of specific genes in a number of species. Unfortunately, few data are available for spontaneous mutation rates in higher organisms because of the great labor required to measure such low values. The data available (see Table 13–1 for an example) demonstrate that the rates vary widely among different genes in the same species. The evidence indicates a given gene may mutate to any one of a number of allelic states, and that the number of states in which some genes can exist is very large. For example, 12 alleles are known for the Rh locus in man, and the gene in cattle responsible for the B system of red blood cell antigens can exist in over 160 allelic forms. Different alleles of the same gene also show great differences in their spontaneous mutation rates.

Although the mutation rate for a given gene is generally low (perhaps 1 in 100,000 on the average), the average gamete contains many genes (perhaps 10,000) and as a consequence the over-all mutation rate per gamete per generation is high. Perhaps one gamete in ten contains a spontaneous mutation of one sort or another.

TABLE 13–1   Spontaneous Mutation Rates for Genes Affecting the Morphology or Pigmentation of the Kernel in Maize (studied by L. J. Stadler, 1942)

MUTATION	NUMBER OF GAMETES TESTED	MUTATION FREQUENCY (PER 10,000 TESTED GAMETES)
$Wx \longrightarrow wx$	1,503,744	0
$Sh \longrightarrow sh$	2,469,285	0.012
$Su \longrightarrow su$	1,678,731	0.024
$Pr \longrightarrow pr$	647,102	0.11
$I \longrightarrow i$	265,391	1.06

Factors influencing mutation

a. Genetic

It has been clearly shown that the rate of mutation is influenced by both genetic and environmental factors. Several genes that increase the rate at which spontaneous lethal and viable mutations occur have been discovered. Demerec, for example, reported in 1937 that a recessive gene located on the second chromosome of *Drosophila melanogaster* increased the spontaneous rate of sex-linked lethal mutations by a fifteenfold factor.

The third chromosomal gene A which in corn is one of the factors responsible for aleurone pigmentation has been referred to previously (p. 81). Rhoades has shown that the rate at which *a* mutates to *A* is influenced by the gene *Dotted* (*Dt*) which resides on chromosome 9. The *Dt* gene itself plays no role in pigment formation. The rate at which such mutations occur can be measured by observing the frequency of pigmented spots on the surface of otherwise colorless kernels. The patch of color results from a cluster of pigmented cells that are the progeny of a single, mutated somatic cell. As the dosage of *Dt* is raised the frequency of mutation increases markedly (see Fig. 13–1).

Subsequently, the *Dissociation-Activator* (*Ds-Ac*) system in maize was discovered by Barbara McClintock during a study of the behavior of loci in the short arm of chromosome 9 at which breakage was occurring. This chromosome arm previously had undergone drastic structural rearrangement as the result of a breakage-fusion-bridge cycle of the type mentioned in Chapter 10. The *Dissociation* and *Activator* loci are recognizable and can be mapped

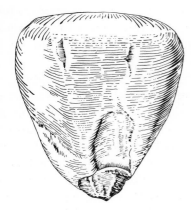 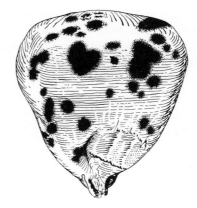

Figure 13-1 Colorless and spotted corn kernels. Only the right kernel carries *Dt*. The relation between the spotting and the number of *Dt* genes is given below.

Genotype			Mutations per seed
dt	dt	dt	0
dt	dt	Dt	7.2
dt	Dt	Dt	22.2
Dt	Dt	Dt	121.9

through their action on adjacent genes and are believed to be blocks of heterochromatin. They are both capable of being "transposed" from one spot to another within and among the chromosomes of the complement, and in this respect they behave like episomes. Transposition presumably occurs through breakage to either side of these loci, their removal, and subsequently their insertion into a new point on the same or a different chromosome. *Ds* appears to initiate changes in genic expression, but it is without effect in the absence of *Ac* which determines the time during morphogenesis when *Ds* acts. *Ac* in many aspects is similar to *Dt*, and McClintock believes that although *Dt* and *Ac* appear not to be the same activator they may both have originated through alterations in heterochromatic chromosomal elements brought about by a breakage-fusion-bridge cycle. The presence of *Ac* and *Ds* in the same nucleus results in increased chromosome breakage. Breakage appears to occur at the locus of *Ds* with subsequent loss of the chromosomal material distal to *Ds* or the production of a chromosome aberration that has one break at the *Ds* locus. McClintock has speculated that "stickiness" of the heterochromatic *Ds* locus may lead to stresses during the anaphase movement of chromosomes which lead to rupture at this locus. *Ds* may also inhibit the action of adjacent genes, making them behave as if they had mutated to an inactive recessive state.

Phenomena reminiscent of the *Ac-Ds* system evidently occur commonly in maize, since Brink has shown similar types of behavior at the *P* locus on chromosome 1 and at the R locus on chromosome 10. In *Drosophila melanogaster* Sandler and Hiraizumi have discovered in the right arm of chromosome 2 near the centromere a region which behaves in a manner analogous to McClintock's elements.

The widespread occurrence of the above phenomena has led McClintock to suggest that there exist within chromosomes (in addition to genes) self-replicating controlling elements. These elements which presumably are associated with heterochromatin influence morphogenesis by initiating a progressive series of responses in different blocks of genes. Brink has suggested that controlling elements (or segments of parachromatin, as he calls them) are sensitive to changes in the cellular environment that specifically accompany the developmental process, whereas genes are not. Parachromatin may thus form the connection between chromosomal heredity and morphogenesis.

b. Environmental

Muller and Altenberg showed as early as 1919 that temperature affected the mutation frequency. The sex-linked lethal mutation rate per generation for *Drosophila* reared at 27° C was three times that observed for those raised at 17° C. It was demonstrated subsequently that brief exposures to either abnormally high or abnormally low temperatures resulted in increased mutation.

The effect of different environmental variables which influence the rate of spontaneous mutations conferring bacteriophage resistance upon *E. coli* (see p. 56) has been studied by Novick and Szilard. To do this they developed a device, called a Chemostat, in which bacterial populations can be kept in a state of continuous division for many generations. Their studies showed that the mutation rates observed were related to the physiology and biochemical state of the bacteria. Thus, if an amino acid was used as the limiting growth factor, the mutation rate was twice that observed when the limiting growth factor used was a nitrogen source, a carbon source, or a phosphorus source. The spontaneous mutation rate per hour was found to be constant and independent of growth rate, at least for bacterial generation times between 2 and 12 hours.

Chemical mutagens

Attempts during World War II by Auerbach and Robson to induce mutations by chemical means were successful in 1941, but this information was not published in declassified form until 1946. In the intervening years the list of mutagenic chemicals has grown longer and longer, and it presently includes such diverse chemicals as formaldehyde, urethane, various acridine dyes, beta propiolactone, manganous chloride, nitrous acid, *mustard gas,* and various *nitrogen mustards, epoxides, ethylene imines,* and *methane sulfonic acid esters* (to name but a few). It is known that chemicals belonging to the groups printed in italics above undergo esterification reactions with the phosphoric acid groups of DNA, and it is assumed that these structural changes increase the likelihood of a mistake being made during subsequent replication which results in a mutation.

Many chemical mutagens are effective in one species, but not another. In a given species they may affect only one sex or only germ cells at one particular stage of gametogenesis. These findings presumably indicate that the germ cell chromosomes react with chemical mutagens only under certain rare circumstances in which the normal physiological barriers protecting the genetic machinery are breached.

Mutational specificities appear to exist since a given chemical mutagen may tend to produce a spectrum of mutations somewhat different than that characteristically produced by radiations or other chemicals and different as well from the spectrum of spontaneous mutations. However, no mutagen is known at present which will produce a mutation at one specific locus. It is assumed that each gene contains all four nucleotides in its DNA and therefore that different genes differ in having the four nucleotides in different sequences. One would therefore expect that a "specific" mutagen would have to react only with a specific assemblage of nucleotides, and this would imply that the mutagen would have to be as complicated in its structure as the gene it mutated. Thus one would expect the relatively simple chemicals which have mutagenic activity to be very unspecific. Chemical mutagens, unlike radiations, often have delayed effects in that the induced mutations may appear several generations after exposure to the agent.

Of a large number of chemicals tested in the Chemostat for mutagenic activity, only one group of compounds was found which exhibited striking mutagenic effects under conditions in which there was no appreciable killing of the bacteria. These mutagens which are either purines or purine derivatives include caffeine, theophylline, paraxanthine, theobromine, and tetramethyluric acid. Subsequently Novick discovered that these induced mutagenic effects could be antagonized by various chemicals and that these "antimutagens" were all purine nucleosides (such as adenosine, guanosine, and inosine). Such antimutagens have no effect on radiation-induced mutations. If adenosine is added to control cultures the *spontaneous* mutation rate is reduced to one-third its normal value. This finding suggests that two-thirds of the spontaneous mutations in the Chemostat are produced by the action of a mutagen of the purine type produced by the normal metabolism of the bacterial cell.

Transformed bacteria

In 1944 a type of "directed mutation" in which a foreign DNA molecule gets incorporated into the genetic machinery of a treated cell was described in *Pneumococcus* by Avery, MacLeod, and McCarty. If DNA is isolated from a strain of encapsulated pneumococci and added to a strain which has lost the ability to produce the polysaccharide capsule (which makes the germ virulent), some of the cells in the second strain are transformed to encapsulated individuals which can transmit this characteristic to their offspring. More recent studies which have shown the simultaneous transfer of two or more characteristics indicate that some DNA preparations carry several genes which seem to travel together as if they were linked. Transformations have been produced in other bacterial species including *Hemophilus influenzae, Escherichia coli, Shigella paradysenteriae,* and meningococci.

It is known from tracer studies that the DNA that accomplishes the transformation actually enters the cell involved in the transformation. Subsequently some type of process equivalent to crossing over may occur between the foreign and the indigenous DNA.

Recent studies by Ottolenghi and Hotchkiss have demonstrated that growing populations of *Pneumococcus* release into the culture medium DNA —containing material with genetic transforming activity. It follows that transformation is not a phenomenon restricted to laboratory conditions, but that transformation in mixed cultures provides natural mechanism for genetic recombination in *Pneumococcus* and possibly in other microorganisms as well.

Radiations as mutagens

The radiations of mutagenic importance are electromagnetic waves of short length (ultraviolet light, X-rays, and γ-rays) and charged and uncharged subatomic particles (see Table 13–2). Electromagnetic radiations

TABLE 13–2 A catalogue of subatomic particles

	PROTON	NEUTRON	DEUTERON	α-PARTICLE	ELECTRON
Charge	+	0	+	+ +	−
Composition	p	n	p, n	2p, 2n	e
Mass (relative to the electron)	1836	1839	3671	7296	1

with wave lengths between 1000 and 4000Å[1] are classified as ultraviolet light. Absorption of a quantum[2] of ultraviolet light by an atom alters the arrangement of the planetary electrons in their orbits. This process is known as *excitation,* and it increases the chemical reactivity of the atom. Excitation of a molecule may cause a reorganization of the electrons which hold its constituent atoms together. If one or more of the weakened bonds rupture, various stable and unstable, chemically reactive fragments may be produced.

X-rays and γ-rays differ only in their origins. The term X-ray was originally reserved for photons[3] from X-ray tubes and the term γ-ray for those from radioactive elements. X-rays from conventional X-ray machines have an average length of 0.5Å; whereas the average γ-ray given off by radium has a wave length of 0.01Å. In practice the energy of a quantum of X- or γ-rays is generally thousands of times greater than that of a quantum of ultraviolet light. Although physically X-rays and γ-rays differ markedly from beams of subatomic particles, their effects are so similar that both are grouped together as *ionizing radiations.* That is, these electromagnetic and corpuscular radiations (in addition to causing excitation) produce ionization as they dissipate their energy in matter. Ionization results when such radiations knock out electrons from the atoms which make up the material through which the photons or particles are passing. The atom from which an electron is released is electron deficient and therefore positively charged. Thus the primary effect of ionizing radiation is to produce countless numbers of ion pairs within tissue.

Two units are used to measure the dose of ionizing radiation, the *roentgen* (abbreviated r) and the *rad* (radiation-absorbed dose). A roentgen of ionizing radiation liberates 2.083×10^9 ion pairs in a cubic centimeter of air (at 0° C and at a pressure of 760 mm. of mercury) or approximately two ion pairs per cubic micron of a substance like protein (which has a density of 1.35). The rad is slowly replacing the roentgen as the preferred unit of radiation dose. The rad is defined in terms of the energy absorbed by irradiated material. Each gram of matter exposed to a radiation dose of one rad absorbs 100 ergs of energy. Since a gram of tissue exposed to one roentgen of ionizing radiation absorbs about 93 ergs, it is obvious that the two units have similar magnitudes.

The slower the ionizing particle and the greater its charge the more ionizations it produces along its path through tissue. Thus a slowly moving alpha particle may liberate 4×10^7 ion pairs per cm. of its track in tissue; whereas the density of ionizations along the track of an energetic electron

---

[1] The Ångström unit (Å) equals 0.1 millimicron (mμ).

[2] Quantum—according to the quantum theory energy is radiated intermittently in units of definite magnitude called quanta and absorbed in a like manner.

[3] Photon—a quantum of electromagnetic energy.

moving at a velocity close to that of light will be perhaps 1000 times less (see Fig. 13–2). The ion density produced by a given radiation is often described by a *LET* value. The LET (linear energy transfer) is defined as the energy (in electron volts[4]) dissipated per micron of tissue traversed by a particular type of ionizing particle.

α β γ

Figure 13–2   Cloud chamber photographs of α, β, and γ-ray tracks. After J. B. Hoag: *Electron and Nuclear Physics*.   (Courtesy of D. Van Nostrand Co.)

The most common molecule found in biological material is water. If through the interaction with ionizing radiation an electron is ejected from water, the molecule becomes unstable and may split into a hydrogen ion and a hydroxyl radical.

$$H_2O + \text{X-ray photon} \rightarrow H_2O^+ + e \rightarrow H^+ + OH + e$$

The OH radicals are initially localized along the path taken by the photon or subatomic particle. The ejected electron will travel a distance determined by the energy it gained from the radiation, and eventually it will combine with a neighboring hydrogen ion or water molecule to produce a hydrogen radical.

$$H^+ + e \rightarrow H \text{ or } H_2O + e \rightarrow H + OH^-$$

Thus, whereas OH radicals are located along the path followed by the radiation, H radicals are produced quite a distance away. If oxygen is dissolved in the water, these H radicals can unite with it to form hydroperoxyl radicals.

$$H + O_2 \rightarrow HO_2$$

Both hydroxyl and hydroperoxyl radicals are very potent oxidizing agents.

---

[4] Electron volt: A unit of energy equivalent to the amount of energy gained by an electron passing through a potential difference of one volt.

Thus a general effect of ionizing radiation is the production of highly reactive molecules which diffuse away from the zones of high concentration, and concurrently react with one another or with such susceptible stable molecules which may be in the vicinity. Molecules of great importance to the functioning of the cell such as DNA may therefore be damaged by being struck by the ionizing photons or particles, or they may react with diffusing free radicals produced by the radiation although they are untouched by the primary events. However, the primary events are far more efficient in damaging genetic material. This is because diffusing free radicals are largely inactivated by the extraneous reducing agents normally found in cells.

Target theory

The target concept first advanced by Crowther in 1924 postulates that there exist within cells being irradiated one or more sensitive targets and that when one (or more) damaging event occurs within said target the observed biological effect is brought about.

Let us consider only the very simplest situation: a cell contains a single sensitive target in which a single damaging event will lead to the death of the cell. Suppose that a population of such cells is subdivided into a series of subpopulations and that each subpopulation is irradiated with a successively higher dose of radiation. Subsequently the proportion of survivors in each subpopulation is determined. In Figure 13–3 the relation between survival and radiation dose is presented graphically. The curvilinear relationship obtained demonstrates that the number of individuals killed is initially proportional to dose, but that as the process continues larger doses are required to produce the same effect. For example, 2000 r kills 20 per cent of the population. To kill a further 20 per cent an additional 3000 r is required and to kill a further 20 per cent an additional 4000 r is required. This behavior results because each increment of dose kills the same proportion of the number of organisms which *survived* until then. Thus a dose of 1000 r kills 10 per cent of the population. The second 1000 r kills 10 per cent of the 90 per cent which survive and kills "a second time" 10 per cent of those already dead. Thus after two doses of 1000 r each to a population of 10,000 cells, 8100 remain alive and 1900 are dead. Of the latter, 1000 were killed by the first 1000 r, 900 by the second 1000 r, and 100 were "killed twice," once by each dose. It is known that at the dose producing 37 per cent survival there is an average of one hit per target, or putting it another way the number of hits equals the number of targets. Of course, at this dose some targets miss being hit and some are hit more than once. In the hypothetical situation described above the 37 per cent survival dose is

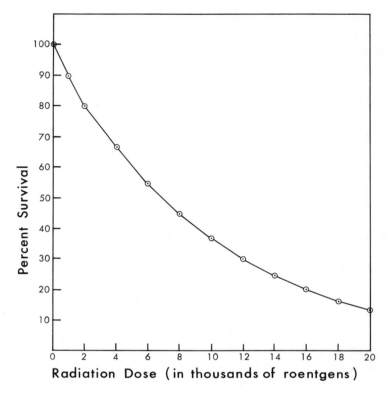

Figure 13–3   A graphical representation of the relationship between survival and the administered radiation dose.

10,000 r. We know that one r liberates 2×10^{12} ion pairs in a cubic centimeter of material the density of protein. Thus the dose producing an average of one hit per target liberates 2×10^{16} ion pairs per cubic centimeter or one ion pair in an average volume of $\dfrac{1}{2 \times 10^{16} \text{ cm.}^3}$ or 50×10^{-18} cm.^{3} or $50 \text{ m}\mu^3$. If the irradiations were carried out upon frozen cells, then diffusion of free radicals cannot occur. If one assumes that the lethal effects are due to the production of a single ion pair within the sensitive volume and that the target is spherical, then the diameter of the target can be calculated to be $4.6 \text{ m}\mu$. Such a target would be resolved by the electron microscope but not by the light microscope.

Through elaborations of this simple target theory, radiation has come to be used as an analytical tool for determining the size, shape, and molecular weight of biologically active macromolecules such as viruses, enzymes, toxins, hormones, and transforming principles (see pp. 251, 255).

Cell lethality due to nuclear damage

Techniques which allow irradiation of parts of cells have demonstrated convincingly that the nucleus is the region of the cell most sensitive to the damaging effects of radiation. Studies with microbeams of radiation have shown that to kill a cell by radiating the cytoplasm radiation doses must be used which are hundreds or thousands of times larger than those which kill the cell if the nucleus is the target.

When a microbeam of protons is directed upon a prophase chromosome it fragments at anaphase. Chromosomal fragmentation is never observed when U.V. microbeams are used. Microbeam irradiation of a small chromosome segment with small doses of protons or U.V. causes the chromosomal region to become sticky. Microbeam U.V. irradiation of a chromosomal segment also causes a decrease in the refractive index of the segment and a reduction in the amount of Feulgen-positive material it contains. Studies by Zirkle's group at the University of Chicago have shown that the photons of ultraviolet light which cause the chromosomal damage referred to above are not absorbed directly by DNA but more probably start their action by absorption in a protein.

Irradiation of centromeres results in the loss of directed chromosomal movement at anaphase. If the nucleolus is exposed to a microspot of high intensity U.V. radiation, mitosis of cells irradiated in stages from late telophase to middle prophase is stopped which demonstrates that the nucleolus plays a vital role in mitosis.

Induced recessive lethal mutations in Drosophila

In 1927 H. J. Muller published the classical paper in which he proved conclusively that the progeny of flies irradiated with X-rays showed frequencies of mutations many times greater than those normally found. The type of induced mutation subjected to intensive study in the early days of radiation genetics was the sex-linked, recessive lethal mutation as detected by Muller's $C \, l \, B$ technique. In this $C \, l \, B$ technique (see Fig. 13–4) the C symbolizes a crossover suppressor (later shown to be an inversion), the l symbolizes a recessive lethal mutation, and the B the dominant gene affecting eye morphology, *Bar*. P_1 males are treated with some mutagenic agent (such as X-rays), and as a result mutations are produced in some of their sperm. These males are then mated to virgin untreated heterozygous $C \, l \, B$ females. The resulting zygotes are of four types, and one of these, the $C \, l \, B$ male, fails to survive because such embryos contain a recessive lethal which expresses itself when hemizygous. Thus only one class of male remains

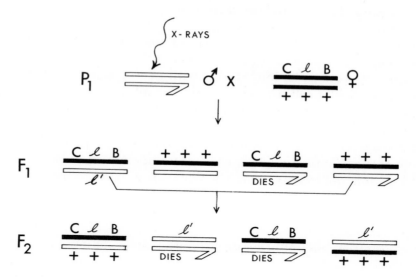

Figure 13–4 A diagram of Muller's classical *C I B* technique for detecting sex-linked, recessive lethal mutations.

to fertilize the F_1 females. Each F_1 heterozygous *C l B* female results from the fertilization of a *C l B* egg by an irradiated X-bearing sperm, and some of these sperm will contain mutated X-chromosomes. In Figure 13–4 one such F_1 female is shown, and the induced recessive lethal mutation is symbolized by *l'*. Mated F_1 heterozygous *C l B* females are distributed individually into culture tubes in which each lays fertile eggs and so produces a single F_2 culture. The cultures produced by females bearing an induced lethal mutation contain only females; whereas females bearing irradiated X-chromosomes in which no recessive lethal has been induced yield cultures containing some wild type males. Thus, if in a population of 1000 cultures 990 contained some males and 10 contained only females, the induced rate of sex-linked, recessive lethal mutations would be 1 per cent.

When studied cytologically, sex-linked recessive lethals proved to be a heterogeneous group of mutations. Some (the "point mutation" category) reside in chromosomes which appear to be completely normal as far as observations with the light microscope can decide. Others are associated with minute deficiencies, and still others with gross chromosomal aberrations such as inversions and translocations.

The curve (determined by Spencer and Stern) relating the frequency of induced, sex-linked, recessive lethal mutations to radiation dosage is a straight line, for the range of doses studied (25 to 3000 r—see Fig. 13–5). The observed rate is 2.15 per cent sex-linked recessive lethals per 1000 r of

90 Kv X-rays. The spontaneous rate is roughly one lethal per 1000 tested sperm. A dose of 50 r of X-rays doubles the spontaneous rate.

Organisms are exposed to low-level chronic irradiation from natural sources which include cosmic rays, radiations from radioactive elements in soils and rocks (such as radium, thorium, and the long-lived radioisotope of potassium, K^{40}) and radioactive elements in tissues (here K^{40} is again important). It is quite clear, however, that this chronic radiation can account for only a very small fraction of the spontaneous mutations observed.

If the frequency of spontaneous mutations is subtracted from the observed frequencies obtained in Spencer and Stern's studies, the straight line of best fit can be drawn through the resulting values. When this line is

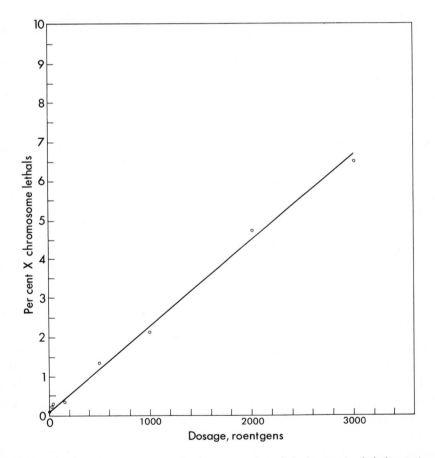

Figure 13–5 The relationship between the frequency of sex-linked, recessive lethal mutations and the administered radiation dose. (Data for *Drosophila melanogaster* from Spencer and Stern. Redrawn with permission from R. P. Wagner and H. K. Mitchell, *Genetics and Metabolism*, 1955, John Wiley and Sons, Inc.)

extrapolated leftward from the lowest observed value, it is found to pass through the point representing zero mutation at zero dose. The only reasonable interpretation of this result is that there is *no* threshold dose below which radiation is harmless but that *any* radiation dose no matter how small produces genetic damage in proportion to the magnitude of the dose.

Recent studies by Lindsley, Edington, and Von Halle have shown that 20 per cent of the sex-linked lethals produced by ionizing radiations in *Drosophila* have gone undetected because their expression is suppressed by the Y-chromosome. When these lethals are added to the orthodox lethals, the total lethal frequency increases *faster* than expected on the basis of a linear relationship between radiation dose and mutation frequency. Most Y-suppressed lethals are position effect lethals associated with gross rearrangements with breaks in chromocentral heterochromatin and in the X-chromosome.

If the apportionment of a large number of induced, orthodox, sex-linked, recessive, lethal, point mutations on the genetic map of the X-chromosome is plotted one finds a very nonrandom distribution. Certain chromosomal regions such as those at 0 and 57 show a great number of mutants, while other regions such as those between 7 and 12 show very few mutants. Why various chromosomal regions differ in their sensitivity to the mutagenic effects of X-rays is not understood.

Extensive studies by Stern and his associates have shown that so-called orthodox, recessive lethals in the X-chromosome of *Drosophila melanogaster* often have a dominant effect upon viability. Most lethals produce an impairment in the viability of heterozygotes of about 4 per cent. A few lethals actually increase the viability of heterozygotes.

Muller and his colleagues have shown that three to five times as many recessive *subvital* mutants (that is, mutations which lower viability but are not completely lethal) are induced by X-rays as recessive lethal mutations.

Induced chromosomal aberrations

The ability of ionizing radiation to induce chromosome breaks is well established. Direct measurements of radiation-induced chromosome breakage have been made in both somatic and germinal tissue of plants characterized by small numbers of large chromosomes, the most favorable genera of which are *Trillium, Tradescantia, Lilium, Allium,* and *Vicia* (see Fig. 13–6).

Broken chromosomes are produced with a frequency which is simply proportional to the radiation dose applied. It has been estimated by Lea that between 15 and 20 ionizations are necessary to break an interphase chromatid of *Tradescantia*. Chromosomal aberrations such as translocations

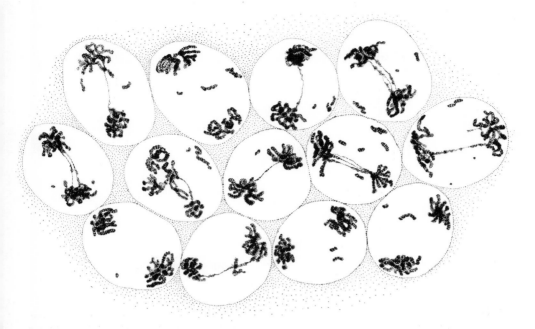

Figure 13–6   Radiation-induced chromosomal bridges and fragments seen during anaphase in cells from X-rayed anthers of *Trillium*.   (After A. H. Sparrow.)

and inversions depend on the formation and union of two broken chromosomes. Broken chromosomes which are close enough to undergo union generally are produced by different ionizing particles in the case of radiations of low LET such as gamma rays. Since a minimum of two independently produced events are required to provide the broken chromosomes which undergo exchange and since each is produced with a certain probability p, the probability of both being produced in the same nucleus is p^2. Since p^2 is proportional to the dose^2, one would expect the frequency of such aberrations to vary as the square of the dose (see Fig. 13–7A). In practice the relation between translocation frequency and dose can often best be fitted to a curve that represents the 1.5 power of the dose. This deviation from the anticipated second power may indicate that in some cases translocations may arise from a single event. Other factors which tend to flatten out the curve are the loss of inviable translocations and the scoring of multiple break rearrangements as simple translocations. In the case of radiations of high LET, such as alpha particles or recoil protons produced by fast neutrons, both chromosomes involved in an exchange are disrupted

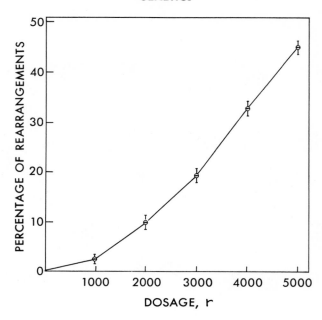

Figure 13–7 (A) A graph of the dose-frequency relation for viable types of chromosomal rear-rangements (determined by cytological tests) induced by X-irradiation of *Drosophila* spermatozoa. The vertical lines represent ± one standard error.   (Data of Bauer. Redrawn with permission from *Radiation Biology*, Vol. 1, part 2, Chapter 9, edited by A. Hollaender, 1955, McGraw-Hill Book Co., Inc.)

simultaneously by the same densely ionizing track. In this case two break rearrangements are produced with a frequency proportional to dose (see Fig. 13–7B).

Restitution of broken chromosomes

Broken chromosomes can undergo restitution, but the breaks remain open for a certain period of time. The length of this time interval varies from seconds to days and depends on what stage of mitosis or meiosis the chromosomes were in when the radiation was administered, on the LET of the radiation, and on the type of chemical bonds ruptured. Broken chromosomes may rejoin and function normally. This repair, however, requires the synthesis of chemical bonds; and for this energy is often needed as well as time. Wolff has shown that metabolic poisons which inhibit the synthesis of protein or ATP also inhibit restitution. Depriving the cell of oxygen or lowering its temperature also retards chromosomal repair. A treatment such as centrifugation which tends to separate broken chromosomes from each other will inhibit rejoining.

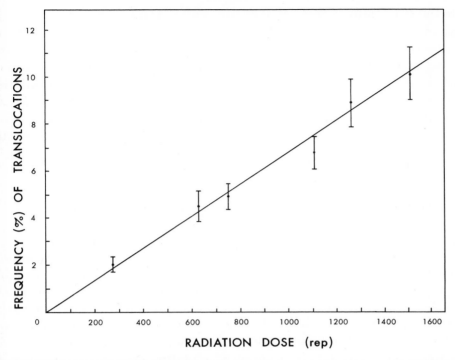

Figure 13–7   (B) A graph of the frequency (%) of viable translocations between chromosomes II and III (induced in *Drosophila* spermatozoa and determined by genetic tests) in the relation to the dose of fast neutrons (measured in *rep*). The *rep* (roentgen equivalent physical) is defined as the dose of radiation which liberates 83 ergs of energy per cm^3 of tissue. The vertical lines represent ± one standard error.   (After Muller.) (Redrawn with permission of *The American Naturalist.*)

The effect of radiation on human cells

The tissue culture techniques of Puck at the University of Colorado allow measurement of the effect of radiation upon the reproductive capacity of single human cells. Determination of the relationship between the frequency of cells which survive with the capability of continued mitosis and the administered X-ray dose shows the 37 per cent survival dose to be only 50 r. The dose of radiation required to produce one chromosome break per cell was found to be about 25 r. The human genetic apparatus thus shows extraordinary sensitivity to radiation. The mean lethal radiation dose[5] for man is between 400 and 500 r of X-rays. Such a radiation dose leaves only about 0.5 per cent of the body's reproducing cells still able to undergo continued mitosis. Since each cell continues to function normally in the

---

[5] The radiation dose which will kill 50 per cent of the individuals in a population.

physiological sense, death is not immediate. Damage shows up first in tissues characterized by the highest mitotic rate. The first symptom of radiation sickness, for example, is a depression in the number of circulating white blood cells. This deficiency results from genetic damage to the blood-cell forming tissues of the bone marrow which prevents the continued reproduction of these cells. Death eventually comes to the irradiated individual, because the surviving cells are not able to restore the needed numbers in time to maintain the physiological functioning of the various vital tissues.

Variables affecting the sensitivity to radiation damage

There are many variables which affect the production of genetic damage by a given radiation. The way in which the germ cells of various organisms respond to radiation depends on the physiological state of the cells, and this in turn depends in part on the genetic constitution of the organism. Since the genetic constitution of one species is vastly different from another, the sensitivity to mutation should likewise differ. W. L. Russell's comparison of the fruit fly and the mouse with respect to the same mutational criteria showed that the mouse has an induced mutation rate fifteen times that of the fly.

There is a very clear-cut relationship between radiosensitivity and the stage of the nuclear cycle irradiated. The relative sensitivity also depends on the mutational criteria studied. In his classical studies upon *Trillium erectum,* Sparrow demonstrated that the amount of chromosome fragmentation produced by 50 r of X-rays depends upon the stage of gametogenesis treated. One of the characteristic changes that occur during meiotic prophase is a shortening of the chromosomes. The relationship between length of the chromonemata and radiosensitivity is shown in Figure 13–8. Increasing radiosensitivity during early prophase is associated with a gradual contraction of the chromonemata. The peak in radiosensitivity corresponds approximately to the most contracted stage. King, Darrow, and Kaye studied different classes of mutations induced by gamma irradiation of *Drosophila* females. They found that the sensitivity of the germ cells to radiation-induced chromosome breakage varied strikingly during oogenesis and that these changes were correlated with the cytology of the developing primary oocytes. Mature ovarian primary oocytes were the most sensitive. In such cells the genetic material is present as a compact Feulgen-positive body which lies free in the ooplasm (that is, it is devoid of a nuclear membrane). Oocytes containing a nucleus in which are located relatively uncoiled chromosomes are much more radioresistant. The above-mentioned

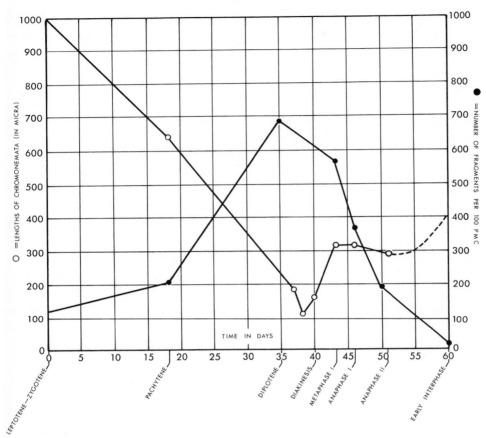

Figure 13–8   The inverse correlation between radiation sensitivity and the length of the chromonemata during different stages of microsporogenesis in *Trillium erectum*. Radiation sensitivity is measured as a function of the number of chromosome fragments per 100 pollen mother cells (PMC).
Note that meiosis in anthers takes about two months.   (Redrawn from *The Chemistry and Physiology
of the Nucleus,* edited by V. T. Bowen, Academic Press, 1952, page 248; paper by A. H. Sparrow.)

workers also demonstrated that mutations associated with chromosomal
aberrations are quickly eliminated from the ovary; whereas recessive lethal
mutations appear never to be completely eliminated from the germ tract.
Therefore, since this is the type of mutation which persists, it is the recessive
lethal and similar subtle genetic changes which must be studied in irradiated
populations, even though this class of mutant requires the most time and
effort to detect.

The age of the individual is very important in considerations of radiosensitivity, since the number of germ cells irradiated, their distribution with
respect to stage, and the rate at which these germ cells mature and are
utilized varies with age. The stage in development of the germ cell deter-

mines whether a given type of mutation will be duplicated, eliminated, repaired, or persist unchanged. If the organism is receiving chronic radiation, the total radiation dose received by germ cells of the organism up to and including the reproductive period is of importance, since certain types of genetic damage are cumulative.

Environmental conditions which modify the physiological state of tissues can influence the effectiveness of radiation. It is known from the work of Steffensen, for example, that the chromosomes of plants fed on a medium deficient in calcium are sensitized to radiation. The degree of hydration of the irradiated material also influences the mutation rate induced. The degree to which oxidizing agents are produced by radiations is related to the oxygen concentration of tissue. However, the degree to which oxygen enhances the effectiveness of radiation depends upon the type of mutation studied and the LET of the radiation used. Those agents which protect the germ cells from damage often do so by lowering the oxygen concentration of tissue, and those which enhance the effectiveness of radiations generally add oxygen, or poison systems which normally remove oxygen from tissue. The effectiveness of these agents depends upon the stage in the nuclear cycle treated. The oxygen concentration is also increased by lowering the temperature, since oxygen is more soluble in water at low than at high temperatures.

The rate at which the radiation dose is delivered and the LET of the radiation are important variables. Radiations of high LET generally are mutagenically most potent and somewhat more damage is often produced if the radiation dose is given in the shortest possible time. However, there is *no* indication of a *threshold dose rate* (a dose rate below which no mutation occurs).

U.V.-induced genetic damage

Since ultraviolet light is not deeply penetrating, it does not produce mutations in the germ line of animals of large size. However, it can be used to irradiate microorganisms, spores, pollen, nuclei which lie near the surface of eggs, etc., and under these conditions U.V. has proved to be a potent mutagen. Ultraviolet light at wave lengths around 257 mμ is strongly absorbed by nucleic acids, and, as one would expect, U.V. of this wave length is most efficient mutagenically.

In 1949 Kelner discovered that ultraviolet-induced lesions in various biological systems could be restored by irradiating the systems with light of longer wave length than that of the damaging radiation. This phenomenon (called *photoreactivation*) has been observed in viruses, microorganisms, plants, and animals. It is known that, whereas the dose rate of inactivating ultraviolet light is relatively unimportant, the dose rate of the photoreacti-vating light is of great importance. The efficiency of photoreactivation also depends upon such variables as pH, temperature, and the physiological state of the cell being treated. It appears that energy from damaging ultraviolet light causes linkages to form between the two complementary DNA strands. Such DNA dimers are rendered biologically inactive because strand sepa-ration during replication is impossible under these conditions. Repair of this damage is accomplished by an enzyme which uses as its substrate the U.V.-induced lesions in DNA. Such a photoreactivating enzyme has been isolated from yeast and shows the unique properties of being involved in a photochemical reaction which results in a constructive action on DNA. There may be a slight photoreactivation of X-ray-induced damage, but in no case is this a large effect.

Another characteristic distinguishing U.V. from other mutagens is the requirement of protein synthesis for the "fixation" of mutations. Witkin has demonstrated that protein synthesis must take place within a critical time interval after exposure of microorganisms to U.V. in order that a maximum yield of mutations be obtained.

Heredity, health, and radiation

It appears that between 2 and 4 per cent of all human beings born are afflicted by hereditary illnesses and handicaps at some time during their lives. According to Newcombe and James approximately one-half of the cases of severe mental deficiency, three-quarters of the cases of blindness occuring before age 15, and about one-half of all cases of blindness, together with many cases of deafness and about one-half of the cases of deaf-mutism, are due to hereditary causes. Deformities such as pyloric stenosis, spina bifida, hydrocephalus, hare lip and cleft palate, club foot, congenital dislo-cated hip, and functional diseases such as diabetes mellitus, albinism, hemophilia, idiopathic epilepsy, target-cell anemia, sickle-cell anemia, gout, galactosemia, and the muscle dystrophies are often of hereditary origin. Thus the human race carries a genetic burden of great magnitude.

Most of this hereditary load of defects results from an accumulation of genes that have spontaneously mutated to inactive or partially active alleles. Some of these hereditary defects may have been caused by chemical muta-gens produced by the normal metabolic processes of the body, others by ingested chemical compounds which are themselves mutagenic or are con-verted by the body into mutagens, and still others by radiations from natu-ral sources. As was mentioned previously, such natural sources include cosmic rays, radiations from radioactive elements in soils and rocks, and radiations from naturally occurring radioisotopes in tissues. To this background radiation, man is adding new sources of radiation. Test explosions of nuclear weapons generate numerous radioisotopes which are carried aloft and eventually fall to the earth's surface. Of these radioactive elements, strontium[90] and cesium[137] appear to be the most important, since they have long half lives[6] and are absorbed by and retained in tissue. By the end of 1958 nearly 300 nuclear detonations had occurred releasing a total explosive force close to 1×10^8 tons of TNT. The radiation dose due to fallout, however, has been calculated to amount to 0.3 per cent that received from natural sources. This calculation was made assuming atmospheric weapons testing would not be resumed, and revisions of the estimate will have to be made now that the U.S.S.R. has broken the test moratorium. The Soviets claim to have bombs of 100 megaton (1×10^8 tons) capacity and may consider testing at high altitudes. Radiation from fallout produced by such devices would produce serious genetic damage to our species. The most important sources of radiation to which the germ plasm of our species is currently exposed are medical and dental X-rays. In technologically advanced countries, radiation from these sources amounts to double that received from natural sources. It is certain that reductions in this exposure can be made by employing the more sensitive X-ray films constantly being developed, shielding the reproductive systems of patients, and by using well-collimated beams of X-rays only in situations in which they are essential for diagnosis or therapy. The main future hazard to the human germ plasm resides in the development of the atomic energy program. Unless extreme care is taken in the construction of nuclear reactors and for the disposal of radioactive wastes produced in them a sizable fraction of the human population will be exposed to far higher levels of radiation than were their ancestors.

---

[6] The time required for a radioactive substance to lose 50 per cent of its activity by radioactive decay. Each radioactive element has a unique half life (Sr[90], 28 yrs., Cs[137], 27 yrs.).

13–1. When determining sensitive volumes care is taken to desiccate the macro-molecules under study. Why?

13–2. Pollard points out that only electrons with energies sufficient to penetrate 125 Å into material of density equivalent to protein can affect bacteriophage T_1. What does this datum suggest?

13–3. Suspensions of a plant virus are irradiated with various doses of X-rays. The activities of the virus suspensions are tested by injecting equal quantities of the virus into leaves. The results are given in the following table.

Dose ($\times 10^5$)r	Number of leaves developing lesions per 1000 leaves tested
0	550
0.5	545
1.0	534
1.5	396
2.0	292
2.5	198
3.0	127
3.5	83
4.0	55
4.5	33
5.0	22
5.5	14
6.0	8

Plot the relationship between relative survival and radiation dose. What type of curve results? How does this curve compare with the curve in Figure 13–3? What conclusions do you reach as to the sensitive targets in the virus?

13–4. It is known that ionizing radiations can cause the fragmentation of DNA molecules. It is also known that "hidden breaks" are produced in the DNA molecule with even greater efficiency by ionizing radiation. In view of your knowledge of the structure of the DNA molecule can you suggest how breaks might be produced in the DNA molecule which would not result in its fragmentation?

13–5. According to the hypothesis that mutations arise as the result of an error in gene replication, the rate of mutations should be proportional to the rate of gene replication. Novick and Szilard observed that the rate of spontaneous muta-tion to resistance to bacteriophage T_5 is independent of growth rate in tryptophan-limited chemostat cultures of *Escherichia coli* for generation times varying from 2 to 12 hours. In view of the above findings defend or attack the error hypothesis of mutation.

13–6. The literature is filled with conflicting reports as to whether oxygen increases or decreases radiation damage. Can you suggest the reason for this confusion?

13–7.   Where polyploid strains of a given species exist and have been studied radiation resistance is found to be a function of the degree of polyploidy. Why should this be so?

13–8.   Organisms which have chromosomes with diffuse centromeres are less sensitive to radiation than those whose chromosomes have a single spindle fiber attachment region. Why should this be so? See question 3–12.

13–9.   *Drosophila* females of genotype y/ClB were irradiated with 2000 r of X-rays and were next mated to $y\,w$ nonirradiated males. In the F_1 population heterozygous Bar and yellow females each made up about 50 per cent of the females. There were approximately half as many males as females. Among the males large numbers of y males and smaller numbers of $y\,w$ males were observed. These $y\,w$ males proved to be sterile. The frequency of these patroclinous males was 45 times higher among the progeny of irradiated than among the progeny of nonirradiated females. Explain these results.

13–10. The dose of radiation which sterilizes adult insects is often very small compared to that required to kill the insects. Thus it is relatively easy to produce large numbers of vigorous sterile individuals which may be let loose in nature. Can you conceive of how such techniques could be used to regulate the populations of various deleterious insects? See the article by E. F. Knipling in *Science 130*: 902–4.

13–11. The rate of reversion of various mutations to wild type can be conveniently studied in microorganisms. When this is done it is generally found that the proportion of X-ray-induced mutations capable of reversion is lower than the proportion of U.V.-induced mutations that can revert. What conclusions can you draw from these findings?

13–12. Mutations may appear in a bacterial population several generations after the mutagen has been administered. Give four possible explanations for this observation.

13–13. Assume (1) that 2 per cent of all individuals in the world suffer serious hereditary handicaps, (2) that 50 r of ionizing radiation doubles the spontaneous mutation rate, (3) that genetic damage from radiation is cumulative, (4) that adult parents by age 30 on the average have produced half the children of the family, (5) that a total dose of 0.1 r is received by the germ cells in 30 years from fallout, (6) that there are a total of 2×10^9 human births per generation, and (7) that 10 per cent of the genetically damaged individuals appear in the first generation. How many handicapped people would appear in the F_1 generation as a result of radiation from fallout? What proportion are these of the total born? Assume a normal incidence of handicapped individuals arising from environmental and genetic causes to be 5 per cent. What increase in handicapped individuals would be caused by fallout? Radiations from medical and dental X-rays account for an accumulated gonadal dose 600 times that from fallout. Calculate the total handicapped people resulting from this radiation source.

13–14. The compound 5-Bromouracil differs from thymine in that the CH_3 group attached to carbon 5 is replaced by a bromine atom. 5-Bromouracil can be incorporated into bacteriophage DNA in place of thymine, if during DNA synthesis 5-Bromouracil rather than thymine is made available to the virus. Once 5-Bromouracil is incorporated into bacteriophage DNA the viruses may be grown in bacteria which provide a plentiful supply of thymine. The frequency of bacteriophage mutants is very high in the progeny. What conclusions can you draw from these findings in view of the observation of Freese that 5-Bromouracil will often pair with guanine?

13–15. Acridine dyes are bound to DNA by sliding between adjacent base pairs thus forcing them 6.8Å, rather than 3.4Å apart. Acridine dyes are powerful mutagens. Can you suggest the mechanism of their mutagenic action? Consult the paper by S. Brenner and his colleagues to see one proposed mechanism.

BIBLIOGRAPHY

Alexander, P.   1957   Atomic Radiation and Life. Pelican Books, Baltimore, Md.

Alexander, P., and K. A. Stacey   1959   Modification of DNA by ionizing radiations and certain mutagenic chemicals. Proc. 4th Intl. Congress of Biochem. *9*: 98–132. Pergamon Press, London.

Auerbach, C., and J. M. Robson   1946   Chemical production of mutations. Nature *157*: 302.

Avery, O. T., C. M. MacLeod, and M. McCarty   1944   Studies on the chemical nature of the substance inducing transformation of pneumococcal types. J. Exper. Med. *79*: 137–58.

Bacq, Z. M., and P. Alexander   1961   Fundamentals of Radiobiology, 2nd ed. Pergamon Press, New York.

Bender, M. A.   1960   X-ray-induced chromosome aberrations in mammalian cells *in vivo* and *in vitro*. *In* Immediate and Low Level Effects of Ionizing Radiations, A. A. Buzzati-Traverso, editor. Taylor and Francis, London, pp. 103–18.

Brenner, S., L. Barnett, F. H. C. Crick, and A. Orgel   1961   The theory of mutagenesis. J. Mol. Biol. *3*: 121–4.

Brink, R. A.   1960   Paramutation and chromosome organization. Quart. Rev. of Biol. *35*: 120–37.

Conger, A. D., and M. L. Randolph   1959   Magnetic centers (free radicals) produced in cereal embryos by ionizing radiation. Radiation Research *11*: 54–66.

Crowther, J. A.   1924   Some considerations relative to the action of X-rays on tissue cells. Proc. Roy. Soc. *96B*: 207–11.

Demerec, M.   1937   Frequency of spontaneous mutations in certain stocks of *Drosophila melanogaster*. Genetics *22*: 469–78.

Demerec, M.   1954   Genetic action of mutagens. Caryologia *6* (Suppl.): 201–17.

Freese, E.   1959   The specific mutagenic effect of base analogues on phage T4. J. Mol. Biol. *1*: 87–105.

Gaulden, M. E., and R. P. Perry   1958   Influence of the nucleolus on mitosis as revealed by UV microbeam irradiation. Proc. Nat. Acad. Sc. *44*: 553–9.

Giles, N. H.   1951   Studies on the mechanism of reversion in biochemical mutants of *Neurospora crassa*. Cold Spring Harbor Symp. Quant. Biol. *16*: 283–313.

Hollander, A., editor   1954–5   Radiation Biology, Vols. I and II. McGraw-Hill, New York.

Hotchkiss, R. D.   1953   The genetic chemistry of the pneumococcal transformations. *In* the Harvey Lectures, Ser. 49, pp. 124–44.

Hutchinson, F.   1961   Molecular basis for action of ionizing radiations. Science *134*: 533–8.

Ives, P. T.   1950   The importance of mutation rate genes in evolution. Evolution *4*: 236–52.

Jagger, J.   1960   Photoreactivation. Radiation Research (Suppl.) *2*: 75–90.

Kelner, A.   1949   Effect of visible light on the recovery of *Streptomyces griseus* conidia from U.V. irradiation injury. Proc. Nat. Acad. Sc. *35*: 73–9.

King, R. C., J. B. Darrow, and N. W. Kaye   1952   Studies on different classes of mutations induced by radiation of *Drosophila melanogaster* females. Genetics *41*: 890–900.

Lea, D. E.   1947   Actions of Radiations on Living Cells. Cambridge University Press, Cambridge, England.

Lindsley, D. L., C. W. Edington, and E. S. Von Halle   1960   Sex-linked recessive lethals in *Drosophila* whose expression is suppressed by the Y chromosome. Genetics *45*: 1649–70.

Marmur, J., and L. Grossman   1961   Ultraviolet light induced linking of DNA strands and its reversal by photoreactivating enzyme. Proc. Natl. Acad. Sci. *47*: 778–87.

McClintock, B.   1951   Chromosome organization and genic expression. Cold Spring Harbor Symp. Quant. Biol. *16*: 13–47.

Muller, H. J., and E. Altenberg   1919   The rate of change of hereditary factors in *Drosophila*. Proc. Soc. Exper. Biol. & Med. *17*: 10–14.

Muller, H. J.   1954   The relation of neutron dose to chromosome changes and point mutations in *Drosophila*. I. Translocations. Am. Naturalist *88*: 437–59.

Neel, J. V.   1957   Special problems inherent in the study of human genetics with particular reference to the evaluation of radiation risks. Proc. Nat. Acad. Sc. *43*: 736–44.

Newcombe, H. B., and A. P. James   1959   Heredity, health and radiation. Canad. J. Pub. Health *50*: 140–47.

Novick, A.   1956   Mutagens and antimutagens. Brookhaven Symposia in Biology *8*: 201–15.

Ottolenghi, E., and R. D. Hotchkiss   1960   Appearance of genetic transforming activity in pneumococcal cultures. Science *132*: 1257–8.

Pollard, E. 1959 Radiation inactivation of enzymes, nucleic acids, and phage particles. Rev. Mod. Physics *31*: 273–81.

Puck, T. T. 1960 The action of radiation on mammalian cells. Am. Naturalist *94*: 95–110.

Rhoades, M. M. 1941 The genetic control of mutability in maize. Cold Spring Harbor Symp. Quant. Biol. *9*: 138–44.

Rupert, C. S. 1960 Photoreactivation of transforming DNA by an enzyme from Baker's yeast. J. Gen. Physiol. *43*: 573–95.

Russell, W. L. 1956 Comparison of X-ray induced mutation rates in *Drosophila* and mice. Am. Naturalist *90*: 67–80.

Russell, W. L., L. B. Russell, and E. Kelly 1960 Dependence of mutation rate on intensity. *In* Immediate and Low Level Effects of Ionizing Radiations, A. A. Buzzati-Traverso, editor. Taylor and Francis, London, pp. 311–20.

Sandler, L., and Y. Hiraizumi 1960 Meiotic drive in natural populations of *Drosophila melanogaster*. V. On the nature of the S D region. Genetics *45*: 1671–89.

Schubert, J., and R. E. Lapp 1957 Radiation: What It Is and How It Affects You. The Viking Press, New York.

Scientific American, Sept. 1959 (issue on Ionizing Radiation).

Sonnenblick, B. P., editor 1961 Protection in Diagnostic Radiology. Rutgers University Press, New Brunswick, N. J.

Sparrow, A. H., M. J. Moses, and R. J. Dubow 1952 Relationships between ionizing radiation, chromosome breakage and certain other nuclear disturbances. Exper. Cell Res. (Suppl.) *2*: 245–67.

Sparrow, A. H., R. L. Cuany, J. P. Miksche, and L. A. Schairer 1961 Some factors affecting the responses of plants to acute and chronic radiation exposure. *Radiation Botany 1*: 10–34.

Spencer, W. P., and C. Stern 1948 Experiments to test the validity of the linear r-dose/mutation frequency relation in *Drosophila* at low dosage. Genetics *33*: 43–74.

Stadler, L. J. 1942 Some observations on gene variability and spontaneous mutation. Spragg Memorial Lectures (3rd series), Michigan State College, East Lansing.

Steffensen, D. 1954 Increased frequency of X-ray-induced chromosomal aberrations in *Tradescantia paludosa* produced by a mineral-nutrient treatment. Genetics *39*: 996–7.

Stern, C., G., Carson, M. Kinst, E. Novitski, and D. Uphoff 1952 The viability of heterozygotes for lethals. Genetics *37*: 413–49.

U. S. 85 Congress. Hearings of the joint committee on atomic energy before the special subcommittee on radiation. May 27, 28, 29, and June 3, 1957, Vol. 2. U. S. Government Printing Office. Statements by Drs. J. Crow, H. B. Glass,

A. H. Sturtevant, H. J. Muller, W. L. Russell, H. B. Jones, and R. Lapp. Papers submitted by L. S. Penrose and J. V. Neel.

U. S. 86th Congress. Hearings of the joint committee on atomic energy before the special subcommittee on radiation. May 5–8, 1959, Vols. 1 and 2. U. S. Government Printing Office. Statements by Drs. D. Graham, J. Crow, W. L. Russell, G. Failla, J. Schubert. Also Vol. 3, Appendices H, I.

Wallace, B., and T. Dobzhansky   1959   Radiation, Genes and Man. Holt, New York.

Witkin, E. M.   1956   Time, temperature and protein synthesis: a study of ultraviolet induced mutation in bacteria. Cold Spring Harbor Symp. Quant. Biol. *21*: 123–40.

Wolff, S., and H. E. Luippold   1955   Metabolism and chromosome-break rejoining. Science *122*: 231–2.

Wolff, S.   1960   Radiation studies on the nature of chromosome breakage. Am. Naturalist *94*: 85–93.

Zirkle, R. E.   1957   Partial-cell irradiation. Advances Biol. & Med. Physics *5*: 103–45.

Chapter **14**

Genes and the Biochemistry of the Organism

Introduction

Myriads of chemical reactions are constantly occurring within living tissue, and each reaction is catalyzed by a specific proteinaceous enzyme. Enzymes catalyze the breakdown of large molecules such as proteins, carbohydrates, and lipids into smaller metabolites, and the energy locked within these compounds is then used in various energy-requiring processes. Enzymes also catalyze the synthesis of proteins and other macromolecules from smaller building blocks. Indeed the metabolism of any organism can be thought of as a chain of interrelated enzymatic reactions. The synthesis of enzymes is in turn under genetic control.

The phenylalanine-tyrosine metabolism of man

The biochemical interrelations between the aromatic amino acids phenylalanine and tyrosine in man (see Fig. 14–1) serve as a useful illustration of such a series of coupled gene-controlled, enzyme-catalyzed reactions. In man, phenylalanine is an *essential* amino acid which must be supplied in the diet. Phenylalanine is hydroxylated to tyrosine (step 1) by an enzyme system present in the liver. Tyrosine is not classified as an essential amino acid, since it need not be supplied in a diet containing sufficient phenylalanine. Tyrosine is converted in turn to 3,4-dihydroxy phenylalanine (nicknamed DOPA) by another enzyme (step 2), and DOPA serves as a precursor for the hormones adrenaline and noradrenaline and for the black pigment melanin. Steps 3 and 4 represent divergent chains formed

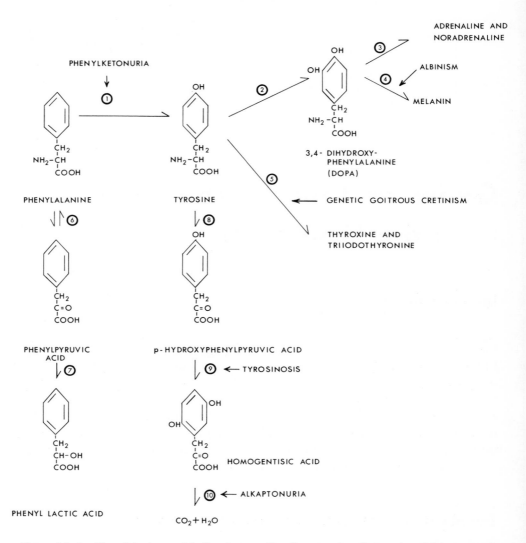

Figure 14–1   Phenylalanine metabolism in man. The diseases phenylketonuria, albinism, genetic goitrous cretinism, tyrosinosis, and alkaptonuria result from blockage of steps 1, 4, 5, 9, and 10, respectively.

by a series of sequential enzymatic reactions. Tyrosine itself serves as a precursor of the hormones thyroxine and triiodothyronine (step 5), and here again a series of reactions is involved. Excess tyrosine is degraded to carbon dioxide and water by a series of steps (not all of which are shown) which involves the formation of p-hydroxy phenylpyruvic acid and homogentisic acid. Excess phenylalanine is degraded by a series of steps to compounds which include phenylpyruvic and phenyl lactic acids.

Genetic disorders of the metabolism of phenylalanine and related compounds

Five rare diseases in man result from improper functioning of five enzyme systems involved in the metabolism of phenylalanine, tyrosine, and their derivatives. Sufficient pedigrees are available (with the exception of tyrosinosis) to show that these diseases are inherited as autosomal recessives.

1. PHENYLKETONURIA.   Individuals with phenylketonuria cannot convert into tyrosine the phenylalanine derived either from the breakdown of tissue proteins or dietary proteins, because such individuals lack the enzyme system concerned in the hydroxylation of phenylalanine. They presumably are homozygous for an inactive allele of the gene responsible for the formation of the phenylalanine hydroxylase system. As a consequence the concentration of phenylalanine rises in the blood plasma, cerebrospinal fluid, and urine. The urine of phenylketonurics contains (in addition to phenylalanine) elevated amounts of phenylpyruvic acid, phenyl lactic acid, and other derivatives of phenylalanine. Nearly all phenylketonurics exhibit some degree of mental impairment, and these mental defects are thought to arise from the abnormal accumulation of phenylalanine or one of its derivatives in the brain. Reduction of the phenylalanine concentration by severe restriction of dietary phenylalanine early in life greatly reduces the degree of mental impairment shown by such phenylketonurics.

2. ALKAPTONURIA.   The enzyme (homogentisic acid oxidase) which catalyzes the oxidation of homogentisic acid appears to be absent in the livers of people suffering from alkaptonuria. The urine of alkaptonurics soon begins to darken when left standing, and this color change is due to the presence of large quantities of homogentisic acid in the urine. Homogentisic acid is itself almost colorless, but it is readily oxidized to a black pigment. Alkaptonuria is a relatively benign disease, and, apart from the excretion of homogentisic acid in the urine, the most notable clinical feature is the deposition in cartilagenous structures during adult life of black pigments derived from homogentisic acid. Alkaptonurics often develop arthritic conditions later in life (particularly of the spine) which may lead to rigidity.

3. TYROSINOSIS.   Only one authenticated example of tyrosinosis has been observed, but detailed study of this patient revealed an inability to convert p-hydroxy phenylpyruvic acid to homogentisic acid.

4. GENETIC GOITROUS CRETINISM.   This rare class of diseases is character-

ized by severe physical and mental retardation and by hypertrophy of the thyroid gland, all due to genetically determined metabolic errors which result in a failure in the formation of the hormones thyroxine and triiodo-thyronine by the thyroid gland.

5. ALBINISM. This inherited condition is characterized by a failure to form the black pigment melanin. Normally melanin is formed from DOPA by an enzyme system referred to as "tyrosinase" present in melanocytes. Melanocytes are present in normal numbers in the skin of albinos, but tyrosinase cannot be demonstrated.

The genetic control of the synthesis of tryptophan and its derivatives

Investigations in a variety of organisms have revealed a complex metabolic pattern of enzymatic reactions involving tryptophan, another aromatic amino acid, and its derivatives.

Since tryptophan cannot be synthesized by *Drosophila melanogaster,* this is a so-called essential amino acid which must be supplied in the diet. Tryptophan enters into a chain of enzymatic reactions (steps 4–7 of Fig. 14–2) and emerges as a portion of the xanthommatin molecule. The dull red compound eye of *Drosophila* contains two classes of pigments, one bright red (the drosopterines) and the other brown (the xanthommatins). The drosopterines (see question 14–3) are readily decomposed by light, and this reaction may play a major role in photoreception. The inert xanthommatin pigments occur in the cells separating the photoreceptor cells, and here these granules presumably serve as masking agents which prevent reflection of light from one facet of the compound eye to another. During the pupal development of the eye the xanthommatins are laid down before the drosopterines. Four recessive nonallelic genes are known which block the synthesis of the brown pigments but which have no effect upon the formation of the red pigments. As a consequence all the mutant insects are characterized by compound eyes which have a bright red color. Individuals homozygous for the sex-linked gene *vermilion* (*v*) cannot perform step 4. Such flies accumulate tryptophan. However, if fed formyl kynurenine or kynurenine, *vermilion* larvae will develop into flies which can form brown pigment. Individuals homozygous for the second chromosomal gene *cinnabar* (*cn*) cannot perform step 6, and as a consequence they accumulate kynurenine. Individuals homozygous for the third chromosomal mutants *scarlet* (*st*) or *cardinal* (*cd*) produce the water-soluble compounds, formyl kynurenine, kynurenine, and hydroxy kynurenine. There is no information available as to what intermediates *st/st* or *cd/cd* flies require, but it is assumed that those

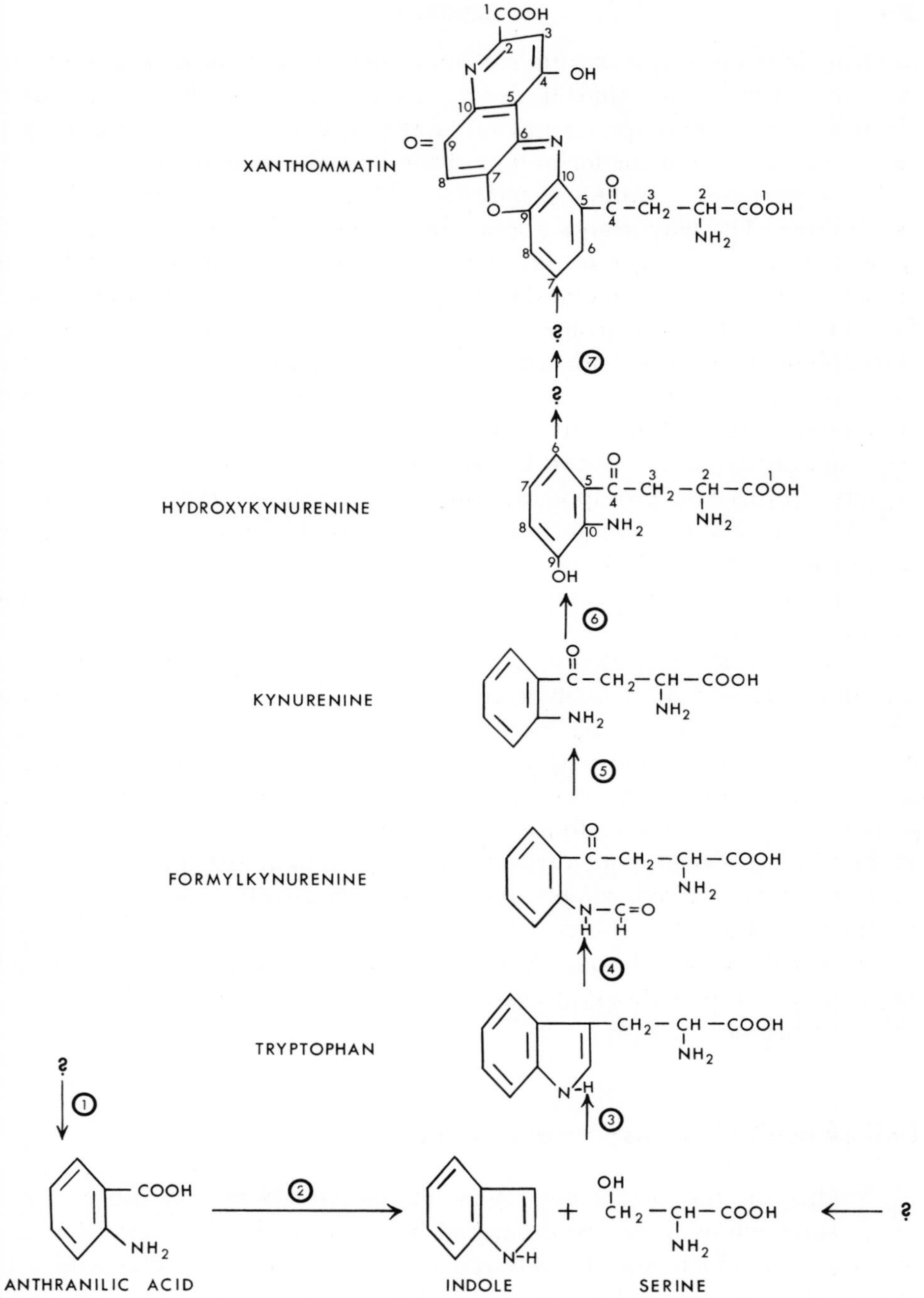

TRYPTOPHAN METABOLISM

Figure 14–2 Structural formulas for the compounds related to tryptophan and their interconversions. The xanthomatin molecule is postulated to arise from the condensation of two molecules of hydroxykynurenine. The carbon atoms of hydroxykynurenine have been numbered in an arbitrary sequence. By referring to these numbers you can locate the modified parent hydroxykynurenine molecules residing in the more complex xanthomatin molecule.

intermediates are water-insoluble compounds normally produced in the eye itself by enzymatic reactions under the control of the + alleles of *st* and *cd*. Thus in flies of genotype *st/st* or *cd/cd* genetic blocks occur subsequent to step 6 which prevent the formation of the brown eye pigments.

Neurospora crassa, unlike *Drosophila melanogaster,* can synthesize its own tryptophan. The way it goes about this synthesis is shown in Figure 14–2, steps 1–3. In working out this metabolic pathway, Tatum and Bonner isolated mutants which required tryptophan for growth. These mutants were found to fall into three groups: A, B, and C. Group A mutants can make tryptophan if supplied with anthranilic acid or indole. The biochemical block in this case occurs at some step prior to the synthesis of the former compound. Group B mutants make anthranilic acid which accumulates in làrge quantities, and they can utilize indole. Evidently the genetic block is at step 2 in this case. Group C mutants can utilize only tryptophan and are therefore blocked at the final stage of synthesis. All group C mutant genes behave as alleles which reside at a specific chromosomal locus (*td*), and all lack the enzyme *tryptophan synthetase* which catalyzes the union of indole and the amino acid serine.

Using *tryptophan synthetase* from wild type *Neurospora* as an antigen, Suskind obtained from rabbits an antibody that completely neutralizes enzyme activity. On testing extracts of several *td* mutants for their ability to react with and remove the tryptophan synthetase antibody, Suskind found that a number of preparations from mutants contained a serologically active, though enzymatically inert, protein. It thus appears that mutation at the *td* locus of *Neurospora* affects the formation of active enzyme, and that as a result an altered, closely related, enzymatically inactive protein is produced. Findings of this sort provide strong support for the *one gene-one enzyme* hypothesis which suggests that "a large class of genes exists in which each gene controls the synthesis, or activity of, but a single enzyme" (Horowitz, 1950).

Indispensable vs. dispensable genes

Studies on the biochemical genetics of *Neurospora* and other micro-organisms such as those just described have led to the discovery of a class of mutations which may be referred to as "dispensable." The wild type alleles of these genes determine the structure of a product such as an enzyme which is nonessential. That is, the enzyme can be dispensed with; since it catalyzes some step in the synthesis of a low molecular weight compound such as a soluble vitamin or amino acid which can be readily supplied to the organism by adding it to its nutrient medium. However, it is reasonable to assume that certain gene functions are "indispensable" and

cannot be compensated for by supplementing the minimal medium. Mutation of such an indispensable gene would be lethal to the microorganism
even when a medium enriched with every conceivable nutrient is used.
With the techniques generally employed by microbial geneticists such
mutants would pass unnoticed.

A method for studying such indispensable mutants was devised by
Atwood and Mukai. The mutants obtained by this method are referred to
as *heterocaryon mutants* because the mutant nuclei exist in symbiosis in the
same cell with nuclei bearing normal genes which can perform the indispensable functions. Such a heterocaryon thus resembles a cell in a diploid
organism which is heterozygous for a recessive lethal. Heterocaryotic cultures produce conidia, some of which contain only mutant nuclei, and these
can be tested to see if growth on *complete* medium can occur. Twenty-six
nonallelic, spontaneous mutants were recovered from 2764 isolates, and of
these 24 could not grow upon complete medium. Thus the majority of the
genes of *N. crassa* belong to the indispensable category. Thus the genome
can be subdivided into two categories. First, there is a class of dispensable
genes whose functions are currently under observation by the methods
already described for studying biochemical mutants. Second, there is a
much larger class of genes that perform entirely unknown functions. It may
be that such genes control the synthesis of complex intermediates which are
used in the fabrication of many enzymes; whereas the dispensable genes
control the final assembly of the complex fragments into dispensable
enzymes. Finally there may be a third class of genes: those so essential that
once having undergone mutation they cannot survive in heterocaryons.
These would be *dominant lethals* in effect, and they could not be detected by
the procedures currently available.

Human hemoglobin types

Oxygen is transported in the red blood cells in reversible combination
with *hemoglobin,* a conjugated protein which is composed of four separate
chains of amino acids and four iron-containing ring compounds (heme
groups). There is a ferroheme group for each protein chain, and each
chain contains approximately 150 amino acids. The chains occur as two
pairs, one pair called α the other β. The members of the β pair are identical but differ from those of the α pair. Pauling and his co-workers in 1949
reported that the formation of an abnormal hemoglobin (hemoglobin S—
symbolized Hb[S]) which differed in its isoelectric point[1] from normal hemo-

---

[1] The isoelectric point of a protein is defined as the pH at which the molecule is neutral because
the number of + and − charges is equal.

globin (Hb^A) was the cause of hereditary *sickle-cell anemia* in man. The red
blood cells of individuals suffering from this generally fatal form of hemolytic anemia undergo a reversible alteration in shape when the oxygen
tension of the plasma falls slightly and they assume elongate, filamentous,
and sicklelike forms (see Fig. 14–3A). Such red cells show a greatly
shortened life span, since they tend to clump together (often causing vascular
obstruction) and are rapidly destroyed (see Fig. 14–3B). Sickle-cell anemics

Figure 14–3A   The sickling phenomenon induced in the erythrocytes of individuals. (upper) heterozygous, and (lower) homozygous, for the gene responsible.   (Redrawn from *Human Heredity* by
J. V. Neel and W. J. Schull by permission of The University of Chicago Press.)

are homozygous for an abnormal gene (H^S). The blood cells of normal
individuals (of genotype H^A/H^A) never sickle, but the blood cells of perfectly healthy heterozygotes (H^A/H^S) can be caused to sickle provided the
oxygen concentration is drastically reduced. The erythrocytes of heterozy-
gotes contain Hb^A and Hb^S, but Hb^A always makes up more than 50 per
cent of the total hemoglobin (which suggests that the H^S gene is less
efficient than the H^A gene in forming hemoglobin). Perutz and Mitchison
discovered that deoxygenated Hb^S was considerably less soluble than
deoxygenated Hb^A and suggested that under conditions of low oxygen
tension the deoxygenated Hb^S molecules aggregate, come out of solution,
and cause the consequent deformation of the red cell which produces

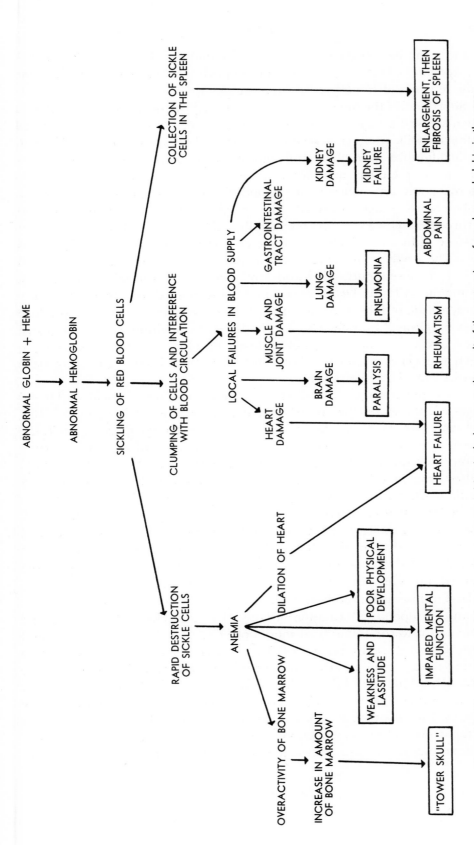

Figure 14–3B The chain of deleterious consequences arising in the human as the result of the possession of an abnormal globin in the case of hereditary sickle-cell disease. (Redrawn from *Human Heredity* by J. V. Neel and W. J. Schull by permission of The University of Chicago Press.)

sickling. In the oxygen-poor venous circulation, 30–60 per cent of the erythrocytes of H^S/H^S individuals are sickled; whereas less than 1 per cent of the red cells of H^A/H^S individuals are deformed.

Shortly after the discovery of hemoglobin S the study of certain families which showed an aberrant pattern of inheritance of sickle-cell anemia led to the identification of a second abnormal hemoglobin (Hb^C). In such atypical families would be found children who suffered from a mild "sickle-cell anemia." Under such circumstances their healthy parents should be heterozygotes, and consequently blood samples taken from them when so treated as to reduce drastically the oxygen content should show sickled erythrocytes. However, in these families the red cells of only *one* parent could be induced to sickle, and these cells were found to contain Hb^A and Hb^S. The erythrocytes from the exceptional parent contained Hb^A and Hb^C, and subsequently Hb^S and Hb^C were isolated from the red cells of the anemic children. Deoxygenated Hb^C does not exhibit the low solubility characteristic of Hb^S and consequently does not cause sickling or produce as severe clinical manifestations. The list of hemoglobin types has grown subsequently and now includes a dozen or more. Studies of families in which the genes producing Hb^S and Hb^C were both segregating have shown them to behave as alleles.

The heme moieties of the different hemoglobins are identical, and it was suggested, therefore, that the differences in the isoelectric points of Hb^A, Hb^S, and Hb^C might be the result of a different charge distribution in the molecule resulting from modifications in the amino acid sequence. Ingram showed subsequently that the difference between hemoglobins A, S, and C resulted from a substitution of one single amino acid for another. At a specific position on each β chain occupied by negatively charged glutamic acid in Hb^A, neutral valine and positively charged lysine are substituted, respectively, in the case of Hb^S and Hb^C (see Fig. 14–4). These amino acid substitutions result in the Hb^S and Hb^C molecules bearing a net charge relative to Hb^A of $2+$ and $4+$. Such charge differences account for the observed differences in the isoelectric points of the three hemoglobins.

In developing a hypothesis to explain the effects of the allelic genes H^A, H^S, and H^C upon the formation of Hb^A, Hb^S, and Hb^C, reference must be made again to the theoretical model of DNA developed by Watson and Crick (Chapter 2). In Figure 14–5A is presented a hypothetical scheme relating the structure of DNA in the genes H^A, H^S, and H^C to the structure of the Hb^A, Hb^S, and Hb^C β chains. Each DNA molecule is represented as a ladderlike structure with the rungs consisting of the purine-pyrimidine pairs, cytosine-guanine (C-G) and thymine-adenine (T-A), projecting from the sugar-phosphoric acid backbone. It is assumed that each of the four sets of three nucleotide pairs shown somehow specifies which amino acid can

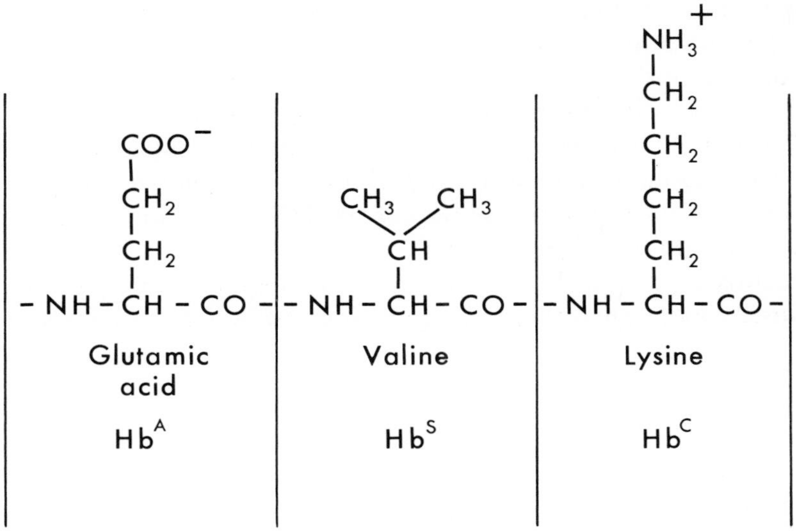

Figure 14-4 The amino acid residues differentiating three types of human hemoglobin.

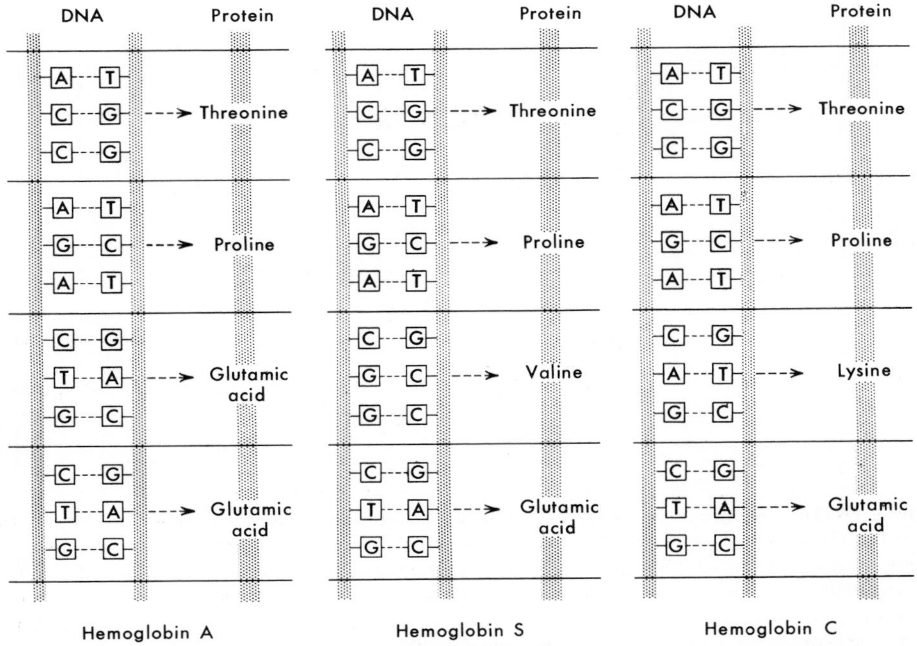

Figure 14-5A Hypothetical scheme showing how the structure of deoxyribonucleic acid might be related to the structures of hemoglobins A, S, and C. It is postulated that there is a correspondence between triplets of purine-pyrimidine base pairs and individual amino acid residues in the beta chain of hemoglobin. Actually several steps must intervene between DNA and completed protein.

(Redrawn with permission from C. B. Anfinsen, *The Molecular Basis of Evolution*, 1959, John Wiley and Sons, Inc.)

occupy each of the four illustrated positions on the forming hemoglobin β chain. The mutation consists of changes in the third DNA triplet. Note that the middle purine-pyrimidine pair is T-A for H^A, G-C for H^S, and A-T for H^C. Thus, according to this model, modifications of a single base pair in the DNA double helix could result in substitutions of different amino acids at a specific position in the forming β chain of hemoglobin. The postulated steps which result in the translation of the DNA code into an amino acid sequence are illustrated in Figure 14–5B.

Recently studies of the inheritance of hemoglobins known as G, I and Hopkins-2 have shown that the genes responsible for their formation are

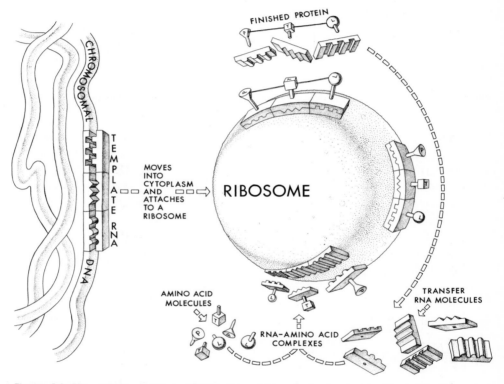

Figure 14–5B   Diagrammatic representation of hypothesized steps in protein synthesis. The inherited chromosomal DNA contains the master set of templates. Complementary templates are constructed out of nuclear RNA molecules which subsequently move to the cytoplasm and attach to ribosomal RNA particles. In the cytoplasm specific transfer RNA molecules combine with specific amino acids (here only tyrosine, T; lysine, L; and phenylalamine, P are represented). Transfer RNA-amino acid complexes fit into available sites on the template RNA. The amino acids which are now arranged in a specific sequence are enzymatically linked together to form a protein polymer which separates from the RNA. The various transfer RNA molecules are then released for future combination with various amino acids. The ribosomal RNA is stable; whereas the template RNA molecules are unstable and are used perhaps only once before disintegrating. In the true situation the protein molecule would contain perhaps 100 amino acids belonging to 20 varieties and the template RNA would be 30 times longer than shown.

not at the same locus as the sickle-cell gene. Furthermore, the changes in the G, I and Hopkins-2 hemoglobins involve changes in the charge of the α chains. It is therefore reasonable to assume that at least two chromosomal loci are concerned in the formation of a single protein (hemoglobin) and that at each locus there occurs a variety of alleles. The one gene-one enzyme hypothesis is therefore best restated as the *one gene-one polypeptide chain hypothesis*.

Blood clotting and enzyme activation

During the process of blood coagulation a protein called *fibrinogen* found in plasma is acted upon by an enzyme called thrombin, and a negatively charged peptide is split off the fibrinogen molecule, leaving monomeric fibrin which is then capable of rapid polymerization to produce a clot. Active thrombin is formed from an inactive precursor called prothrombin also found in blood plasma. The conversion of prothrombin into thrombin is a very complex process which requires a lipoprotein factor liberated from rupturing blood platelets, a proteinaceous plasma thromboplastin component (PTC), antihemophilic globulin (AHG), calcium ions, and several other factors. Patients suffering from *Christmas disease* and *hemophilia* (see p. 107) show a deficiency in the activity of PTC and AHG, respectively. The occurrence of these inherited conditions suggests that the + alleles of these amorphic or hypomorphic genes are responsible for the formation of two different substances which serve to activate a single enzyme. A third inherited disorder of the clotting system is *afibrinogenemia* which is characterized by the inability to synthesize fibrinogen.

The genetics of antigen-antibody reactions

The introduction of foreign compounds of high molecular weight into the body of adult birds and mammals generally elicits the formation of antibodies. The foreign substance or antigen has been shown to enter the nucleus of immature lymphoid cells of the recipient. It is these cells which subsequently form antibodies which belong to a class of proteins called gamma globulins. If antigen molecules form a surface component of introduced cells, the reaction these molecules undergo with complementary antibodies may cause agglutination or lysis of the foreign cells.

It is antigen-antibody reactions of the type just described which make it generally impossible to transplant tissues between human beings other than identical twins or between mice unless both come from the same highly inbred strain. This incompatibility depends on the inheritance of the genes which produce tissue antigens. If, for example, skin transplants are made between mice belonging to either of two highly inbred strains (A or B) or to a population of F_1 hybrids (A/B), it will be observed that skin transplants between A individuals or between B individuals or between A/B individuals are accepted and incorporated into the host. However, patches of skin from A individuals transplanted to B hosts are destroyed. Reciprocal grafts are also rejected. Patches of skin from hybrids transplanted to parental animals also fail to survive. However, F_1 hybrids will accept skin grafts from either parent. The genotypes characterizing each strain are

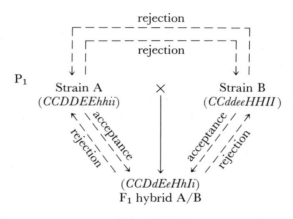

Figure 14–6

shown in parentheses. Genes symbolized by capital letters form specific antigenically active macromolecules; whereas genes symbolized by lower case letters are inactive in this respect. Genes concerned in such transplantation specificities are called histocompatibility loci, and in the mouse at least 15 such loci are known. A given host will accept a graft of foreign skin provided the foreign cells contain no antigens to which the host is unfamiliar. Thus mouse A rejects skin from mouse B because mouse A recognizes B skin as foreign since it contains the unfamiliar gene products H and I. Hybrids contain all antigens and are therefore tolerant to parental grafts.

The situation during embryonic life is different, for embryos repeatedly exposed to foreign antigens develop an immunological tolerance to them and upon reaching adulthood cannot form antibodies against these foreign antigens. This tolerance has been found in dizygotic twin cattle who during embryonic life shared red cells because of anastomosing extra-embryonic circulatory systems. Such twins may retain throughout life a stable mixture of erythrocytes of two antigenic types and will also accept skin grafts from each other.

Experimental and theoretical efforts by Medawar, Burnet, Lederberg, and others have led to a theory which seeks to explain the mechanism of immunity and immunological tolerance. According to this theory during embryonic development a population of lymphoid cells is produced which possess the ability to synthesize a vast array of different antibodies. This genic diversity arises from the hypermutability (solely at this stage) of genes responsible for globulin production. Subsequently there is a selection of only those cells which produce antibodies with configurations which are not complementary to any antigens normally present in the embryo (or administered to the embryo from foreign sources at this stage). It is assumed that embryonic plasma cells which produce antibodies that react with normal compounds found in the embryo are inhibited or destroyed. As a result, upon reaching adulthood the animal has lymphoid cells capable of reacting to a host of foreign antigens. When a foreign antigen finds its way into the body, it reacts with those few lymphoid cells capable of producing a complementary antibody. The antibody-antigen complex stimulates such cells to intense proliferation, and as a consequence, subsequent exposure to antigen elicits a greatly magnified immunological response.

It is obvious that immunological responses play a vital role in combating infections, but the possibility also exists in complex, large, long-lived vertebrates that immune reactions play a role in eliminating cells that bear potentially dangerous somatic mutations which lead to "foreign" molecular configurations.

The blood group antigens

One of the most thoroughly studied examples of the genetic control of antigenic structure is that of the human blood group substances. Acquisition of knowledge in this area first led to an understanding of the cause of the often fatal agglutinations of red blood cells in the recipient following a transfusion.

On the basis of cross agglutination tests of the type shown in Table 14–1, Landsteiner in 1900 was able to differentiate sharply between four classes of people as to whether they possessed on their red blood cell surfaces one, both, or neither of two antigenic substances—A and B. These antigens are now known to be closely related stable mucopolysaccharides made up of sugars, amino sugars, and amino acids and which have molecular weights of 300,000 or more. The A and B mucopolysaccharides are not restricted to the erythrocytes but are constituents of all the mucilaginous secretions

TABLE 14–1   In cross agglutination experiments erythrocytes of one type are mixed with serum of another type. The result of a given combination is presented in a given square in the checkerboard. (Plus signs signify clumping of erythrocytes; minus signs, the absence of agglutination.)

SOURCE OF SERUM

	O	A	B	AB
O	−	−	−	−
A	+	−	+	−
B	+	+	−	−
AB	+	+	+	−

SOURCE OF CELLS

of the body. In 1925 Bernstein put forward the currently accepted hypothesis that the inheritance of the A B O system is determined by a series of three allelomorphic genes as outlined in Table 14–2. Subsequently it was discovered that the A antigen is heterogeneous and consists of two distinct antigens A_1 and A_2, and that there are two antibodies, α which reacts with A_1 and A_2 and α_1, which is specific for A_1. Bernstein's original theory can be extended to include the A_1 and A_2 antigens in the fashion shown in Table 14–3. Gene l is now considered to be associated with the production of a polysaccharide which acts as a very weak antigen.

It appears, therefore, that there exists at a specific locus on a human chromosome a gene which has as its function the production of a specific

TABLE 14–2   The relationship between genotype, blood group phenotype, and the antigen and antibody composition of the blood.

GENOTYPE	BLOOD GROUP	ANTIGENS ON SURFACE OF RED BLOOD CELLS	ANTIBODIES IN BLOOD SERUM
$l\,l$	O	none	Anti-A and Anti-B
$l^A\,l^A$ or $l^A\,l$	A	A	Anti-B
$l^B\,l^B$ or $l^B\,l$	B	B	Anti-A
$l^A\,l^B$	AB	A and B	none

type of polysaccharide which accumulates in the cell wall of the erythrocyte and in other tissues as well. The gene has undergone mutation and exists at present in at least four allelic states, and each allele produces a detectably different polysaccharide.

Two types of incompatibility can occur when a person is transfused with blood of a type different from his own: (1) the agglutination of the cells of the recipient by the serum of the donor and (2) the agglutination of the donor erythrocytes by the serum of the recipient. In the first instance the antibodies included in the blood donation are almost instantaneously diluted below the concentration required for agglutination. Consequently an AB individual, for example, can receive blood from an O donor without ill effects. In the second case the entire antibody content of the serum of the recipient is available to agglutinate the erythrocytes from the donor.

TABLE 14–3 The modified relationship between genotype and blood group necessitated by the discovery of the A_2 antigen.

GENOTYPE	PHENOTYPE
$I^{A1} I^{A1}$ or $I^{A1} I^{A2}$ or $I^{A1} I$	A_1
$I^{A2} I^{A2}$ or $I^{A2} I$	A_2
$I^B I^B$ or $I^B I$	B
$I^{A1} I^B$	$A_1 B$
$I^{A2} I^B$	$A_2 B$
$I I$	O

Thus all the erythrocytes from an AB donation would be rapidly agglutinated in the circulatory system of an O recipient, causing vascular occlusions and death.

Mother-fetus incompatibilities

A pregnant placental mammal should produce antibodies against all foreign antigens possessed by the fetus. Thus one would expect rejection of the fetus in the same way the parent rejects skin grafts from offspring. Obviously this is not the case, and it is believed, therefore, that the placenta serves as a barrier which prevents passage of most antigens and antibodies. However, Rh incompatibilities serve as clear-cut examples of transplacental immunization in man.

The Rh system contains several antigens (C,c,D,d,E, and e), but the one known as D is by far the most important, and we shall consider only it in the following discussion. The Rhesus system received its name from the fact that the antigen in question (D) was discovered first in the Rhesus monkey and subsequently in humans of certain genotypes. The humans in which no D antigen can be detected are referred to as Rh-negative. The clinical significance of the D antigen was established by the observation that 90 per cent of the white mothers with infants suffering from a hemolytic disease called *erythroblastosis fetalis* were Rh-negative, whereas the frequency of Rh-negative women in the white population as a whole was about 15 per cent. Almost invariably the fathers of the diseased infants were Rh-positive and the infants were found to be Rh-positive as well. It was therefore postulated that the fetus arose from a fertilized egg containing a gene of paternal origin which was responsible for the formation of the D antigen and an inactive allele of maternal origin. The D antigen from the developing fetus crossed the placenta, entered the circulation of the Rh-negative mother, and there elicited an immunization reaction. Maternal antibodies against the D antigen next crossed the placenta and caused agglutination in the baby's blood with resulting anemia.

The mother who is Rh-negative never produces erythroblastotic children, if her husband is also Rh-negative. If he is Rh-positive but carries the inactive allele (i.e. is of genotype R/r), half the children will be Rh-negative and will never develop the anemia; whereas the others will be Rh-positive and are potential victims of the disease. The transplacental immunization reaction referred to above is a relatively slow one and as a consequence the mother may produce insufficient antibodies to damage her first child. However, she will be sensitized as a result of the first pregnancy and will be a more efficient antibody producer in subsequent pregnancies. As a consequence the second fetus will have a more perilous embryonic development. The situation described above is complicated by the fact that the relative permeability of the placenta to antigens appears to vary between women in the population. Roughly one in 12 pregnancies involves an Rh-negative mother carrying an Rh-positive fetus, but erythroblastosis fetalis occurs in only about 1 in 200 pregnancies.

Newer blood groups

In addition to the A_1, A_2, B and the six Rhesus antigens there are now known to exist the H, M, N, P, Lutheran, Kell, Lewis, Duffy, and Kidd blood antigens. The fact that these recently discovered antigens do not have naturally occurring antibodies as is the case with the A B O system makes it possible to transfuse blood containing them even to an incompatible individual at least once. However, such a transfusion to an incompatible individual will stimulate the production of antibodies, thus sensitizing the individual against future transfusion with the same agglutinogen. Some of these factors (Kell, Lewis, Duffy, and Kidd) are named after the person who yielded the first specific antibody. Some of the antigens were discovered following study of transfusion incompatibilities, and of families containing infants suffering from hemolytic diseases.

Suppressor mutations

Wild type individuals are sometimes observed among a population of homozygous mutant individuals. These "reversions" when tested genetically are often found to be the results of mutation of the mutant gene back to the wild type allele. However, it is often found that the reverted individual contains the original mutant genes, and that an additional mutation at another locus has modified the mutant phenotype toward wild type. Thus *suppressor mutations* are changes which, although occurring at a genetic locus distant from the site of the primary mutation, reverse its effect. Numerous suppressor mutations have been found in *Drosophila, E. coli,* and *Neurospora.* Suppressor genes often exhibit striking allele specificity, that is, the suppressor gene may affect one or more alleles of a series, but not the others of the same series.

There are several means by which suppressor genes have been found to act. They may, for example, allow the synthesis of the required compound by means of an alternate enzymatic reaction. A second mechanism involves the removal of an inhibitory substance. This relief of inhibition may occur, if the primary mutation resulted in the formation of an enzyme so modified that it is inactivated by some normal cellular component. Any mutation acting to reduce the concentration of the normal component would in these circumstances suppress the effect of the primary gene. A suppressor gene may also act by introducing a second block which lowers the production of an inhibitory substance which is accumulating in supernormal amounts as a result of the primary genetic lesion. Finally, suppressor genes sometimes act by forming a new, enzymatically active protein, possibly by modifying the defective enzyme produced by the primary mutation.

Thalassemia, another hereditary anemia, is commonly found among populations living in the northern Mediterranean area. The disease occurs in two forms, minor and major. Patients afflicted with thalassemia major, the severer disease, are homozygous for a gene which in heterozygotes results in the much milder abnormality (thalassemia minor). No abnormal type of hemoglobin detectable by current methods has been identified from patients with thalassemia major, and the abnormal gene is clearly nonallelic with the sickle-cell gene. It has been postulated that the thalassmias result from amino acid substitutions in the α or β chains which do not alter the net charge but manifest themselves by depressing the rate of synthesis of hemoglobin. The reduction in hemoglobin synthesis is so severe that the erythrocytes cannot fill themselves with pigment. In individuals heterozygous for both the *thalassemia* gene and the *sickle-cell* or *hemoglobin C* gene the circulating hemoglobin is largely or exclusively Hb^S or Hb^C. It appears, therefore, that in this particular combination the *thalassemia* gene suppresses the synthesis of normal hemoglobin but leaves intact the synthesis of a protein differing by a single amino acid.

The hemoglobin of the fetus has different properties from Hb^A. The differences arise from the fact that fetal hemoglobin contains α chains identical to adult hemoglobin and γ chains which differ from the adult β chains. Newborn infants contain hemoglobin 70 per cent of which is of the fetal type and 30 per cent of which is Hb^A. However, by the end of the first year all the fetal hemoglobin has been replaced by Hb^A. In some infants abnormal variants of fetal hemoglobin have been detected which are subsequently replaced by Hb^A. Thus during infancy the activity of the gene controlling the γ chain is suppressed and the activity of the β chain gene is switched on, while the α chain gene remains active all the time. Findings of this sort suggest that independent genes may exist which control the formation of related polypeptide chains, and that during development the manufacture of one product is suppressed while a second pair of genes takes over. We have cytological circumstantial evidence for cycles of this sort in the swelling of certain chromosomal regions in specific tissues at specific times during development (see Fig. 2–7). There are even some reported instances (see Fujii, Callan, Acton, and Beermann) of loci in homologous chromosomes showing cytochemical or morphological differences which can be interpreted as visible manifestations of heterozygosity.

An equally attractive hypothesis to explain the shift in hemoglobin types which in man accompanies maturation is that two nonallelic genes occur; one of which is responsible for the synthesis of the α chain and the other for the β *or* γ chain. The second gene produces the γ chain when operating in a fetal environment; whereas in the adult environment makes a modified chain we recognize as the β-component of hemoglobin. It has been suggested that the γ chain represents the evolutionarily more primitive form which in the past occurred in the adult as well. Indeed a gene has been found recently which appears to be allelic to the genes for hemoglobin S and C which results in the production of hemoglobin F in adults.

Perhaps this gene represents a back mutation to the DNA structure characteristic of the ancient gene.

The nature of the gene

Throughout the previous chapters genes have been defined rather loosely as chromosomal segments having spatial, mutational, and physiological properties. From the spatial standpoint the gene as the ultimate unit of recombination is that chromosomal segment interchangeable but not divisible by crossing over. A gene so defined has been nicknamed the *recon*. Each gene also may be defined as the smallest element which when altered gives rise to a mutant form of the organism. Genes mutate at specific rates to one or more allelic forms and in so doing do not alter their recombinational relations with neighboring genes. The gene defined as the unit of mutation is nicknamed the *muton*. Finally the gene as the ultimate unit of physiological action or the *cistron* has a specific functional role to play, one duplicated by no nonallelic gene. There is evidence that cistrons often control the formation of polypeptide chains. There is no self-evident reason for thinking that the recon, the muton, and the cistron need always correspond to the same physical unit, although such may often be the case. Many instances are now known where a cistron is composed of several recons, and the evidence for this statement will now be developed.

Tests for allelism

Let us suppose that in *Drosophila* two, second chromosomal, recessive mutants a and b are discovered independently, both of which affect eye color in a similar way. By inbreeding, homozygous stocks of each mutant are produced. Crosses are then made between individuals from the two stocks (aa x bb), and the offspring are observed. If the offspring are wild type, the genes are nonallelic, and the cross may be symbolized as follows:

$$P_1 \frac{a\ +^b}{a\ +^b} \times \frac{+^a\ b}{+^a\ b} \longrightarrow F_1 \frac{a\ +^b}{+^a\ b}$$

The F_1 individuals are wild type, since each mutant-bearing chromosome carries the wild type allele of the other mutant gene. Conversely, if the genes are allelic and are given the symbols x^a and x^b, the cross is

$$P_1 \frac{x^a}{x^a} \times \frac{x^b}{x^b} \longrightarrow F_1 \frac{x^a}{x^b}$$

Here the offspring will show a mutant phenotype generally intermediate between the parental phenotypes. Thus by the allelism test one can decide whether or not two genes control the same physiological process.

Pseudoallelism

Pseudoalleles are genes that behave as alleles in the allelism test but which can be separated by crossing over. Pseudoallelism has been demonstrated in *Drosophila,* maize, *Aspergillus, Gossypium, Neurospora, E. coli,* and in various bacteriophages. In Table 14–4 are listed various pseudoallelic loci in *Drosophila.*

TABLE 14–4

PSEUDOALLELIC LOCI IN DROSOPHILA

CHROMOSOME	POSITION	LOCUS	MINIMUM SUBUNITS
1	0.0	*yellow* (*y*)	2
1	1.5	*white* (*w*)	4
1	3.0	*Notch* (*N*)	7
1	21.0	*singed* (*sn*)	3
1	27.7	*lozenge* (*lz*)	3
1	33.0	*vermilion* (*v*)	2
1	36.1	*miniature* (*m*)	2
1	44.0	*garnet* (*g*)	3
1	56.7	*forked* (*f*)	2
2	1.3	*Star* (*S*)	2
2	13.0	*dumpy* (*dp*)	7
2	104.5	*brown* (*bw*)	2
3	52.4	*rosy* (*ry*)	3
3	58.2	*Stubble* (*Sb*)	2
3	58.8	*bithorax* (*bx*)	5

One of the first physiological genes to be shown to consist of subunits was *lozenge.* In 1940 a small number of wild type *Drosophila* from a cross involving two *lozenge* alleles, lz^g (*glossary*) and lz^s (*spectacle*), was recovered which could be interpreted by assuming that the locus was compound. Subsequently Green and Green published a series of papers which constitutes one of the most complete analyses of pseudoallelism. A study of recombination among 18 independently discovered *lozenge* alleles demonstrated that each mutant could be assigned to one of three subloci (see Fig. 14–7). No case where an lz mutant involved more than one locus could be found. All mutants were localized to section 8D of the salivary X-chromosome. The lozenge mutants can be separated into three phenotypic classes on the basis of the effect of each allele when homozygous on the morphology and pigmentation of the compound eyes, on the morphology of the tarsal claws, and on female fertility. These phenotypes, however, do not correspond to the subloci, since class I and II mutants occur at all three loci. Spontaneous and radiation-induced mutants occur at each locus.

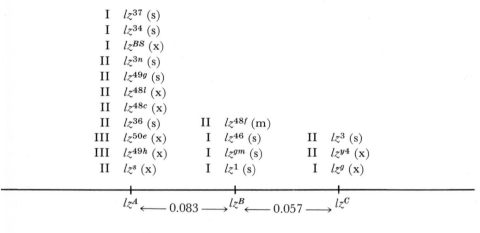

$$\text{I} \quad lz^{37}\ (\text{s})$$
$$\text{I} \quad lz^{34}\ (\text{s})$$
$$\text{I} \quad lz^{BS}\ (\text{x})$$
$$\text{II} \quad lz^{3n}\ (\text{s})$$
$$\text{II} \quad lz^{49g}\ (\text{s})$$
$$\text{II} \quad lz^{48l}\ (\text{x})$$
$$\text{II} \quad lz^{48c}\ (\text{x})$$

$$\text{II} \quad lz^{36}\ (\text{s}) \qquad \text{II} \quad lz^{48f}\ (\text{m})$$
$$\text{III} \quad lz^{50e}\ (\text{x}) \qquad \text{I} \quad lz^{46}\ (\text{s}) \qquad \text{II} \quad lz^{3}\ (\text{s})$$
$$\text{III} \quad lz^{49h}\ (\text{x}) \qquad \text{I} \quad lz^{gm}\ (\text{s}) \qquad \text{II} \quad lz^{y4}\ (\text{x})$$
$$\text{II} \quad lz^{8}\ (\text{x}) \qquad \text{I} \quad lz^{1}\ (\text{s}) \qquad \text{I} \quad lz^{g}\ (\text{x})$$

$$lz^{A} \longleftarrow 0.083 \longrightarrow lz^{B} \longleftarrow 0.057 \longrightarrow lz^{C}$$

(s) spontaneous
(x) X-ray induced
(m) induced with mustard gas
I, II, III phenotypic class to which mutant belongs

Figure 14–7 The distribution of various lozenge alleles among the subloci of the lozenge gene.

In the left-hand column of Figure 14–8 are presented symbolically the X-chromosome configurations of three flies, each heterozygous for two alleles of lozenge (lz^{BS}/lz^{1}, lz^{1}/lz^{g}, and lz^{BS}/lz^{g}). All the mutants belong to phenotypic class I and all behave as alleles; since in combination they produce the mutant phenotype. Yet as a result of crossing over between the mutants, individuals are produced containing one homologue with the double mutant and one with three + alleles in tandem, and such individuals are wild type. Thus the *cis* configuration gives wild type; whereas the *trans* configuration gives the mutant phenotype.

Various hypotheses have been advanced to explain such cis-trans effects, and among these, two are particularly appealing: the *multirecon-cistron* and

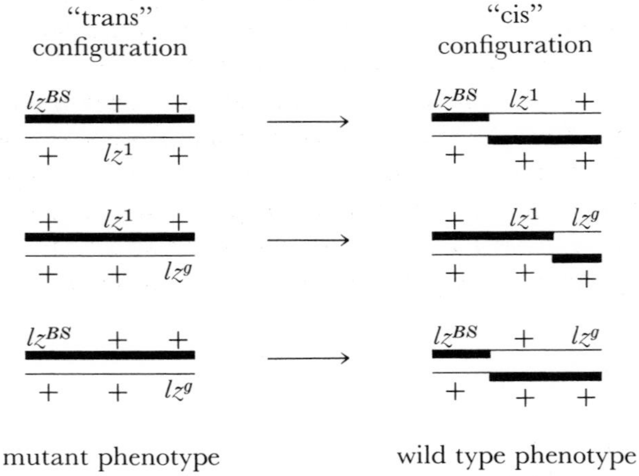

Figure 14-8

the *multi cistron-assembly line* hypotheses. According to the multirecon-cistron hypothesis the + alleles of lz^{BS}, lz^1, and lz^g would each represent a recon and the three together a cistron. That is, the functional unit which controls the phenotype of the eyes, female reproductive system, and tarsal claws is the entire lozenge locus. However, it is divisible by crossing over into three subunits and mutation in any one of them will inactivate the entire cistron. However, the proper crossover between two cistrons, each inactivated at a different recon, can produce a functional cistron. According to the alternative multi cistron-assembly line hypothesis lz^{BS}, lz^1, and lz^g are separate genes (that is, each constitutes a cistron, muton, and recon). Each of these genes acts on a consecutive step in the biosynthesis of a compound which is essential for the normal development of the compound eyes, tarsal claws, and femal reproductive system. The precursor substances formed are unstable or nondiffusible and consequently the alleles of the three genes must form a tandem assembly line on the chromosome for proper functioning. Such is the case in the cis configuration. Such is not the case in the trans configuration (see Fig. 14–8).

Working with *Salmonella typhimurium*, the germ causing typhoid fever in mice, Demerec and his colleagues were able to classify a series of tryptophan-requiring mutants into four groups: (A) those which fail to synthesize anthranilic acid; (B) those which cannot convert anthranilic acid into an as yet unidentified intermediate X; (C) those which fail to convert X to indole; and (D) those which are blocked in the conversion of indole to tryptophan (see Fig. 14–2).

It will be recalled (see p. 60) that during transduction a fragment of genetic material from a host bacterium can be carried by a virus to a second host where it is integrated into the genetic material of the second host. If two marker genes are near one another on the first host's chromosome, they may be included on the transduced chromosomal element. Conversely both genes physically distant from one another would rarely be included in the same transduced element. Using transduction experiments, Demerec was able to determine the linkage relationships of the four classes of tryptophan-requiring mutant genes referred to above. All four loci associated with the tryptophan requirement were found to be closely linked. The order of the loci on the linkage map was found to be A,B,C,D, and this order coincided exactly with the sequence with respect to the biochemical steps in the synthesis of tryptophan. Thus the genes controlling tryptophan synthesis in *Salmonella* serve as a good example of a multi cistron assembly line. Four instances of sequentially linked loci for biochemical syntheses have thus far been found in microorganisms. The occurrence of such integrated gene systems constitutes the best explanation for position effect (see Chapter 10).

Complementation

The phenotype of a heterozygote compounded with two independent *lozenge* alleles in the trans configuration is usually intermediate between the phenotypes shown by either allele when homozygous. However, the mutants belonging to class III do not behave characteristically in this respect. A fly of genotype lz^s/lz^{50e}, for example, has an eye which represents only a slight departure from wild type; whereas lz^s/lz^s and lz^{50e}/lz^{50e} individuals have eyes which are markedly abnormal. Thus lz^{50e} and lz^s, both of which occupy the same recon, are called complementary alleles. The fact that lz^{50e} and lz^s show a nearly wild phenotype when present in the trans configuration demonstrates that the functional deficiencies of lz^{50e} are not identical with lz^s, and that the mutation process may only cause a gene to lose *part* of its function. Such cases of *complementation* are hypothesized to involve situations where each mutant produces inactive polypeptides which are deficient in different regions. Recombination in the cytoplasm between the inactive products supplied by the complementary mutants results in sufficient active protein to allow the production of an almost normal phenotype. This suggestion is supported by recent studies by D. Woodward, who investigated two mutants of *Neurospora* capable of complementing each other in heterocaryons. He found that inactive extracts obtained from each mutant would form an active enzyme when mixed together *in vitro*.

The fine structure of the r II region

The subdivision by Benzer of the r II region of the T₄ bacteriophage chromosome into two multirecon cistrons constitutes one of the major advances in genetics of recent years. Wild type-T₄ produces similar plaques on two strains of *Escherichia coli* (B and K). The K strain is lysogenic for phage lambda. Mutants of the r II type, however, fail to produce plaques on K (because they fail to multiply, although they do infect and kill the cells) and produce markedly altered plaques on B. All mutants of this type are found located within a small portion of the T₄ linkage map, about 6 units in length. Thousands of r II mutants were recovered for the analysis. If a colony of *E. coli* K cells is infected simultaneously with two different r II mutants and massive lysis of the colony occurs subsequently, it is obvious that the functional deficiency of mutant 1 is not identical with that of mutant 2. If the two mutants fail to complement each other, no lysis of the colony occurs, and the mutants are placed in the same class (i.e. they belong to the same cistron). Application of this test to various pairs of mutants leads to a division of the r II region into an A and a B cistron. Mutants belonging to class A or B can now be tested in pairs to see if they behave as pseudoalleles. When this is done certain mutants are found to behave anomalously. For example (see Fig. 14–9), when five mutants are tested against each other it is found that recombination occurs between 1 and 2,

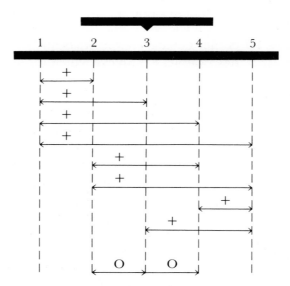

Figure 14–9 An illustration of the recombinational behavior of an anomalous mutant (number 3). A plus sign signifies the production, a zero the lack of production, of wild type recombinations in a cross.

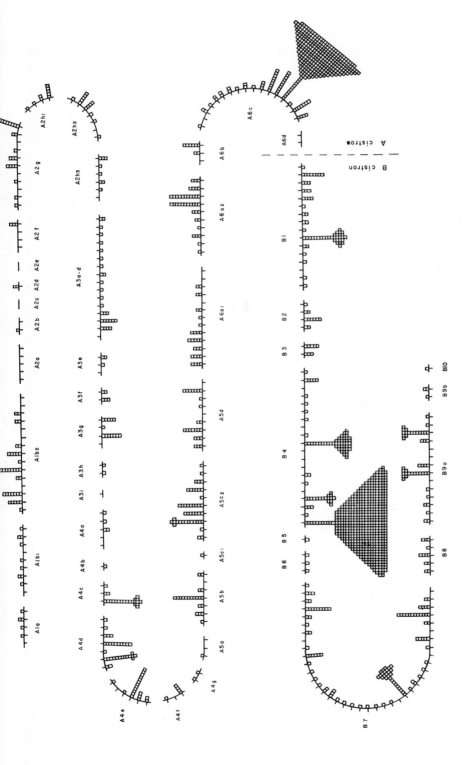

Figure 14–10 The location of 1612 spontaneous mutations on the genetic map of the r II region of the chromosome of phage T₄ of *Escherichia coli*. Each square represents one occurrence observed at the indicated site. Sites with no occurrences shown are known to exist from the occurrence of experimentally induced mutations. Deletions were used to divide the r II region into 47 distinct segments. A segments reside in the A cistron; B segments in the B cistron. While the order of the segments is known the arrangement of sites within each segment is arbitrary. Over 300 sites are known for the r II region. Note the conspicuous "hot spots" (sites tending to mutate frequently) in segments A6C and B4.

(From Benzer, Proc. Nat. Acad. Sci. *47*: 403–15.)

1 and 4, 1 and 5, 2 and 4, 2 and 5, 1 and 3, 4 and 5, and 3 and 5; but recombination does not occur between 2 and 3 or 3 and 4. Furthermore, mutants 1, 2, 4, and 5 commonly back mutate, whereas mutant 3 never does. Such behavior is best explained by assuming that mutant 3 is a deficiency which encompasses point mutations 2 and 4. The occurrence of overlapping deletions in each cistron allowed the cistron to be subdivided further. Each point mutant can then be located within a specific deletion and placed in the correct order with its neighbors by crossover tests. Mutants showing negligible recombination and similar reversion rates are assumed to be recurrences of identical mutations (see Fig. 14–10).

By comparing the length of the total linkage map and the total DNA content of a T_4 particle, a rough conversion factor was calculated by Benzer for translating linkage distances into molecular ones. According to these calculations the A cistron of 4 crossover units is 400 nucleotide pairs long. The minimum recombination frequency between mutations was found to be about 0.02 per cent. This then is the value of the recon, and it corresponds to a distance of two nucleotide pairs, if the assumption that exchange is equally likely anywhere along the DNA chain is a valid one. The various mutants which can back mutate are between 0.01 and 0.05 crossover units in length. This range of values (corresponding to between one and five nucleotide pairs) defines the muton.

Thus in viruses it appears that crossing over can occur between almost any two of the many nucleotides making up a cistron. Here genetic continuity appears to be complete; whereas in higher organisms, exemplified by *Drosophila,* the genetic material shows a clear-cut segmentation. In most cases where sufficient data are available to allow lengths to be assigned to cistrons, mutons, and recons, the cistron is the largest. The current tendency is to equate the terms gene and cistron.

14–1. It has been observed that phenylalanine serves as a competitive inhibitor of the tyrosine-tyrosinase system *in vitro*. It is also known that phenylketonurics tend to have lighter hair and skin pigmentation than their normal brothers and sisters. Suggest a reason for the latter finding in view of the former fact.

14–2. Determinations of the levels of phenylalanine in the blood plasma at 1-, 2-, and 4-hour intervals after feeding a standard dose of phenylalanine demonstrate that the "normal" parents of phenylketonurics have a phenylalanine level about double that of controls. What do you conclude from these findings?

14–3. In *Drosophila melanogaster* a chain of enzymatic reactions is postulated for the formation of the bright red pigments of the compound eye. Some of these reactions are shown below. Wild type flies contain the yellow compound in the

BIOPTERIN

YELLOW PIGMENT

DROSOPTERIN (BRIGHT RED PIGMENT)

walls of their testes. Flies homozygous for the second chromosomal mutant *brown* (*bw*) accumulate no drosopterins in the eye and have colorless testes. Flies homozygous for the third chromosomal gene *sepia* (*se*) have yellow testes but lack drosopterins in the compound eyes. Do these facts suggest the points in the reaction chain controlled by the + alleles of *bw* and *se*? Does the above information suggest differences in gene action in different tissues?

14–4. A. H. Sturtevant reported in 1920 the occurrence of a bilateral gynandromorph in *Drosophila melanogaster* which developed from an egg of genotype $\frac{sc\ +\ ec\ +\ ct\ v\ g\ f}{+\ w^e\ +\ rb\ +\ +\ +\ f}$. The male side of the fly showed the mutant phenotypes scute bristle, echinus eye texture, cut wing shape, garnet eye color, and forked bristle. The female tissues showed the forked bristle phenotype. Explain the method of origin of the gynandromorph and the reason for the failure of the gene *v* to manifest itself on the male side of the fly.

14–5. Beadle and Ephrussi in 1936 reported the results of transplantations of eye primordia from larvae of one genotype into hosts of different genotype. In cases

GENETICS

where the transplantations were successful an adult was produced containing the donor eye in its abdominal cavity. The eye was next dissected from the host and its color recorded. The results were as follows:

HOST

		+	v	cn	cd	st
DONOR	+	■	+	+	+	+
	v	+	■	+	+	+
	cn	+	cn	■	+	+
	cd	cd	cd	cd	■	cd
	st	st	st	st	st	■

Note that +, cd, and st eye primordia develop autonomously. That is, they develop in accordance with their genotype irrespective of the host in which they reside. The v eye primordium develop + type pigmentation in all the hosts tested. The cn eye primordium develop + type pigmentation in all hosts tested except v. Explain these observations.

14–6. Assume that the *cd* gene acts before the *st* gene in the chain of reactions, then fill in the blanks in the following table. Use P for present, A for accumulates in excessive amounts, O for absent.

GENOTYPE WITH RESPECT TO					TRYPTOPHAN	FORMYL KYNURENINE	KYNURENINE	HYDROXY KYNURENINE	cd + SUBSTANCE	st + SUBSTANCE	XANTHOMMATIN	DROSOPTERN	EYE PIGMENTATION
v	cn	cd	st	bw									
v	+	+	+	+									bright red
+	cn	+	+	+									bright red
+	+	cd	+	+									bright red
+	+	+	st	+									bright red
+	+	+	+	bw									brown
v	+	+	+	bw									colorless

water soluble   water insoluble

14–7. Several instances have been discovered in *Neurospora* where the inactivation of a single gene results in the organism exhibiting a double growth factor requirement. Discuss the possible mechanisms for such a phenomenon.

14–8. Sanger received the Nobel prize for elucidating the structure of beef insulin. It is made up of two polypeptides, an A or acidic chain comprising 21 amino acids, and a B or basic chain containing 29 amino acids. The only differences in the insulins of the various species studied lie in the $8 \cdot 9 \cdot 10$ sequence of amino acids in the A chain. Discuss how these differences might have arisen.

Organisms	8	9	10
Cattle	alanine	serine	valine
Sheep	alanine	glycine	valine
Pig and sperm whale	threonine	serine	isoleucine
Horse	threonine	glycine	isoleucine
Sei whale	alanine	serine	threonine

14–9. Consider the hazards of an RH-positive mother carrying *in utero* an Rh-negative fetus.

14–10. If other sources of blood exist, a woman should not be transfused with her husband's blood even if the two have the same A B O and Rh blood types. Why?

14–11. Legal disputes often arise over the paternity of a child. The most common situation is that in which a woman accuses a man of fathering her child, which he denies. On other occasions controversies may arise over an accidental interchange of babies at a hospital. In situations of this sort, determination of a variety of blood group antigens for the child and the adults concerned will often exclude certain individuals as the parents. It is obvious, for example, that the antigens possessed by the child must be present also in one or the other parent. Thus if the child's erythrocytes contain an antigen not found in the mother or in the alleged father, then the man is not the father.

The Jones have a boy Tom and a girl Alice. The Browns have a boy Archie and a girl Martha. Martha and Alice were born at the same time in the same hospital, and it is suspected that they were accidently interchanged. The blood of all eight individuals is tested for antigens A_1, A_2, B, M, N, P, and D. The results are shown below.

	A₁	A₂	B	M	N	P	D
Mrs. Jones	+	−	−	+	−	−	+
Mr. Jones	+	−	−	−	+	−	−
Alice Jones	−	+	−	+	−	+	+
Tom Jones	−	−	−	+	+	−	−
Mrs. Brown	−	+	−	+	−	+	+
Mr. Brown	−	−	−	+	−	+	+
Martha Brown	+	−	−	+	+	−	+
Archie Brown	−	+	−	+	−	−	+

Does it appear that the suspected exchange occurred?

14–12. Blood group antigens have found use in solving questions of disputed parentage in cattle. In the following table (taken from Irwin) data are presented from blood tests run in solving a case in which the dam of a calf was known, but in which either of two bulls could have been the sire.

BLOOD TYPES

	A	B	C₁	F	H	J	O	R	S	V	W	X₂	Y₁	Y₂	Z	A'	E₃'	H'	I'	J'	K'	L'
Possible sire (1)	A	B		F		J	O					X₂			Z				I'			L'
Possible sire (2)	A	B	C₁	F		J	O	R	S	V	W	X₂	Y₁	Y₂	Z	A'	E₃'	H'		J'	K'	
Dam	A			F	H	J	O			V		X₂						H'		J'	K'	L'
Calf	A				H		O	R		V	W	X₂		Y₂	Z			H'		J'	K'	L'

Which bull can be excluded as sire of the calf?

14–13. In man, linkage studies have placed the genes for hemophilia, colorblindness, Christmas disease, and glucose-6-phosphate dehydrogenase deficiency on the X-chromosome, the genes for the Lewis and Lutheran blood group antigens on one autosome, the genes for the Rh system and elliptocytosis on a second autosome, and the genes for the A B O system and for the nail patella syndrome on a third autosome. Why do you suppose linkage studies in man are in such a primitive state? Can you suggest a few genes in man which might serve as useful chromosome markers?

14–14. Studies in *Drosophila* involving recombination between pseudoallelic loci are very laborious because of rarity of recombinant types. Can you think of a way that crossing over between these loci might be increased?

14–15. If Benzer's A cistron of the r II region of the chromosome of T_4 phage is 400 nucleotide pairs long, what would be the size of the polypeptide it could specify? (See Fig. 14–5.)

14–16. Whereas the genetic material of bacterial viruses is DNA, that of the tobacco mosaic virus (TMV) and related plant viruses is RNA. The TMV consists of a central core of RNA which controls the synthesis of a proteinaceous coat. Nitrous acid is known to undergo a reaction with the bases of nucleic acids which causes a substitution of OH groups for NH_2 groups. Tsugita and Fraenkel-Conrat have treated RNA isolated from TMV with nitrous acid and have demonstrated that the protein isolated from the coat formed subsequently has an altered amino acid composition. What do you conclude from these findings?

14–17. What would be the size of the template RNA molecule required to specify a β chain of hemoglobin? How would such a template molecule fit upon a ribosome of 20 mμ diameter? Assume the distance between successive nucleotide pairs is 0.34 mμ.

BIBLIOGRAPHY

Acton, A. B. 1958 The gene contents of overlapping inversions. Am. Naturalist *92*: 57.

Allison, A. C. 1959 Metabolic polymorphisms in mammals and their bearing on problems of biochemical genetics. Am. Naturalist *93*: 5–15.

Anfinsen, C. B. 1959 The Molecular Basis of Evolution. Wiley, New York.

Atwood, K. C., and F. Mukai 1953 Indispensable gene functions in *Neurospora*. Proc. Nat. Acad. Sc. *39*: 1027–35.

Baglioni, C., V. M. Ingram, and E. Sullivan 1961 Genetic control of foetal and adult human hemoglobin. Nature *189*: 467–9.

Baldwin, E. 1959 Dynamic Aspects of Biochemistry, 3rd ed. Cambridge University Press, Cambridge, England.

Beadle, G. W. 1946 Genes and the chemistry of the organism. Am. Scientist *34*: 31–53.

Beadle, G. W., and B. Ephrussi 1936 The differentiation of eye pigments in *Drosophila* as studied by transplantation. Genetics *21*: 225–47.

Beermann, W. 1959 Chromosomal differentiation in insects. *In* Developmental Cytology, edited by D. Rudnick. Ronald Press, New York. (See also references on p. 29 above.)

Benzer, S. 1955 Fine structure of a genetic region in bacteriophage. Proc. Nat. Acad. Sc. *41*: 344.

Benzer, S. 1961 On the topology of the genetic fine structure. Proc. Nat. Acad. Sc. *47*: 403–15.

Brown, C. L. 1960 DNA and specific protein synthesis. 10th Symposium of Society for General Microbiology, pp. 208–38. Cambridge University Press, Cambridge, England.

Brenner, S., F. Jacob, and M. Meselson   1961   An unstable intermediate carrying information from genes to ribosomes for protein synthesis. Nature *190*: 576–80.

Burnet, F. M.   1961   Immunological recognition of self. Science *133*: 307–11.

Callan, H. G., and L. Lloyd   1956   Visual demonstration of allelic differences within cell nuclei. Nature *178*: 355–7.

Carlson, E. A.   1959   Comparative genetics of complex loci. Quart. Rev. Biol. *34*: 36–67.

Crawford, I. P., and C. Yanofsky   1959   The formation of a new enzymatically active protein as a result of suppression. Proc. Nat. Acad. Sc. *45*: 1280–87.

Crick, F. H. C.   1958   On protein synthesis. Symposia of the Society for Experimental Biology. *12*: 138–63.

Crick, F. H. C.   1959   The present position of the coding problem. Brookhaven National Laboratory Symposium *12*: 35–9.

DeBusk, A. G.   1956   Metabolic aspects of chemical genetics. Advances Enzymol. *17*: 393–476.

Demerec, M., and Z. E. Demerec   1956   Analysis of linkage relationships in *Salmonella* by transduction techniques. Brookhaven National Laboratory Symposium *8*: 75–87.

Dixon, M.   1949   Multi-enzyme Systems. Cambridge University Press, Cambridge, England.

Fujii, S.   1940   An abnormal staining capacity of the sixth salivary gland chromosome of *Drosophila virilis*. Cytologia *10*: 294–301.

Goldsmith, K. L. G., editor   1959   Blood groups. British Medical Journal *15*: 89–174.

Green, M. M., and K. C. Green   1949   Crossing-over between alleles at the *lozenge* locus in *Drosophila melanogaster*. Proc. Nat. Acad. Sc. *35*: 586.

Harris, H.   1959   Human Biochemical Genetics. Cambridge University Press, Cambridge, England.

Horowitz, N. H.   1950   Biochemical genetics of *Neurospora*. Advances Genet. *3*: 33–71.

Hsia, D. Y.   1959   Inborn Errors in Metabolism. Year Book Pub., Chicago.

Hubby, J. L., and L. H. Throckmorton   1960   Evolution and pteridine metabolism in the genus *Drosophila*. Proc. Nat. Acad. Sc. *46*: 65–78. (Concerns the bright red eye pigments.)

Irwin, M. R.   1956   Blood grouping and its utilization in animal breeding. 7th International Congress of Animal Husbandry, Proceedings. Altamira, Talleres Gráficos, S. S., Madrid.

Itano, H. A., and E. A. Robinson   1960   Genetic control of the α and β chains of hemoglobin. Proc. Nat. Acad. Sc. *46*: 1492–1500.

Kabat, E. A.   1956   Blood Group Substances. Academic Press, New York.

Kabat, E. A. 1961 Experimental Immunochemistry. Thomas, Springfield, Ill.

Lederberg, J. 1959 Genes and antibodies. Science *129*: 1649–53.

Levine, P. 1954 The genetics of the newer human blood factors. Advances Genet. *6*: 183–234.

Lewis, E. B. 1948 Pseudoallelism and gene evolution. Cold Spring Harbor Symp. Quant. Biol. *16*: 159–74.

Medawar, P. B. 1961 Immunological tolerance. Science *133*: 303–6.

Morgan, T. H. 1926 The Theory of the Gene. Yale University Press, New Haven, Conn.

Nolte, D. J. 1959 The eye-pigmentary system of *Drosophila*. IX. Heredity *13*: 233–41.

Pontecorvo, G. 1958 Trends in Genetic Analysis. Columbia University Press, New York.

Race, R. R., and R. Sanger 1958 Blood Groups in Man, 3rd ed. Blackwell, Oxford, England.

Rich, A. 1960 A hybrid helix containing both deoxyribose and ribose polynucleotides and its relation to the transfer of information between nucleic acids. Proc. Nat. Acad. Sc. *46*: 1044–53.

Rich, A., and D. W. Green 1961 X-ray studies of compounds of biological interest. Ann. Rev. Biochem. *30*: 93–132.

Roberts, G. F. 1957 Comparative Aspects of Haemolytic Disease of the Newborn. Heinemann, London.

Schultz, J. 1959 Antigens and antibodies as cell phenotypes. Science *129*: 937–43.

Snyder, L. H. 1959 Fifty years of medical genetics. Science *129*: 7–13.

Stadler, L. J. 1954 The gene. Science *120*: 811.

Strauss, B. S. 1960 An Outline of Chemical Genetics. Saunders, Philadelphia.

Sturtevant, A. H. 1920 The *vermilion* gene and gynandromorphism. Proc. Soc. Exper. Biol. & Med. *17*: 70–71.

Suskind, S. R. 1957 Gene function and enzyme formation. *In* The Chemical Basis of Heredity, W. D. McElroy and H. B. Glass, editors. Johns Hopkins Press, Baltimore, Md, pp. 123–9.

Tatum, E. L., and D. Bonner 1944 Indole and serine in the biosynthesis and breakdown of tryptophane. Proc. Nat. Acad. Sc. *30*: 30–37.

Tsugita, A., and H. Fraenkel-Conrat 1960 The amino acid composition and c-terminal sequence of a chemically evoked mutant of TMV. Proc. Nat. Acad. Sc. *46*: 636–41.

Vogel, H. J., and D. M. Bonner 1959 The use of mutants in the study of metabolism. Encyclopedia of Plant Physiology *11*: 1–32. W. Ruhland, editor. Springer Verlag, Berlin.

Wagner, R. P., and H. K. Mitchell   1955   Genetics and Metabolism. Wiley, New York.

Weiss, S. B., and T. Nakamoto   1961   On the participation of DNA in RNA biosynthesis. Proc. Natl. Acad. Sci. *47*: 694–7.

Woodruff, M. F. A.   1960   The Transplantation of Tissues and Organs, C. C. Thomas, Springfield, Ill.

Woodward, D. O.   1959   Enzyme complementation *in vitro* between adenlysuccinaseless mutants of *Neurospora crassa*. Proc. Nat. Acad. Sc. *45*: 846–50.

Woodward, D. O.   1960   A gene concept based on genetic and chemical studies in *Neurospora*. Quart. Rev. Biol. *35*: 313–23.

Zueler, W. W., and A. R. Robinson   1961   Haemoglobin F: its significance in the genetics and evolution of haemoglobin. Nature *190*: 237–40.

Chapter 15

The Interaction of Genic and Nongenic Hereditary Units

Introduction

Most of the thousands of inherited characters in various organisms (whose mode of transmission during sexual reproduction has been studied) follow the rules of Mendelian heredity. However, clear-cut examples of hereditary transmission different from gene transmission do exist. In general such anomalous conditions are first detected by the occurrence of dissimilar F_1 individuals in the case of reciprocal crosses (where the different phenotypes cannot be accounted for by sex linkage).

Maternal effects

An example of a situation where reciprocal crosses give dissimilar results occurs in the moth *Ephestia kühniella*. In this case the autosomal gene $+^a$ must be present for the conversion of tryptophan to kynurenine (see Fig. 14–2). In females of genotype a/a no kynurenine is formed, and tryptophan is accumulated; whereas females of genotype $+/a$ form kynurenine and store some of it in their eggs. Thus when reciprocal crosses of the types shown in Figure 15–1A are made, the F_1 larvae of genotype a/a have pale ocelli in the first cross but pigmented ocelli in the second cross. Eventually, however, as these larvae grow their stores of kynurenine run out, and since they contain no $+^a$ gene, they can make no more kynurenine (and as a consequence, no brown pigment). By the end of larval development the ocelli are pale in accordance with the genotype of the larvae.

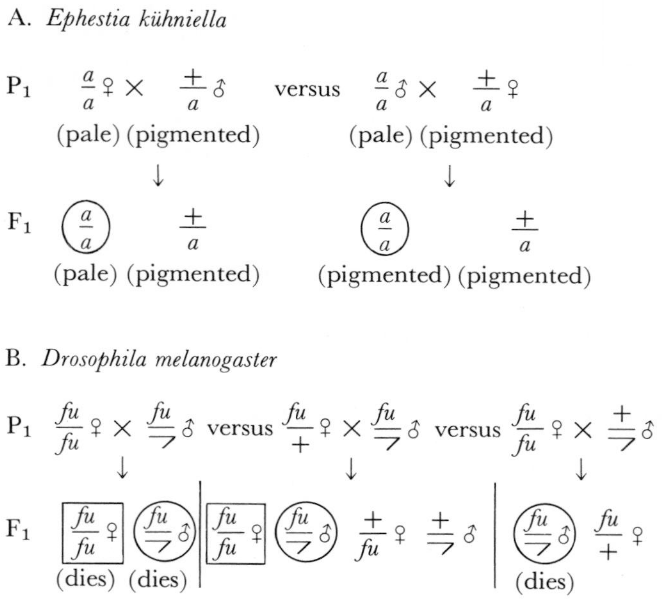

A. *Ephestia kühniella*

P$_1$ $\frac{a}{a}$ ♀ × $\frac{+}{a}$ ♂   versus $\frac{a}{a}$ ♂ × $\frac{+}{a}$ ♀

    (pale) (pigmented)   (pale) (pigmented)

      ↓   ↓

F$_1$ $\left(\frac{a}{a}\right)$ $\frac{+}{a}$ $\left(\frac{a}{a}\right)$ $\frac{+}{a}$

   (pale) (pigmented)   (pigmented) (pigmented)

B. *Drosophila melanogaster*

P$_1$ $\frac{fu}{fu}$ ♀ × $\frac{fu}{\nearrow}$ ♂ versus $\frac{fu}{+}$ ♀ × $\frac{fu}{\nearrow}$ ♂ versus $\frac{fu}{fu}$ ♀ × $\frac{+}{\nearrow}$ ♂

      ↓   ↓   ↓

F$_1$ $\boxed{\frac{fu}{fu} ♀}$ $\boxed{\left(\frac{fu}{\nearrow}\right) ♂}$ $\left|\frac{fu}{fu} ♀\right|$ $\left(\frac{fu}{\nearrow}\right) ♂$ $\frac{+}{fu}$ ♀ $\frac{+}{\nearrow}$ ♂ $\left|\left(\frac{fu}{\nearrow}\right) ♂\right.$ $\frac{fu}{+}$ ♀

  (dies) (dies)   (dies)

Figure 15–1   Crosses which illustrate situations in which individuals of identical genotypes (enclosed) show dissimilar phenotypes because of maternal inheritance. Work of A. Kühn in the moth (A) and of C. Lynch in the fruit fly (B).

The recessive X-chromosomal gene *fused* (*fu*) in *Drosophila melanogaster* produces manifold effects which include partial sterility in females, abnormalities in the pattern of the longitudinal wing veins, and reduction in the number of ocelli. A homozygous *fused* female fertilized by a *fused* male produces no offspring. If fertilized by a + male, however, she produces only daughters. Heterozygous *fused* females produce offspring of the expected genotypes. These results are summarized in Figure 15–1B. The simplest explanation for the action of *fused* upon viability is that the plus allele of *fused* is responsible for the production of a substance necessary for embryogenesis. The nurse cells (see p. 49) of females of genotype + /*fu* manufacture and transmit this substance to the ooplasm, and as a consequence fertilized eggs can develop normally regardless of whether or not they contain the +^{fu} gene. Homozygous females form eggs devoid of the *fused* plus substance, and thus normal embryogenesis can occur only if the +^{fu} gene is contributed by the fertilizing sperm. Thus *fu/fu* females can produce only + /*fu* daughters.

In both examples cited above the phenotypic differences found between individuals of identical genotype must be ascribed to an effect of the maternal cytoplasm. In these cases, however, the cytoplasmic determinants were themselves produced by the action of nuclear genes of parental tissues. That these maternal effects are temporary is demonstrated by the a/a moth larvae eventually losing their pigmentation and by the fact that surviving fu/fu embryos develop into females which are phenotypically fused and are sterile unless mated to wild type males. Thus in the case of maternal effects we are dealing with transient changes in the phenotype of the cytoplasm. In the case of the true cytoplasmic inheritance of a certain characteristic the condition must persist with no diminution over a large number of generations, and this prerequisite implies the existence of self-reproducing cytoplasmic particles.

Hereditary transmission of self-reproducing particles

The hereditary viruslike agents of *Drosophila*

Normal *Drosophila* can be kept for hours in an atmosphere of pure CO_2 without permanent injury. However, in 1937 L'Héritier and Teissier discovered an *ebony* strain of flies very sensitive to carbon dioxide. Exposure for a few seconds to this gas paralyzes and eventually kills them. It seems likely that the toxic effect of CO_2 is due to injury to the thoracic ganglia, but as yet the biochemical mechanism of the toxicity is obscure.

Soon after the discovery of CO_2 sensitivity, breeding experiments by L'Héritier demonstrated that the character did not follow Mendelian laws and exhibited no linkage with any chromosome. Rather, CO_2 sensitivity was found to result from the flies harboring a viruslike agent (nicknamed sigma, σ). Studies of inactivation of the virus by X-rays made possible the calculation of a target diameter of 40 mμ. The particle as yet has not been observed in electron micrographs.

Under normal circumstances σ is not contagious and is propagated through the eggs and sperm. However, injection of extracts from σ-infected flies into σ-free flies can cause them to become infected and simultaneously to develop sensitivity to CO_2. Such injected flies carry σ in the "nonstabilized" condition. The growth cycle of the virus is carried out presumably in cellular receptors of the host and extracts of such flies give high yields of the virus. Transmission of σ to the progeny is rare, occurring in a fraction of the eggs but never in sperm. However, from some of the σ-infected oocytes arise stabilized females. Extracts of such females contain only about 10 per cent as much σ as that found in extracts from nonstabilized females. Stabilized females, however, transmit σ to all their progeny. It is presumed that a stabilized fly is more or less equivalent to a culture of lysogenized

bacteria (see p. 60) and that the virus of stabilized flies may exist within
the host nuclei although not associated with any particular chromosome.
The hereditary virus of *Drosophila* shows numerous mutant forms, and several genes in the host are known which inhibit viral growth. Recently
recombinant types of σ have been recovered from flies developing from eggs
infected by a mutant virus of maternal origin and fertilized by spermatozoa
carrying a different viral mutant.

Drosophila harboring the CO_2 sensitivity virus are very common in
nature, and it appears that the condition confers some selective advantage
upon the insect. The virus displays a tendency to become lost under laboratory conditions. The virus has been experimentally transmitted to many
species of *Drosophila* other than *melanogaster* and has been observed in other
species in nature as well.

Recently a maternally inherited condition known as "sex-ratio" has
been reported in *Drosophila bifasciata, prosaltans, borealis, willistoni,* and
paulistorum. In all cases a cytoplasmically transmitted agent dependent upon
the nuclear genotype of the host is involved in the production of females
which give rise to progenies which are exclusively or mainly female. In
willistoni the unisexual progenies arise through the lethal effect of the agent
upon XY zygotes. Ooplasm from lethal XY zygotes when injected into the
abdomens of females from a previously normal strain causes the females to
produce unisexual progenies after a latent period of two weeks. The sex-
ratio agent in *D. willistoni* has been identified as a spirochete.

Kappa

Kappa is the name given by Sonneborn to a remarkable particle, populations of which are found in the cytoplasm of *Paramecium aurelia.* During
early stages in its development the kappa particle is capable of continued
reproduction by transverse division. Subsequently it ceases to divide,
enlarges until it reaches dimensions averaging 0.8×2.3 micra, and develops a highly refractile bright granule within it. Cytochemical tests show
kappa to contain DNA and protein, and studies with the electron microscope by Dippell demonstrate a complex internal structure. The mature
particles are liberated into the medium where they undergo a transformation to a P particle which acting as a toxic agent can cause sensitive paramecia to become abnormal in behavior and morphology and to die in the
course of some hours or days. Animals of some stocks of sensitive paramecia
can be killed by a single particle, whereas others require more than one.
Paramecia containing kappa particles are protected against the action of
the toxin they liberate. Such paramecia are called *killers.* The kappa
particle also exists in a mutant form called pi. The presence of pi particles
does not confer protection against, or result in the liberation of, a toxic

agent; whereas the presence of kappa particles in the cytoplasm somehow protects the organism from damage from its own P particles. Mutant kappas also are known which, while protecting the organism against damage from P particles, cannot themselves transform into P particles. The number of kappa particles varies between 100 and 3000 per paramecium. The amount of kappa is halved at fission and during the first third of the subsequent growth period the number of particles doubles. On the average, kappa reproduces at the same rate as the host. However, the paramecium can be induced to multiply more rapidly than kappa. Under these circumstances the mean amount of kappa per animal declines with successive generations and eventually a kappa-free, sensitive population may result. Kappa may be eliminated from paramecia by exposing them to the anti-biotics aureomycin, terramycin, and penicillin G.

The transmission of the killer and sensitive character is presented diagrammatically in Figure 15–2. The maintenance of kappa requires the presence of a dominant gene K. Individuals of genotype kk lose their kappa within about five fissions. KK and Kk individuals need not carry kappa, but if they do KK individuals contain twice as many kappa particles as do Kk individuals.

Another particle, called mu, which is related to kappa, occurs in the cytoplasm of certain strains of paramecia. For their maintenance mu particles also depend on the presence of a dominant gene in the host. Mu, unlike kappa, is not liberated into the medium to form a toxic agent. However, when mu is present in large numbers, the paramecia (which are called *mate killers*) kill or injure sensitives with which they conjugate. The presence of mu in a paramecium protects it from the action of other mate killers. Under conditions of rapid reproduction by the host mu may also be lost by progressive dilution.

The significance of kappa is that it furnishes an instance of a situation in which a unicellular, infectious symbiont and its host have become exquistitely co-adapted genetically. As far as kappa is concerned the relation is an obligatory one, since kappa cannot multiply outside the paramecium. The gene K could be postulated to allow the synthesis of some nutrient required by the symbiont. The relationship with kappa is beneficial to a paramecium of genotype KK, since the P particles it liberates and to which it is immune cause the death of sensitive competitors. Thus K could be looked upon as a dominant gene conferring susceptibility to a beneficial disease.

The mammary tumor agent (MTA)

In a series of papers beginning in 1936, J. J. Bittner brought forward evidence that several causative factors interacted in the development of

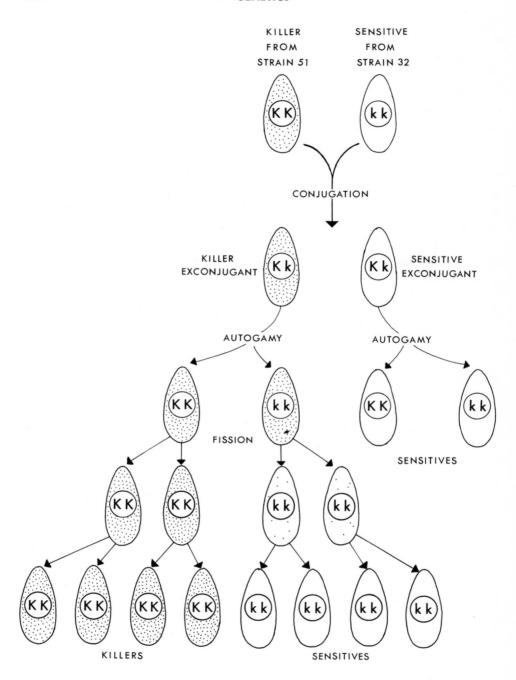

Figure 15–2   The transmission of the killer and sensitive character in *Paramecium aurelia*. Kappa particles are symbolized by dots. The toxic effect of killers on sensitives is not rapid enough to prevent conjugation of sensitive and killer paramecia. A minimum of 140 kappa particles per organism is essential for protection against P particles.

spontaneous mammary cancer in mice. These factors are: the inherited susceptibility for spontaneous mammary cancer, hormonal stimulation of the mammary glands, and a milk-borne nursing influence with properties of an infectious agent or virus. Several inherited hormonal patterns have been described, and from genetic studies it appears that the same genes do not control the inheritance of susceptibilty for mammary cancer and the inheritance of the hormonal influence. As the work proceeded, evidence was obtained that males of cancerous strains with MTA may infect MTA-free females with the virus at coitus.

The mammary tumor agent has been observed in electron micrographs and shown to be a complex organelle consisting of a membranous sac containing an internal core or nucleoid. Determination of the target size by deuteron bombardment suggests that the nucleoid is the site of tumorigenic activity. The agent appears to arise from protrusions of the outer walls of the mammary cells. The MTA from one cancerous stock may have different antigenic properties after being introduced into mice having a different genotype, and antiserum produced against the latter may not neutralize the virus obtained from the original strain.

Chlorophyll inheritance

All the cells which carry on photosynthesis contain chloroplasts in which the chlorophylls and carotenoids are found. In electron micrographs chloroplasts are seen to be ellipsoidal bodies surrounded by a membrane which is known to be semipermeable. The stroma or proteinaceous matrix of the chloroplast contains long columns called grana made up of stacks of dense disks. It is in these disks that the chlorophyll is found. Adjacent grana are connected through a series of fine lamellae which extend through the grana. Large pigment granules are also present in the stroma. A schematic picture of a chloroplast similar to those found in spinach leaves is shown in Figure 15–3. Chloroplasts reproduce themselves by undergoing fission, can mutate, and can reproduce the mutant condition. In fact much of the variegation in plants arises from the somatic segregation of mutant and wild type plastids. Chloroplasts are generally but not invariably transmitted to the next generation through the ooplasm and consequently are derived from the maternal line. The antibiotic streptomycin rids plant cells of their chloroplasts. Once they are lost from a cell they cannot be regenerated *de novo*. In addition to chlorophylls, carotenoids and proteins chloroplasts are known to contain DNA, RNA, and lipids.

Plastids presumably require various nutrients for their maintenance and reproduction, and many of these are synthesized under the control of

GRANA

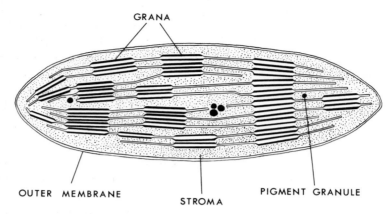

OUTER MEMBRANE   PIGMENT GRANULE

STROMA

Figure 15–3   A schematic diagram of a chloroplast.   (Redrawn from Diter von Wettstein,
"Developmental changes in chloroplasts and their genetic control" in *Developmental Cytology*, edited by
Dorothea Rudnick, copyright 1959, The Ronald Press Co.)

nuclear genes. Hundreds of mutants are known in various plants (particularly maize and barley), and in some cases the effects of mutations upon
the ultrastructure of the chloroplast have been studied. In the case of the
barley mutant *xantha 3,* for example, von Wettstein has shown that the
chloroplast accumulates excessive numbers of pigment granules and never
develops an orderly array of grana. Von Wettstein suggests that the granules
provide a morphological counterpart of the accumulated precursors often
detected in the case of biochemical blocks caused by genetic lesions in
Neurospora.

Some plastid characters may be under nuclear control to the extent that
a gene mutation may induce a change in plastid characteristics. Subsequently, however, the changed plastid may behave autonomously. A recessive gene *i o j a p (i j)* located on chromosome 7 in maize and studied by
Rhoades furnishes an example of the above situation. Plants homozygous
for *ij* are green and white striped. Ears from *Ij/Ij* plants when pollinated
with *ij* pollen yield green plants containing normal chloroplasts. The reciprocal cross produces green plants, green-white striped plants, and white
seedlings which fail to survive. White tissues contain small, colorless chloroplasts. Pollination of ears from striped F₁ plants of genotype *Ij/ij* with
pollen from green plants of genotype *Ij/Ij* produces kernels from which arise
green, green-white striped, and white seedlings. The phenotype of the
plant is independent of its genotype and depends upon whether the ear
developed in a green, green-white striped, or white sector of the F₁ plant.
Thus the *i o j a p* gene seems to have produced mutant plastids which

subsequently behave autonomously. Sporogenous tissues can be made up of cells containing normal or mutant chloroplasts or both and from such tissues arise green, white, or striped plants.

Petite and poky

Ephrussi and his colleagues in 1949 found that many populations of baker's yeast (*Saccharomyces cerevisiae*) yield dwarf (petite) colonies at a frequency of 1 per cent. Cells from petite colonies upon vegetative reproduction (budding) produce more petite colonies. Such cells lack various respiratory enzymes, and it is assumed that petite mutants have lost their mitochondria. Normal cells grown on medium containing the acridine dyes (euflavine and acriflavine) give rise to identical petite mutants. Presumably acridine dyes destroy yeast mitochondria. Subsequently a mutant was discovered in a French yeast strain phenotypically similar to the vegetative petites but whose characteristics were due to a recessive gene. In the absence of the normal allele of this gene the yeast mitochondria were inactivated. By crossing cells of the above mutant (the "segregational petite") with cells from the vegetative petite it was possible to obtain diploid cells containing a wild type allele (from the vegetative petite parent) and previously inactive mitochondria (from the segregational petite parent). Such cells showed the normal growth habit, and the inactive mitochondria recovered their full activity. Thus the synthesis of respiratory enzymes in *Saccharomyces* requires an interaction between the genome and cytoplasmic particles.

A parallel situation was found by Mitchell and Mitchell in their studies of a mutant of *Neurospora* designated as *poky* (*po*) because of its slow mycelial growth. Poky and a second strain mi-3 (also characterized by slow growth) exhibited maternal inheritance and were found to carry an altered system of respiratory enzymes. Presumably cells of both strains contained mutant mitochondria which are unable to form certain enzymes. In the case of *po* and mi-3 the mitochondria behave autonomously. However, mutants are known in *Neurospora* where the upset of the respiratory system is controlled by nuclear genes as in the case of segregational petite in yeast.

Pollen abortion in maize

Genes and cytoplasm have evolved together over many centuries and have accomplished an effective, harmonious interrelationship which provides for normal growth, development, and transmission to future generations. Abnormalities often occur when this normal relationship is disturbed by hybridization between individuals of different races, species, or genera.

The most common disturbance observed in the case of plant hybrids is
pollen abortion.

Several cytoplasmic conditions which affect pollen production have been
identified in maize. However, the expression of these cytoplasmic conditions
is under genetic control. Environmental conditions such as humidity, day
length, and soil fertility also influence the system. As shown in Table 15–1

TABLE 15–1

TYPE	GENOTYPE	CYTOPLASMIC COMPONENT	PHENOTYPE
A	*ss*	sterile	pollen abortion
B	*ss*	fertile	normal pollen
C	*SS* or *Ss*	fertile	normal pollen
D	*SS* or *Ss*	sterile	normal pollen

pollen abortion occurs only when the cytoplasmic male sterility component
is present and pollen-restoring genes (symbolized by *S*) are absent. The
pollen-restoring genes have been shown not to be alleles of the various
"male-sterile" genes in maize which produce genetic abortion of pollen
which is independent of cytoplasmic influences. If restored sterile plants of
genotype *Ss* (type D in Table 15–1) are self-fertilized, one-fourth of the offspring will be *ss* in genotype, and these will have sterile anthers. Thus the
S gene does not produce a permanent change in the cytoplasm. By using
ears from plants of type A and pollinating with pollen from plants of type
B, pollen abortion can be propagated to all the progeny. A cross of this type
produces plants which are in effect " genetically detasseled." Such plants
are no longer hermaphroditic and can only be cross fertilized. In the production of commercial hybrid corn, crosses are made between two highly
inbred lines of corn. The F_1 hybrids show a uniform level of high grain yield.
Normally the P_1 plants must be detasseled to prevent self-fertilization, and
detasseling is a laborious procedure with very large populations of plants.
The genetic detasseling procedure outlined above has been exploited in the
production of commercial hybrid corn seed with great savings in time and
money.

15–1. Stabilized female *Drosophila* transmit σ to all their progeny. Male offspring when mated to CO_2-resistant females in turn produce F_1 females which yield sensitive and resistant offspring and F_1 males which produce only resistant offspring. What do you conclude from these findings?

15–2. Boycott and his colleagues detected a situation where reciprocal crosses give dissimilar results with respect to the inheritance of the direction of the coiling of the shells in *Limnea peregra,* a common, British, hermaphroditic snail. Normally the shell is coiled in a right-handed spiral (the dextral condition), but rarer, pure breeding, sinistral (left-handed spiral) races also exist. Reciprocal crosses between homozygous dextrals and sinistrals give the following results:

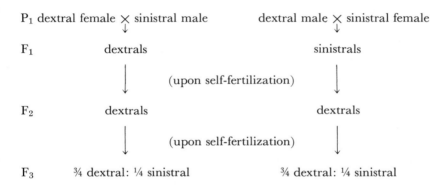

P_1 dextral female $\times$ sinistral male   dextral male $\times$ sinistral female

F_1 dextrals   sinistrals

          (upon self-fertilization)

F_2 dextrals   dextrals

          (upon self-fertilization)

F_3 ¾ dextral: ¼ sinistral   ¾ dextral: ¼ sinistral

Sturtevant explained these results by a very ingenious hypothesis. Can you?

15–3. Put forth a series of crosses which would demonstrate that CO_2 sensitivity in a certain strain of *Drosophila* is not chromosomally transmitted.

15–4. In *Drosophila subobscura* an autosomal recessive gene exists which has been called *grandchildless* (*gs*) by Spurway. When homozygous, *gs* produces no change in the phenotype of flies homozygous for it. In the progeny of *gs/gs* females, no matter by what father, all females have rudimentary ovaries and most males (98 per cent) have no testes at all. The *gs/gs* males are viable, fertile, and have grandchildren. Try to explain this sex-limited "delay in gene action."

15–5. An attempt was made to produce species hybrids between *Drosophila melanogaster* and *D. simulans.* The following results were obtained (see Sturtevant, 1929):

> *simulans* male x *melanogaster* female ⟶ 3210 females; 0 males
> *simulans* female x *melanogaster* male ⟶ 2110 males; 0 females

From these results what conclusions can you draw about the interactions between genome and cytoplasm?

15–6. Let us assume that a plant exists which shows patches of white and green tissue. White regions on these plants contain colorless plastids, whereas the green regions contain normal chloroplasts. Flowers from a colorless branch when fertilized by pollen from a branch bearing green plastids produce F_1 plants which contain colorless plastids, cannot photosynthesize, and die as seedlings. The reciprocal cross yields viable green seedlings. How can these results be explained?

15–7. According to Billingham when black skin from a black and white spotted guinea pig is grafted to a white area on the same individual there is an outward encroachment of pigmentation into the white skin from the margins of the graft. Such pigment spread occurs naturally in spotted cattle, pigs, sheep, and dogs (such as dalmatians). How can you account for pigment spread and how would you go about testing your hypothesis?

15–8. Fukasawa obtained an amphidiploid from the cross *Aegilops ovata* ♀ x *Triticum durum* ♂. A series of subsequent back crosses using *T. durum* as the pollen parent eliminated all *Aegilops* chromosomes, and only *Triticum* chromosomes were left. These plants with *Triticum* chromosomes in an *Aegilops* cytoplasm were male sterile. Discuss these results.

BIBLIOGRAPHY

Billingham, R. E., and W. K. Silvers   1960   The melanocytes of mammals. Quart. Rev. Biol. *35*: 1–40.

Bittner, J. A.   1958   Genetic concepts in mammary cancer in mice. Ann. New York Acad. Sc. *71*: 943–75.

Boycott, A. E.,C. Diver, S. L. Garstang, and F. M. Turner   1930   The inheritance of sinistrality in *Limnea peregra* (Mollusca, Pulmonata). Phil. Tr. Roy. Soc. *219B*: 51–131.

Brookhaven Symposia in Biology *11*   1959   The Photochemical Apparatus: Its Structure and Function.

Caspari, E.   1948   Cytoplasmic inheritance. Advances Genet. *2*: 2–68.

Cavalcanti, A. G. L., D. N. Falcao, and L. E. Castro   1958   The interaction of nuclear and cytoplasmic factors in the inheritance of the "sex-ratio" character in *Drosophila prosaltans*. Report 22 of the Centro de Pesquisas de Genetica da Faculdade Nacional de Filosofia da Universidade de Brasil, Rio de Janeiro.

Dippell, R. V.   1959   The fine structure of kappa in killer stock 51 *Paramecium aurelia*. J. Biophys. Biochem. Cytol. *4*: 125–8.

Ephrussi, B.   1953   Nucleo-cytoplasmic Relations in Microorganisms. Oxford University Press, London.

Fukasawa, H.   1953   Studies on restoration and substitution of nucleus in *Aegilotricum*. I. Appearance of male sterile durum in substitution crosses. Cytologia *18*: 167–75.

Granick, S.   1955   Plastid structure, development and inheritance. Encyclopedia of Plant Physiology *1*: 507–64. W. Ruhland, editor. Springer Verlag, Berlin.

Jones, D. F., H. T. Stinson, Jr., and U. Khoo   1957   Transmissible variations in the cytoplasm within species of higher plants. Proc. Nat. Acad. Sc. *43*: 598–602.

Jones, D. F.   1956   Genic and cytoplasmic control of pollen abortion in maize. Brookhaven Symposia in Biology 9: 101–12.

Kühn, A.   1936   Versuche über die Wirkungsweise der Erbanlagen. Naturwissenschaften 24: 177, 194, 280.

Lederberg, J.   1952   Cell genetics and hereditary symbiosis. Physiol. Rev. 32: 403–30.

L'Heritier, P. L.   1948   Sensitivity to CO_2 in Drosophila—a review. Heredity 2: 325–48.

L'Héritier, P. L.   1958   The hereditary virus of Drosophila. Advances Virus Res. 5: 195–245.

Lynch, C.   1919   An analysis of certain cases of intraspecific sterility. Genetics 4: 501–33. The behavior of fused is described here.

Malagolowkin, C., D. F. Poulson, and E. Y. Wright   1959   Experimental transfer of maternally inherited abnormal sex-ratio in Drosophila willistoni. Genetics 44: 59–74.

Michaelis, P.   1954   Cytoplasmic inheritance in Epilobium and its theoretical significance. Advances Genet. 6: 287–401.

Mitchell, M. B., and H. K. Mitchell   1952   A case of "maternal" inheritance in Neurospora crassa. Proc. Nat. Acad. Sc. 38: 442–9. (Description of "poky.")

Moore, D. H., E. Y. Lasfargues, M. R. Murray, C. D. Haagensen, and E. C. Pollard   1959   Correlation of physical and biological properties of mouse mammary tumor agent. J. Biophys. Biochem. Cytol. 5: 85–92.

Poulson, D. F., and B. Sakaguchi   1961   Nature of the "sex-ratio" agent in Drosophila. Science 133: 1489–90.

Poulson, D. F.   1962   Cytoplasmic inheritance and hereditary infection in Drosophila. In Methodology in Medical Genetics, vol. 3. Holt and Day, San Francisco.

Rhoades, M. M.   1955   Interaction of genic and non-genic hereditary units and the physiology of non-genic inheritance. In Encyclopedia of Plant Physiol. 1: 19–57. W. Ruhland, editor. Springer Verlag, Berlin.

Sonneborn, T. M.   1959   Kappa and related particles in Paramecium. Advances Virus Res. 6: 229–356.

Spurway, H. S.   1948   Genetics and cytology of D. subobscura. 4. An extreme example of delay in gene action, causing sterility. J. Genetics 49: 126–40.

Sturtevant, A. H.   1923   Inheritance of direction of coiling in Limnea. Science 58: 269–70.

Sturtevant, A. H.   1929   Contributions to the genetics of Drosophila simulans and Drosophila melanogaster. Publ. Carnegie Instn. 399: 1–62. Washington, D. C.

von Wettstein, D.   1959   Developmental changes in chloroplasts and their genetic control. In Developmental Cytology, pp. 123–60, ed. by D. Rudnick. Ronald Press, New York.

Wolken, J. J.   1959   The chloroplast and photosynthesis—a structural basis for function. Am. Scientist 47: 202–15.

Chapter **16**

Developmental Genetics

Introduction

In all biology no phenomenon is more exciting and puzzling than the development of an embryo. This process occurs with a fantastically precise ordering of a sequence of exquisitely complex events in space and time. Cells resulting from cleavage of a fertilized egg move about, differentiate into morphologically different types, and organize themselves into tissue and organ systems. Integration of the organ systems eventually yields an adult organism capable of reproducing its kind and possessing morphological, physiological, and behavioral characteristics which mark it as belonging to its own sex and species and to no other. The entire process is obviously a hereditary one, for on the same rock in the same tide pool, for example, barnacles and seaweeds develop side by side, each according to its own pattern, year in year out, generation after generation.

It has been demonstrated in many different species that in most instances each cell of which the multicellular organism is composed contains the same chromosomal complement. Evidence will be presented in this chapter showing that differentiation involves a continual interaction between nucleus and cytoplasm with the cytoplasm acting upon the nucleus so as to suppress (or stimulate) certain of its gene-controlled activities. Since the biochemical stratification of the cytoplasm is itself under genetic control there is produced an endless series of cycles of interaction between nucleus and cytoplasm during embryogenesis which results in a continual restriction of the alternative types of development any cell and its descendants can undergo. In situations where multicellular organisms have been well studied from both the embryological and the genetic standpoints (the fruit fly, silkworm, chicken, and mouse, for example) many mutants exist which are blocked at various steps in development. From studies on such developmental mutants we can gain some understanding of how normal genes control growth and form.

The genetic control of oogenesis

During oogenesis various complex materials are formed and subsequently localized in parts of the cytoplasm of the maturing egg. Work by experimental embryologists like Driesch, Morgan, Lillie, Wilson, Spemann, and Conklin at the turn of the century demonstrated that the position of the main organ areas of the embryo was often determined, directly or indirectly, by the characteristic distribution of cytoplasmic "morphogenetic" substances. Following oblation of a certain cytoplasmic area the developing embryo often exhibited deficiencies of certain tissue types.

That oogenesis is itself under genetic control is demonstrated by the fact that numerous mutants are known which when homozygous cause female sterility. In *Drosophila melanogaster,* for example, about 60 nonallelic, female sterile mutants have been reported, and cytological studies have been made by R. C. King and his colleagues on about two dozen mutants. Of these, 12 showed clear-cut abnormalities in the morphogenesis of the developing oocyte. The process of oogenesis in this insect has already been briefly outlined (p. 48). It will be recalled that the developing oocyte is nourished by a group of 15 daughter nurse cells. Intercommunication of cytoplasm between all members of the 16-cell cyst is made possible by large pores in the walls separating adjacent cells, and a continual flow of materials from the nurse cells to the oocyte occurs during vitellogenesis. A fact which

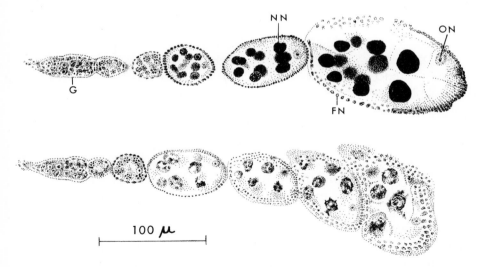

Figure 16–1   Drawings contrasting developing oocytes from (upper) wild type *Drosophila* and from (lower) flies homozygous for *singed*[36a]. The ovaries were treated according to the Feulgen whole mount procedure which stains only structures containing DNA. Note that the nurse cell nuclei of *sn*[36a] females are cytologically abnormal in that they contain reduced amounts of DNA. The oocyte nuclei and follicle cell nuclei are not affected. Vitellogenesis is markedly reduced in *sn*[36a] oocytes. G = germarium, N.N. = nurse cell nucleus, F.N. = follicle cell nucleus, O.N. = oocyte nucleus.

should be stressed is that the nurse cells are of maternal genotype. It appears that the wild type alleles of the genes *apterous, minus, tiny, diminutive, morula, female sterile 2.1, rotund, raspberry,* and *singed* play a direct or indirect role in vitellogenesis, since it is retarded to a greater or lesser extent in females homozygous for any of these mutants. In the case of the last five mutants the abnormalities in yolk production can be correlated with cytological changes in the nuclei of the nurse cells (see Fig. 16–1). It appears that further studies on mutations affecting oogenesis in different organisms will provide insight into the nature of the cytoplasmic localizations found in oocytes, their mode of origin, and their function during early embryogenesis.

Genes affecting cytological processes

In maize certain mutants are characterized by sticky chromosomes, abnormal behavior of spindles and centromeres, and by abnormal coiling of chromosomes. Also numerous mutants affecting meiosis in various ways have been described. In some mutant strains of corn the onset of meiosis is suppressed, in others cytokinesis during meiosis is abolished, or supernumary cell divisions may occur without chromosomal duplication. Conversely, in *Drosophila hydei* and in barley, mutants exist where supernumerary chromosomal duplications occur without cytokinesis or nuclear division. Asynaptic and desynaptic mutants are known in maize, wheat, the tomato, *Crepis, Datura,* and in different *Drosophila* species. In man and the rabbit, mutants are known which produce abnormal segmentation of the nuclei in specific tissues. In no instance is the mechanism of gene action understood, but the existence of mutants of the types described above demonstrates that the morphology and behavior of the chromosomes and the mitotic apparatus are under direct or indirect genetic control.

There are also many instances in which genes have been implicated in the control of cell proliferation. Tumors of species hybrids (presumably resulting from genic imbalance) have been described in mice, fish (see Fig. 16–2), and plants. Different related species and various races of a single species differ radically in cancer proneness, and such differences have in many cases a genetic basis. In mammals, Huxley has pointed out the extraordinary case of proneness to malignant melanomas exhibited by gray horses. The incidence of this type of uncontrolled multiplication of pigment cells is ten times higher in gray horses than in other breeds. In man, certain rare tumorous conditions (xeroderma pigmentosum, retinoblastoma, multiple intestinal polyposis, and multiple neurofibromatosis) have shown single factor inheritance. The pioneer work of Drs. Slye, Little, MacDowell,

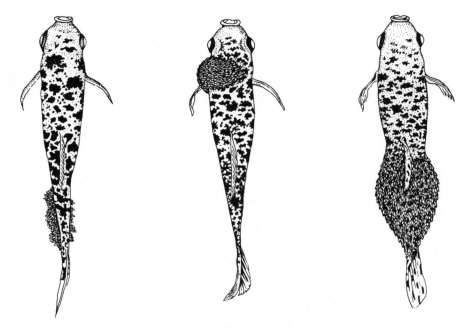

Figure 16–2 Melanotic tumors which have developed in hybrid fish produced by mating spotted platyfish (*Xiphophorous maculatus*) and Mexican swordtails (*X. helleri*). Shown at 1.5 × life size.
(Redrawn from M. Gordon, *Transactions of the N. Y. Academy of Sciences*, Series II, Vol. 15, 1953.)

and Strong has demonstrated the existence of large numbers of genes in the laboratory mouse which influence susceptibility to various types of cancer. In *Drosophila* three genes are known which cause uncontrolled cell proliferation in the ovaries of adults which results in sterility. The genes in question are *female-sterile* (*fes*) and *narrow²* (*nw²*) both of which have their loci on chromosome 2 and the sex-linked gene *fused* (*fu*). The *fes* and *nw²* females have ovaries which are completely tumorous from the time of eclosion (see Fig. 16–3); whereas freshly eclosed *fu* females show no tumors. Tumors begin to appear on the second day, and eventually the *fu* ovary becomes completely tumorous. In the case of *fu* a study of four alleles of independent origin by King, Burnett, and Staley demonstrated ovarian tumors in each case. Thus in every instance where the + allele of *fused* has undergone mutation, abnormal proliferation of cells in a specific tissue at a specific developmental period has followed.

In the case of the more common types of human cancer it is difficult to demonstrate a sizable hereditary component. Such demonstrations depend upon the construction of pedigrees, and this is difficult for a number of reasons. Diagnostic skills have changed markedly over the past 50 years,

Figure 16–3 Tumorous ovarian chambers in *Drosophila melanogaster* homozygous for the gene *female sterile*. The drawing is of a section stained with the basic dye, azure B. Distributed within some of the tumorous chambers are large cells with nuclei which resemble those of nurse cells. These nuclei contain large nucleoli and banded polytene chromosomes. The tumors are often surrounded by a follicular epithelium.

and it is difficult to know what weight to give to the causes of death stated in death certificates of a generation or two ago. Certain types of cancer are so common that they may appear in one family group purely by chance, and so give a spurious suggestion of a hereditary predisposition to the disease. Furthermore, members of a family share not only genes but social patterns and dietary habits which may influence cancer-proneness both positively and negatively. However, human twin statistics provide decisive evidence of a genetic component in cancer susceptibilty. Here identical (one-egg) and fraternal (two-egg) twins are contrasted with respect to concordance or discordance of cancer. When both twins of the pair develop cancer the pair is said to show concordance, whereas if only one member develops the disease the twins are said to be discordant. Concordance of cancer in identical twins is generally double that found in dizygotic twins. However, the fact that 40 per cent of monozygotic twins are discordant demonstrates that environmental influences likewise play an important role in carcinogenesis.

Evidence for nuclear differentiation

Circumstantial evidence for nuclear differentiation during development has come from direct observations on the polytene chromosomes of developing dipterans. It will be recalled that certain regions of certain chromosomes in the cells of specific tissues undergo reversible changes in circumference during larval development (Fig. 2–7), whereas in other tissues the same chromosomal segment remains quiescent. These puffs presumably represent areas of intense chromosomal synthesis of compounds required during specific developmental stages.

A second line of evidence comes from direct chemical analyses of nuclei from various differentiated tissues. Here one finds variations in the amount of RNA and of nonhistone proteins between different tissues and within the same tissue at different stages of development or under different physiological conditions. On the other hand the DNA-histone content remains remarkably constant in the different somatic cells of the organism.

The most direct evidence for nuclear differentiation during the development of multicellular organisms comes from the nuclear transplantation studies of R. Briggs and T. J. King (see Fig. 16–4 *upper*). Using the frog *Rana pipiens,* they developed a method for enucleating eggs and subsequently injecting them with nuclei from cells at various stages of development. The nature of the ensuing development of the injected egg revealed the character of the transplanted nucleus. The first experiments involved the injection of nuclei from frog blastulae into enucleated eggs. Such eggs

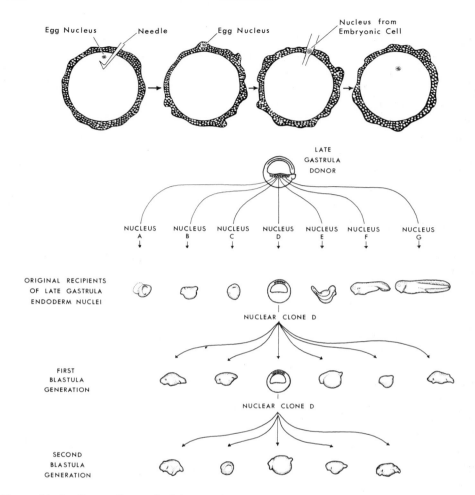

Figure 16–4 Upper: The method for enucleating an egg and subsequently injecting it with a diploid nucleus from an embryonic cell.   (Redrawn from Maurice Sussman, *Animal Growth and Development,* copyright 1960, Prentice-Hall, Inc., Englewood Cliffs, N. J.)

Lower: A diagrammatic representation of the results of experiments involving the serial transplantation of endoderm nuclei. Nuclei are first transferred from endodermal cells of a late gastrula into enucleated eggs. Here the donated nuclei promote the various types of development shown for the "original recipients" in the diagram. One of the original recipients upon reaching the blastula stage provides nuclei for a new series of transfers, and one of these recipients upon reaching the blastula stage provides nuclei for still another generation. The individuals from such "nuclear clones" develop in a more uniformly abnormal manner than did the original recipients of gastrula nuclei.

(Redrawn from Briggs and King, Cold Spring Harbor Symposium on Quantitative Biology *21*: 227, 1956.)

completed normal embryonic and larval development which indicated that blastula nuclei are undifferentiated and equivalent to the zygote nucleus at the beginning of development. However, when cells from embryos in the late gastrula stages of development were used to provide the nuclei, the embryos which resulted ceased to develop at a certain stage and showed marked deficiencies of certain cell types. In the late gastrula the main organ areas are laid down and display determination with respect to the general type of tissue. The transplantation experiments show that late gastrula nuclei are not equivalent to the nucleus of the egg or to blastula nuclei. Furthermore, nuclei from cells of differently determined regions when transplanted into enucleated eggs produce embryos composed mainly of cells of the same type as donated the nucleus and containing subnormal amounts of other cell types. That these nuclear differentiations are stable has been shown by serial transplantations (see Fig. 16–4 *Lower*). Such experiments involve first the transfer of nuclei from endodermal cells of late gastrulae to enucleated eggs. One of the original recipients upon reaching the blastula stage is sacrificed and provides nuclei for a new series of transfers. These recipients upon reaching the blastula stage are sacrificed and provide nuclei for still another generation, and so on. The individuals developing from such nuclear clones develop in a uniformly abnormal fashion. Here then is clear-cut evidence that nuclei become progressively modified as development proceeds, that the modification is often a stable one, and that it constitutes restriction of the alternative types of differentiation the nucleus can induce.

Cellular differentiation and protein synthesis

Cellular differentiation must involve transformations of protein populations. After all, the morphological changes seen during the differentiation of embryonic cells are manifestations of specific sorts of protein synthesis, since proteins are known to serve as the framework for all sorts of structural entities in tissues. Using the methods of enzymology and immunochemistry, numerous workers have shown in organisms as different as echinoderms, amphibians, and birds that specific changes in serologically detectable proteins and in patterns of enzyme activity occur during embryogenesis. The fact that certain adult cells contain specialized proteins suggests that tissue specificity extends to the molecular level. Among the better known examples of proteins specific for certain tissues are: the hemoglobin of the erythrocyte, insulin of the pancreatic beta cell, actin, myosin and tropomyosin of the muscle fiber, and α-crystallin of the lens.

From the foregoing discussion it should be obvious that to understand cellular differentiation we must discover how restrictions are placed upon the alternative types of protein synthesis that cells can undertake. Some of the most pertinent information on this subject comes from studies on the genetics of induced enzyme formation.

Intergenic regulation

It is a well-documented fact that the enzymes found in living organisms can be subdivided into two classes: *constitutive* and *inducible*. Constitutive enzymes are always produced irrespective of environmental conditions; whereas inducible enzymes are synthesized only in response to the presence of inducers. The inducers are nearly always substrates for the enzymes they induce. The ability of an organism to manufacture many enzymes only when they are needed is obviously useful from the standpoint of economy.

Recently Pardee, Jacob, and Monod have reported work that sheds considerable light on the difference between inducible and constitutive enzyme systems. In *Escherichia coli,* strain K 12, three closely linked genes (*y, i,* and *z*) play a role in the metabolism of a class of sugars called β-galactosides. The capacity to synthesize galactoside permease, an enzyme responsible for allowing galactosides to enter the cell, is controlled by the + allele of gene *y.* The capacity to synthesize intracellular β-galactosidase, an enzyme responsible for the hydrolysis of β-galactosides, is controlled by the + allele of gene *z.* The + allele of gene *i* which resides between genes *y* and *z* is responsible for the inducibility of the two enzymes. In the presence of the inactive allele of *i* the enzymes function in the constitutive sense. Pardee, Jacob, and Monod have shown that gene *i* in its active form controls the synthesis of a product which when present in the cytoplasm specifically inhibits either primarily or secondarily the action of the genes adjacent to it unless inducer is present in the environment. The inducer in this case is the substrate, β-galactose. Thus when the inactive allele of *i* is present β-galactosidase and galactoside permease are formed continuously. The above workers suggest that the $+^i$ gene synthesizes a chemical repressor which is antagonized by the inducer. If such findings are confirmed in other organisms, the *E. coli* system may lead to a generalizable picture of the regulation of the synthesis of proteins. According to this scheme, genes would exist whose function is to regulate the expression of neighboring genes according to environmental conditions. We can only guess at present how gene-produced repressors work. Perhaps these inhibitors form a coating over the genes they regulate and so prevent their action. McClintock's *Ac-Ds* system (see p. 186) may represent such a regulatory system which is functioning abnormally. The effect of heterochromatin upon euchromatic genes (see p. 146) again gives us a hint that intergenic regulation although best understood in microorganisms may be working in multicellular plants and animals. A system of the sort outlined above could be responsible for dosage compensation (see p. 175).

In the adult organism we find cells such as those of nervous tissue which never divide, cells such as those of liver, which never divide unless called upon to regenerate damaged material, and cells which continually divide (such as the erythrocyte mother cells of the bone marrow). Most adult cells face to different degrees the problem of how to *avoid* duplicating in the presence of an abundance of those substances needed for cell duplication. Presumably an elaborate system of checks and balances operates in the nucleus to prevent proliferation. When this system is disturbed by spontaneous, chemically induced or radiation-induced damage to the genetic material or by viral attack, the cell may start dividing and transmit to its progeny the ability of unrestrainable proliferation. It follows that studies that seek to discover the chemical mechanisms whereby activity of nuclear genes can be regulated by products from other genes, by viruses, or by cytoplasmic influences are of great practical importance. Once these processes are understood, they can be mimicked, and by mimicking gene action man will find the cure to many of the diseases that plague his species.

The cytoplasmic control of nuclear differentiation

Sonneborn and his students have studied this phenomenon as it pertains to the control of mating type in *Paramecium aurelia*. As mentioned earlier (p. 53), during the mating reaction, cells of different mating types bump into each other in the course of random swimming movements, and the cilia of the different animals adhere. Such clumping is followed by conjugation. The exconjugants contain diploid nuclei of identical genotype; yet their mating types remain unaffected unless transfer of appreciable amounts of cytoplasm has occurred between the members of the pair. In this case both members of the pair form clones, all of which belong to one mating type. Sonneborn has shown that the immature macronucleus when developing in cytoplasm of a particular genotype is irreversibly determined to produce that mating type in the future. An immature macronucleus of identical genotype can be determined to produce an alternate mating type, if it undergoes its development in cytoplasm of the alternate type. When two types of cytoplasm are mixed one suppresses the other, and nuclei differentiate in accordance with the unsuppressed cytoplasmic factor. However, once the macronucleus has matured it is no longer susceptible to the action of the cytoplasmic factors and is itself responsible for what cytoplasmic factors are produced. These studies demonstrate that cytoplasmic factors can regulate nuclear action by deciding which of a set of alternative phenotypes the nucleus will produce. At different times the nucleus causes cytoplasmic differentiation and the cytoplasm causes nuclear differentiation. Such a sequence of cycles of nuclear and cytoplasmic interaction undoubtedly plays a major role in the differentiation of multicellular organisms.

Visible manifestations of the cytoplasmic control of the activity of specific chromosomal regions have been detected by Kroeger. In this study, salivary gland nuclei from larvae of *Drosophila busckii* were transplanted into exudates formed by rupturing early embryos of *Drosophila melanogaster* at different stages of development. Different regions of the polytene chromosomes responded to their new cytoplasmic environments in specific fashions, which demonstrates that chromosomal puffing may occur as a reaction to extragenic cytoplasmic conditions.

Nuclear control of cytoplasmic differentiation

Hammerling's studies of regeneration patterns in *Acetabularia* serve as a good illustration of the nuclear control of cytoplasmic morphology. The Acetabulariae are unicellular green algae commonly found in tropical and subtropical seas. Each mature toadstool-shaped cell consists of a large, complicated fruiting body (generally called the cap or hat) connected by a stalk to a root-like process which attaches it to the substratum (see Fig. 16–5). The nucleus lies at the base of the stalk. The cap of *Acetabularia mediterranea* is umbrella-like, whereas that of *A. crenulata* is deeply indented. Hammerling demonstrated that grafting a stem of *A. crenulata* to the nucleated base of *A. mediterranea* results in the regeneration of a hat similar to *A. mediterranea*. In the reciprocal experiment the hat resembled *A. crenulata*. It is obvious therefore that the nucleus controls the developmental pattern of the cytoplasmic cap.

Cytoplasmic self-regulation

Evidence has been presented that the nucleus can regulate itself in response to changes in its cytoplasmic environment, that the nucleus can itself regulate its cytoplasmic environment, and that the cytoplasm in turn can cause nuclear differentiation. Finally, the cytoplasm can often act in a self-regulatory fashion independent of the nucleus. Many instances are known where the activity of the initial enzyme in a chain of enzymatic reactions is inhibited by the final product. Thus, when the internal pool of the product reaches a certain critical concentration the entire synthetic process is shut off. In a population of cells a constant interaction is taking place where the synthetic processes of certain cell types stimulate or suppress specific reactions occurring in their neighbors.

Figure 16–5   *Acetabularia.* The umbrellalike cap of each organism is about 8 mm. in diameter.
(Courtesy of the General Biological Supply House, Inc., Chicago.)

The time of gene action

Developmental geneticists often start their analyses with some easily detectable collection of morphological abnormalities known to originate as the result of a single gene mutation, and then try to trace back, in terms of descriptive and chemical embryology, the pathological effects to their earliest appearance. An example of such an analysis is the study by Lees and Waddington of the effects of the third chromosomal dominant gene *Hairless* (*H*), which is lethal when homozygous but which in the heterozygous condition eliminates certain bristles from body surface of *Drosophila*. Each bristle organ consists of three cells: the bristle cell, the socket cell which secretes the ring which encloses the bristle, and a sensory nerve cell whose process ends near the base of the bristle. All three cells are daughters which arise from a single ancestral epidermal cell. In *Hairless* individuals the two cells of the bristle apparatus *both* differentiate into socket cells and as a consequence no bristle is produced. The reason that there is no bifurcation in differentiation is thought to be that in *Hairless* individuals the two cells lie side by side, instead of one lying on the outside and the other on the inside of the differentiating epidermis. The fact that the cells lie side by side may be due to the plane of cell division being perpendicular instead of parallel to the layer of epidermis. Perhaps the plane of division was shifted because of modifications of the viscosity of the cytoplasm caused in some mysterious way by the *H* gene.

A study which traces development backward in a mutant as illustrated above shows the time when the lack of the substance normally elaborated by the + allele becomes critical. Such a finding does not necessarily imply that the normal gene is inactive prior to that time, however. A discussion of the mutant *rosy* (*ry*) of *Drosophila* is illustrative in this respect. The mutant was originally picked up because of its effect upon eye color. Homozygous *ry* individuals have brownish eyes because they do not form the bright red pigments (see p. 241), but can form the xanthommatins (see Fig. 14–2). The bright red pigments are laid down in the developing compound eye during the pupal period, and consequently a student of morphogenesis might suspect that the $+^{ry}$ gene is inactive prior to this time. However, as a result of biochemical studies on this mutant by Hadorn, Mitchell, Forest, and Glassman it was found that flies of the *ry* genotype lacked the enzyme xanthine dehydrogenase. If the + allele of *ry* is responsible for the formation of xanthine dehydrogenase, then whenever this enzyme is detected the $+^{ry}$ gene must be active. Since the enzyme has been detected in wild type individuals at all developmental stages, the gene is obviously active throughout the entire life of the insect.

Deficiencies and development

There is very good evidence that many genes are not essential for the achievement of a certain developmental process. For example, Poulson studied embryogenesis in *Drosophila* males missing the left half of the X-chromosome and found that an apparently normal blastoderm was formed. After this performance the separation of germ layers failed, and development came to a standstill. It follows that the many genetic loci missing in the deficiency had no essential functions with respect to those developmental steps preceding the lethal effect. At the same time a study of the effect of deletions and inactivations of different chromosomal regions has proven the existence of genes which are essential for almost every step in embryonic development (see Fig. 16–6). Studies by Hadorn and others have uncovered numerous mutants that block development at post-embry-onic stages as well. A comparative study of these lethal factors has led to the conclusion that there exist along the developmental time axis sensitive periods during which there is an enhanced chance that genetic malfunction will bring development to a standstill. In *Drosophila* these sensitive periods correspond to the onset of embryonic, larval, pupal, or adult development, and it is during such periods that many new systems are differentiated and put to immediate test.

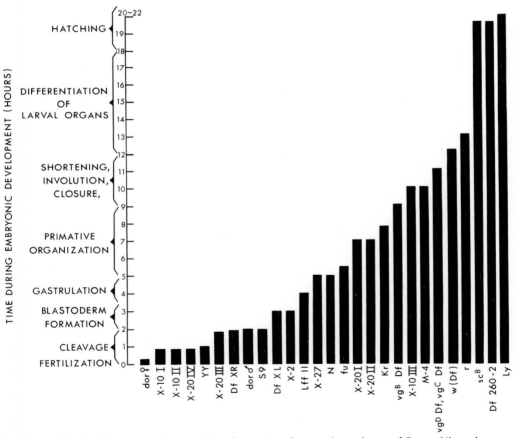

Figure 16–6 The amount of normal development undergone by embryos of *Drosophila melanogaster* homozygous or hemizygous for various specified deficiencies or lethal genes.

(After D. F. Poulson.)

Genes and cellular dynamics

Paul Weiss has compared the organism to a system of concentric shells (see Fig. 16–7) with the gene occupying a central position. The gene is enclosed in the chromosome, the chromosome in the nucleus, the nucleus in the cytoplasm of the cell, which in turn forms part of a tissue, which forms part of the organism, which is surrounded by the external environment. The point Weiss makes is that no external agent can influence an inner shell except through the mediation of the shells in between which may or may not modify the factor during its transit between the shells. Similarly, materials produced within inner shells (by genes, for example) may not reach outer shells as such, but may be screened to varying degrees or altered chemically during their transit. The student when exposed to the statement that a given gene "controls" the production of a particular feature of the organism should keep in mind Weiss's remark that the gene

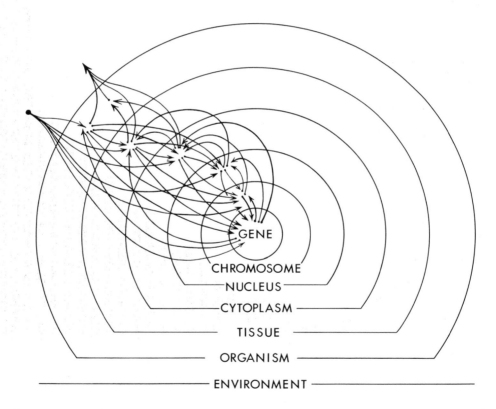

Figure 16–7   A diagram of the network of possible interactions in an organism.
(Redrawn with the permission of the American Physical Society, from P. Weiss, *Reviews of Modern Physics,* 1959, Vol. 31, Number 1.)

can operate "only through interactions with outer shells, which in them-selves have become progressively modified in their long developmental history by countless chains of interactions with other shells, including, of course, the innermost, the gene."

When we think in terms of such complex systems, the observations that many mutations produce manifold effects (are pleiotropic) become far less mysterious. Examples of such pleiotropic genes have already been described (*fused*, see pp. 250, 265, and 289; and the sickle-cell gene, see Fig. 14–3). In mice an example of a pleiotropic gene is *mb* (*myelencephalic blebs*). Indi-viduals homozygous for this gene show abnormalities in the growth of hair, clubbed feet or feet with extra toes, and eye defects which range from the lack of an eyelid to complete absence of the eye. Such abnormalities arise because during embryonic development fluid which normally is drained off from the neural canal through a temporary opening of the brain is secreted in excessive amounts or is not resorbed sufficiently by the surrounding tissue. As a result fluid accumulates to form blisters under the skin at various regions of the body and interferes with normal development at these points. How the normal allele of *mb* controls fluid balance in the mouse is as yet a mystery.

Again when thinking in terms of the complex system diagrammed in Figure 16–7 one would predict that the form and function of any organ whether as simple as a bristle or as complex as a gonad must be directly influenced by dozens of genes. That such is the case is borne out by looking through a catalogue of some 450 nonallelic mutants of *Drosophila melano-gaster* which produce modifications of adult structure and function. Forty-seven mutants affecting bristle pattern, 54 affecting bristle morphology, 63 affecting eye color, 76 affecting eye morphology, 142 producing sterility in one or both sexes, and 222 affecting wing morphology were found to occur.

Embryonic induction

In 1922 Hans Spemann and Hilde Mangold, his student, undertook a series of experiments which was to demonstrate that a living part of an embryo can exert a morphogenetic stimulus upon another part and so bring about its morphological differentiation. For these experiments a darkly pigmented and an albino species of salamander were used. Tissue from the upper lip of the blastopore of an early gastrula of the albino species was transferred to the belly of a pigmented embryo of the same stage. In this embryo, gastrulation occurred at *each* place with ectodermal cells on the top side migrating over the embryo's own blastoporal lip and those on the underside migrating over the transplanted blastoporal lip into the mesodermal layer beneath. Development proceeded, and eventually there developed two perfect axial systems, each containing a spinal column and associated structures. Eventually Siamese-twin baby salamanders were formed. Since the tissues of the extra salamander arising from the implant contained sectors of pigmented and nonpigmented cells, it was obvious that the tissue transplanted from the albino embryo had extended its organizing power to multiplying cells of the host. Spemann named the active tissue of the upper blastoporal lip the "organizer" and supposed that the entire process of development was directed by a succession of different organizers producing chains of inductions upon adjacent tissues (see Fig. 16–8). Subsequently it was shown that the process whereby organizers induce the formation of new embryonic rudiments consists of a reaction between the target tissues and specific, labile, poorly diffusible, proteinaceous inductors produced by the organizers.

Genic effects upon organizer systems

From the foregoing account one would expect developmental abnormalities to arise, if organizer and inducible tissue fail to make contact. Also, if the inductor fails to be produced (or is produced in abnormally small or large amounts or is qualitatively modified) or if the inducible tissue fails to respond (or responds excessively) to the inductor, abnormal development might ensue.

For an example of a genetically controlled modification of development arising from failure of organizer and inducible tissue to make contact we may turn to a discussion of a gene in the mouse called *Danforth's short tail* (*Sd*). Mice heterozygous for this gene show a variety of abnormalities of the kidney and ureter. During embryogenesis the developing ureter is thought to act as an organizer which induces the formation of a portion of the kidney. In *Sd/+* individuals, however, the ureteric bud fails to elongate, to branch properly, or to make proper contact with the nephrogenic mesenchyme which it normally induces to form Bowman's capsules and the secretory tubules of the kidney. As a result the kidney is reduced in size or is absent in the mice of this genotype.

The question often arises as to whether a given tissue rudiment from an embryo of a particular mutant genotype develops abnormally because of its failure to respond to certain diffusible factors which are present in adequate amounts or because these growth substances are not formed in the necessary concentrations by the mutant. Transplantations of mutant organ rudiments to wild type environments (and vice versa) will often decide this question one way or the other. Most chickens which are homozy-

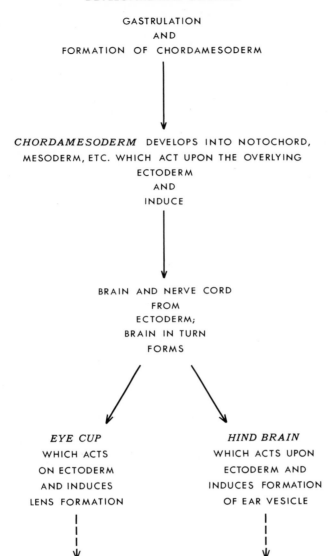

Figure 16-8   An example of organizers acting in a chain.   (Reprinted with permission from
R. P. Wagner and H. K. Mitchell, *Genetics and Metabolism,* copyright 1955, John Wiley & Sons, Inc.)

gous for the *Creeper* gene (*Cp*) die as embryos during the third or fourth
day of incubation, but some survive until almost the end of the incubation
period. These individuals show extreme malformations of the limbs and
eye abnormalities of a less severe nature. In transplants *Cp* limbs behave
autonomously; whereas the *Cp* eye primordia develop normally when trans-

planted to normal hosts. Here then is an example where in a mutant organism abnormal development occurs because of subcritical amounts of growth factors. Yet when these factors are made available in concentrations suitable for wild type tissues certain specific tissues fail to respond to them while others do.

In the chick the limb forms from a mound of mesoderm covered by ectoderm. Zwilling by suitable transplantation experiments has shown that, in the case of a polydactylous mutant, mesoderm induces in the ectodermal component a ridge which is excessively large and from which excessive numbers of digits develop. Presumably in this case excessive amounts of inductor are elaborated by the inducing mesoderm.

The *homeotic mutants* of *Drosophila melanogaster* are characterized by the transformation of an organ from its usual form to that of a homologous organ characteristic of a neighboring segment (see Fig. 16–9). Thus in the case of *aristapedia* the arista of the antenna is transformed to a leg, in *Antennapedia* the antenna itself becomes a leg, in *proboscipedia* mouth parts are changed into leglike organs, in *tetraptera* and *bithorax* the halteres are changed into winglike appendages, and in *tetraltera* the reverse transformation occurs. These mutants all seem to have their loci in the middle of chromosome 3. Waddington has suggested that these striking morphogenetic abnormalities may arise from the production of a modified inductor by mutant organizers or by a changed response of the mutant imaginal disk to a normal inductor.

Genes and growth hormones

Instances of morphological and physiological abnormalities resulting from the inability of certain mutants to synthesize hormones are fairly common, and in fact one has already been discussed (genetic goitrous cretinism). In several plant species mutants are known which are deficient in their ability to synthesize the growth hormone *gibberellic acid*. Such plants grow as dwarfs unless supplied with gibberellic acid from an external source. Mice homozygous for the autosomal recessive gene *dw* are dwarfs because the anterior pituitary fails to produce *growth hormone* (see Fig. 16–10). Normal growth of such mice may be obtained by giving them daily injections of extracts from normal anterior pituitary glands.

In *Drosophila* certain lethal mutants are known (*l* (2) *gl*, for example) which are characterized by malfunction of the ring gland which in diptera plays a key role in larval growth, molting, and metamorphosis. Variations in the genetic control of the production of the juvenile hormone may be

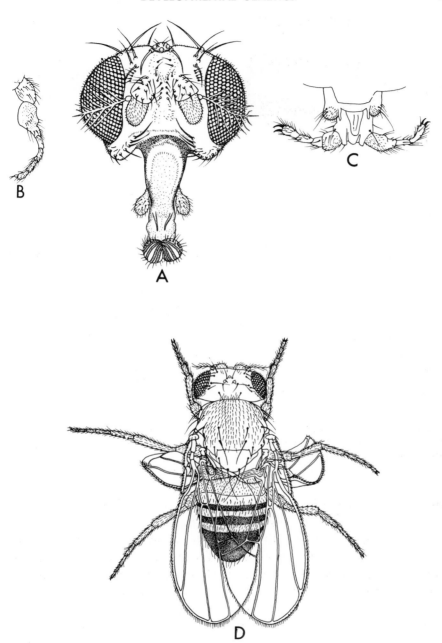

Figure 16-9   Homeotic mutants of *Drosophila melanogaster*. (A) Frontal view of a normal head. (B) The leglike antenna of *aristapedia*. (C) The proboscis of *proboscipedia* showing a pair of leglike structures. (D) *Bithorax*; in this mutant male the halteres are changed into winglike appendages.

(After Stern.)

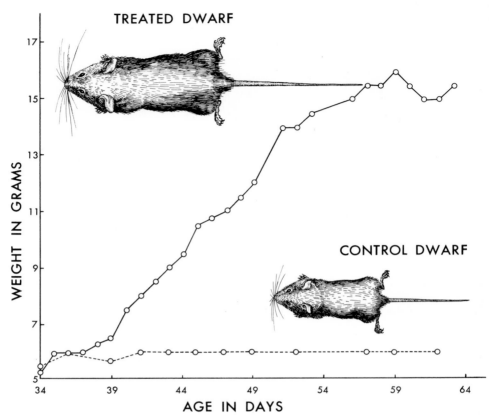

Figure 16–10 The relation between weight and age for hereditary dwarf mice. The control dwarf fails to grow; whereas the litter mate which received daily injections of pituitary gland extracts from normal mice grows normally.

responsible for races of silkworms which undergo one less or one more molt than the four larval molts customary for *Bombyx mori.*

Morphological abnormalities may also arise from an abnormal distribution of a normal growth hormone. Van Overbeek has reported a mutant strain of maize called "lazy" which is characterized by a stalk which grows flat on the ground (see Fig. 16–11). This curious growth habit is due to the fact that indole acetic acid, the plant hormone, remains evenly distributed throughout the stalk. Normally indole acetic acid accumulates on the lower side of a horizontal plant stem and stimulates cell elongation in this region which causes the tip of the stem to turn upward.

Genetic control of patterns in time and space

It will be recalled (p. 47) that during insect metamorphosis many larval tissues undergo histolysis, and that simultaneously imaginal disks

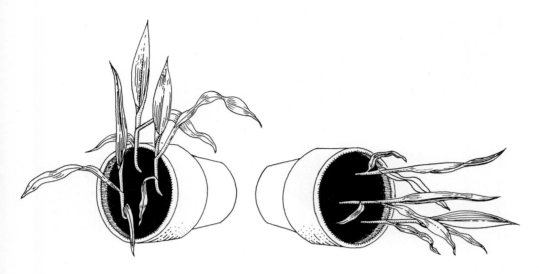

Figure 16-11   Normal (left) and *lazy* (right) maize plants showing contrasting growth habits. Potted seedlings were placed on their sides for a two-month period. *Lazy* plants continue to grow in the way they started (indifferent to the pull of gravity). Normal plants grow away from the gravitational pull of the earth (exhibit negative geotropism).   (After Van Overbeek.)

grow to produce the adult organs. The individuals of certain *Drosophila* strains are characterized by aggregations of blackened cells (often misnamed *melanotic tumors*). Normally these pseudotumors become visible relatively late in larval life (see Fig. 16–12) and persist throughout the adult period. Rizki has shown that in the pseudotumorous strains tu^W and mt^A the "tumors" result from encapsulation and subsequent melanization during the larval stage of certain tissues by a type of blood cell called the lamellocyte. Those tissues which become encapsulated have undergone a precocious histolysis. Thus the genotype responsible for "tumor formation" actually results in an asynchrony of developmental rates between different tissues, and the development of tissues in certain regions of the organism has been moved forward in time.

Pigment patterns in vertebrates often arise as the consequence of the migratory movements of pigment cells. Dalton has shown that migratory behavior of pigment cells is genetically regulated. By a series of transplantation experiments he was able to demonstrate that the initial effect of the *white* gene in the axolotl is exerted *not* on the pigment cells but rather on the embryonic tissues through which pigment cells must migrate from their point of origin. Somehow the tissue environment is modified so that migration of pigment cells is inhibited, and as a result the tissue fails to develop pigment.

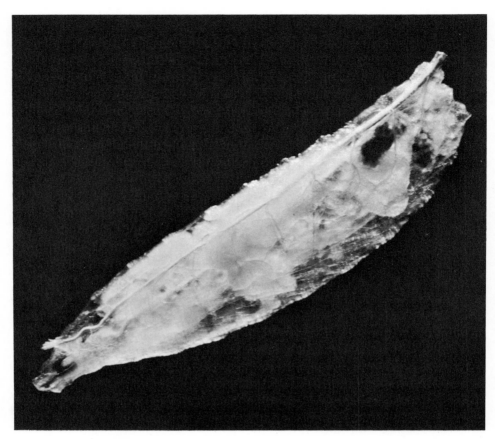

Figure 16–12　A photomicrograph of a third instar larva from the tu^W strain of *Drosophila melanogaster*. Note the blackened pseudotumor in the posterior portion of the animal below the tracheal trunk.

Some 40 bristles grow in a specific pattern from the dorsal surface of the head and thorax of *Drosophila melanogaster* (see front end paper). The bristle pattern must be inherited, since it is constant enough to be useful in taxonomical considerations. As Stern and Hannah-Alava have pointed out, the origin of such patterns must involve an interaction between the cells which differentiate into bristles and a "prepattern" which is superimposed upon the population of hypodermal cells which cover the dorsal surface of the insect. The origin of such "prepatterns" or "embryonic fields" is one of the great mysteries facing the embryologist. These fields cannot be defined in terms of their physical or chemical properties as yet, but only by their ability to incite regional differentiations. Normally, differentiation of a bristle organ occurs in a limited region of a "bristle field," and once differentiation has occurred no other differentiations are allowed within this region. As a result bristles are found certain distances apart. If the differentiation of a bristle organ is prevented from occurring at its characteristic site, however, then a bristle may arise in a neighboring region where bristles normally do not occur. Thus the embryonic field is plastic and capable of regulation to a certain degree.

In *Drosophila* many mutants are known in which specific bristles are missing. Stern and Hannah-Alava have demonstrated from a masterful analysis of induced genetic mosaics that many of these genes do not affect the prepattern but rather control the competence of the hypodermal cells to respond or not to respond to the physical or chemical inhomogeneities which represent the prepattern. A second group of mutants is known (*extra sex comb, esc; Polycomb, Pc;* and *Extra sex comb, Scx*) that produces sex combs on the second and third legs of males (see p. 48). Hannah-Alava has presented convincing evidence that these genes act by changing the prepattern of the embryonic legs. Subsequently, cells of male genotype respond to the changed pattern by the formation of sex comb teeth. It seems likely that the *transformer gene* (see p. 171) and the homeotic mutants represent even more extreme cases of genetically induced changes in prepattern systems.

Genetics and behavior

Inherited, stereotyped patterns of behavior are often just as characteristic of a given species as are its morphological attributes. Such a stereotyped behavior pattern is shown by the worker honey bee who gives her hive companions information as to the location of a new, rich source of food by means of a dance performed on the vertical honeycomb of the dark hive. Von Frisch has shown that by standardized variations in the choreography she indicates the relative distance between the hive and the food source and in which direction her companions must fly to seek the food. Furthermore, different species of *Apis* and different subspecies of *A. mellifera* can be distinguished by specific differences in the dances performed. Thus the "language" of the bees comes in a variety of "dialects." The web-spinning behavior of the spider constitutes another example of an inherited behavior pattern. So unique is the web spun by different species of spiders that the web pattern can aid the taxonomist in classifying the arachnid.

Although much of behavior has a hereditary component, the mechanisms involved are far from clear. Genes could exercise an effect upon behavior through positive or negative influences upon the endocrine systems, through modifications of the anatomy and physiology of the sense organs or the nerves innervating the voluntary or involuntary muscles, or by direct action upon the biochemistry of the central nervous system. Since sexuality is a hereditary characteristic, certain patterns of behavior distin-

Figure 16–13 A graphical representation of the results of experiments carried out by R. C. Tryon on the inheritance of maze-learning ability in rats. Members of an unselected sample of rats were tested with respect to the number of times they entered blind alleys while passing through a specialized maze. Each rat was given 19 consecutive trials. "Bright" rats (those making few mistakes) were mated to other bright individuals; "dull" rats were mated to other dull individuals. Similar tests were carried out on the progeny of each group, and the experiment was extended for eight generations. Note that by generation 8 there is virtually no overlap in maze performance between the bright and dull groups.   (Redrawn from J. L. Fuller and W. R. Thompson, *Behavior Genetics*, 1960, John Wiley and Sons, Inc.)

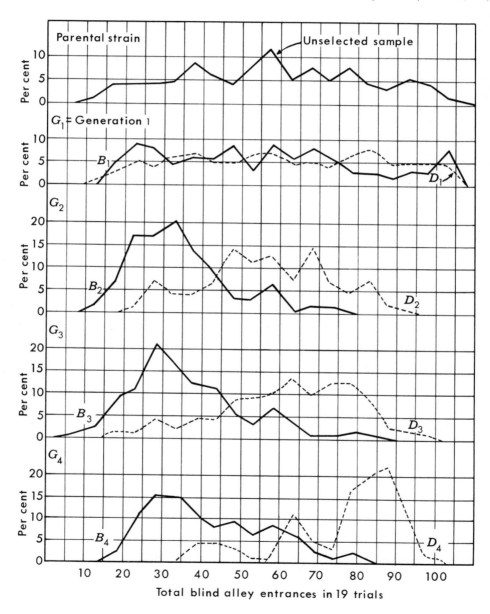

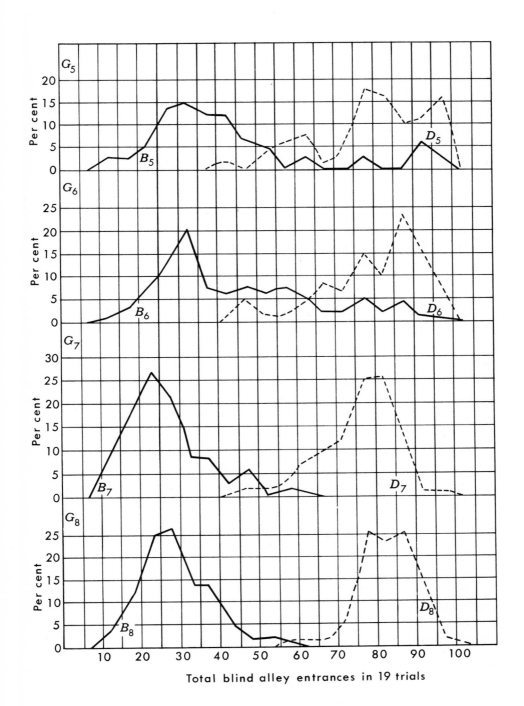

Total blind alley entrances in 19 trials

guishing males from females are inherited. In this sense the *transformer gene* of *Drosophila melanogaster* has a most marked effect upon behavior.

It has been demonstrated many times that selective breeding can influence certain behavioral traits both positively and negatively (see Fig. 16–13). In the case of wild birds the tendency of the female to show the desire to incubate eggs is an essential aspect of the reproductive process. In domesticated fowl it has proved more desirable, however, to keep hens laying and to hatch fertilized eggs in incubators. As a consequence poultrymen have attempted successfully to reduce the incubation habit (broodiness) by selection. Hutt has pointed out that over the years the proportion of hens showing broodiness in a flock of Rhode Island Reds was reduced by negative selection from 91 per cent to 2 per cent. While it is known that the urge to incubate eggs results from the action of the anterior pituitary hormone prolactin, the genetic basis of the characteristic differences in the degree of broodiness between various breeds of chickens is unknown.

Over a hundred breeds of dogs are now recognized by the American Kennel Club. These breeds all result from human selection of different characteristics, which has been going on during a good portion of the 8000-year period which has elapsed since the domestication of wolves. Selective breeding has led to a great increase in the expression of genetic variability, an earlier sexual maturity, and a decreasing wildness. Not only do different breeds of dogs differ greatly in morphology (contrast the Chihuahua and the St. Bernard) but in behavior as well, since selection for learning of specialized tasks has been carried further in dogs than in any other species. Scott has shown that genetically controlled differences in the behavior of dogs affect emotional traits such as aggressiveness, motivational traits such as response to rewards, and sensory and motor abilities as well.

Geneticists have often noted that certain mutations exercise among their pleiotropic effects modifications in behavior. Thus the genes *white* and *yellow* affect the courtship behavior of *Drosophila*. Certain mutants in the mouse influence tameness. In man many inherited abnormalities in metabolism (phenylketonuria and amaurotic idiocy are examples) lead to marked deficiencies in intellectual ability.

Twin studies in man have shown a much higher concordance between identical twins than between fraternal twins for epilepsy and various conditions, like schizophrenia, characterized by psychotic behavior patterns. It is also fairly well established that identical twins resemble each other in intelligence more than do fraternal twins. The correlation between members of pairs on intelligence tests is greater for identical twins reared apart than for ordinary siblings reared together. Thus intelligence represents a basic inherited capacity, but this capacity can be greatly and permanently influenced by environmental stimulation, particularly during early life.

16–1. The $C\,l\,B$ and y^4 chromosomes contain inversions. In the case of the $C\,l\,B$ chromosome the breakage points are between sc and bi and between sy and fu. The lethal is at the left break. In the case of $In\,y^4$ the breakage points are between y and the telomere and between fu and the centromere. The locus of each mutant is: y (0.0), sc (0.0+), bi (6.9), B (57.0), sy (59.2), and fu (59.5). The centromere is at 70. Demonstrate that a chromosome deficient for *fused* is produced when crossing over occurs between the $C\,l\,B$ and $In\,y^4$ chromosomes. Devise a system of crosses to produce females hemizygous for *fused*. Hemizygous *fused* females have been shown by R. C. King to have a more extreme ovarian abnormality than fu/fu females. What conclusion can you draw from this observation?

16–2. Ionizing radiations, ultraviolet light, mustard gas, urethane, and various nitrogen mustards are known to be potent carcinogens (cancer producing agents). What interesting parallelism does this finding demonstrate?

16–3. It has been argued that the existence of virus-induced tumors rules out mutation as a factor in carcinogenesis. Discuss this argument in view of lysogenic phenomena.

16–4. Evidence is accumulating from studies of tissue cultures of human tumor cells that they are almost always aneuploid. However, there is no characteristic aneuploid chromosome number. What do you conclude from these findings?

16–5. Give examples of situations in which it has been demonstrated experimentally that (a) genes can regulate each other, (b) the nucleus can control the synthesis of cytoplasmic substances, (c) the nucleus can control the presence or absence of complicated cytoplasmic organelles, (d) the cytoplasm can regulate the nucleus, and (e) the cytoplasm can regulate itself.

16–6. Although courtship patterns are basically similar in the platyfish and swordtail, Clark, Aronson, and Gordon have demonstrated a number of qualitative and quantitative differences between these related species. Thus about 70 per cent of the platyfish males observed during courtship perform a swimming motion referred to as "retiring" which is not found in male swordtails. About 20 per cent of the males in the F_1 and F_2 hybrid generations show "retiring" behavior during courtship. When a back cross is made between an F_1 hybrid and a platyfish 10 per cent of the offspring show the behavior in question, whereas when the back cross involves a swordtail none of the offspring show "retiring" behavior. How is this behavior pattern inherited?

16–7. Merogonic hybrids are produced experimentally by combining the sperm nucleus of one species with the enucleated egg of a second species. The more distantly related the two species are, the earlier the development of the hybrid is terminated. Try to explain this observation.

16–8. It will be recalled (Fig. 15–1) that fu/fu females when fertilized by fu males fail to produce offspring. Counce has shown that the fertilized eggs produced by these females undergo early embryogenesis. However, five hours after fertilization there is established a general asymmetry in germ layers which is responsible for many ensuing aberrations. Such embryos never hatch but remain alive long after normal embryos have emerged as larvae. You will also recall that embryogenesis is normal in *fu* eggs fertilized by sperm bearing the $+^{fu}$ gene and in *fu* eggs (from *fu*/ + mothers) fertilized by *fu*- or Y-bearing sperm. What can you conclude from these findings as to the time of action of the + allele of *fused*? What is the function of the *fused* + substance?

16–9. W. Beermann has recently studied a balanced heterozygous strain of *Chironomus* which regularly segregates approximately 25 per cent nucleolusless progeny. Nucleolusless zygotes undergo early embryogenesis but fail to gastrulate properly and die. What conclusions can you draw from these findings?

16–10. Humphrey has discovered a fluid imbalance in embryos of the Mexican axolotl which is inherited as a simple Mendelian recessive.

genotype of		
mother	offspring	class
+/*f*	+/+ or +/*f*	1
	f/*f*	2
f/*f*	+/*f*	3
	f/*f*	4

Embryos of class 1 develop normally; whereas those of class 2 become bloated. Once the circulation is established, this distension disappears, however, and the embryos survive. Embryos of class 3 also become bloated, but the excess fluid eventually escapes and most individuals survive. Excess fluid fails to escape in the case of class 4 individuals, which die. The ovaries of *f*/*f* females behave autonomously when transplanted to +/+ females. Class 4 individuals can survive if united surgically (in parabiosis) with +/+ individuals. Put forward a theory that explains Humphrey's findings.

16–11. Cartilage is formed by groups of cells which secrete into the intercellular space a ground substance containing a protein (collagen) and a polysaccharide called chondroitin sulfuric acid. Cartilage forming a limb grows in compact, whorl-shaped masses; whereas that producing a coating over the eye forms a plate-shaped lamellated structure. P. Weiss and A. Moscona separated cartilage cells (originating from limb or eye coat) from one another by exposing them to the proteolytic enzyme trypsin. The separated cells were seeded out in a tissue culture and allowed to grow. The cells aggregated, continued their cartilage-forming activities, and eventually produced cartilage characteristic of the source which provided the cells (i.e. limb or eye coat). What do you conclude from these findings?

16–12. The salamander newt has nothing corresponding to the sucker of a frog tadpole. Yet Spemann and Schotté have demonstrated that a newt will develop a sucker if frog ectoderm is grafted into the newt in a position equivalent to that where the sucker develops in the frog. What do you conclude from this finding?

16–13. Galls often arise on plants as a result of a stimulus to meristematic tissues caused by an insect parasite. An insect will often cause galls of very similar morphology when attacking a variety of plants, and conversely plants of a single species may develop morphologically different galls, each characteristic of the insect parasitizing the plant. What do you conclude from these observations?

16–14. Give several examples, including situations described in earlier chapters, where reorganization of a developmental pattern involving the interaction of different types of tissues accompanies a change in genotype.

16–15. Give examples where the direction of cell division is genetically determined.

16–16. Rabbits belonging to the Himalayan strain are genotype $c^h c^h$ and are characterized by a pattern of pigmentation which is temperature dependent. At temperatures above 34°C these rabbits are entirely white; whereas when reared at room temperature they develop black fur upon the ears, forepaws, tail, and nose. Black pigment may be induced in any white area of the body by cooling it below 34°C. Rabbits of genotype CC are completely pigmented independent of temperature. Speculate as to the mechanisms involved.

16–17. M. Vogt has shown that wild type ovaries not only from *Drosophila melanogaster*, but from *D. virilis, funebris,* and *pseudoobscura* develop normally in *melanogaster* hosts of *fes/fes* genotype. This being the case what conclusions can you draw as to the effect of the *fes* gene upon the production of ovarian tumors?

16–18. During metamorphosis a characteristic puff forms in the first chromosome of the dipteran *Chironomus tentans* while in a second chromosomal region a previously puffed area returns to the usual diameter. In experiments performed by Clever and Karlson the purified hormone "ecdysone" (which is known to initiate metamorphosis) was injected into last instar larvae. The above mentioned sequence of changes in chromosomal morphology followed. Speculate as to the mechanisms involved.

16–19. The polyoma virus isolated by Stewart and Eddy from parotid gland tumors of mice has been inoculated into newborn individuals belonging to several species. In mice the virus causes tumors of a wide variety of tissues, in hamsters a more limited variety of tumors develop (but at a faster rate), in rats induced tumors are generally restricted to the kidney, rabbits develop tumors which regress, and monkeys fail to develop tumors. Injection of virus after mice are 48 hours old appears to be harmless. What conclusions can you reach from these findings?

16–20. The Frizzle feather mutation in domestic fowl has already been alluded to (Question 5–5). It will be recalled that FF individuals are "extreme frizzle" with bristle feathers which wear off easily; whereas Ff individuals are "mild frizzle" with curly feathers which are more normal. Extreme frizzle fowl are poorly insulated and lose heat rapidly. The body temperature is often subnormal, and the birds show a reduced ability to adjust to changes in the temperature of their environment. A host of morphological and physiological changes take place within the bird to compensate for the abnormal heat loss. The primary aberration seems to be in the feather protein itself. Krimm has shown that Frizzle keratin shows a much less well-ordered crystalline structure and that its amino acid composition differs from normal feather keratin. Construct a diagrammatic scheme similar to that shown in Figure 14–3B showing the relationship between the Frizzle DNA, the Frizzle keratin, and the various abnormalities shown by the mature bird. Can you conceive of a situation where Frizzle might be considered a beneficial mutation?

BIBLIOGRAPHY

Balinsky, B. I.   1960   An Introduction to Embryology. Saunders, Philadelphia.

Barth, L. G.   1953   Embryology. Dryden Press, New York.

Beermann, W.   1960   Der Nukleolus als lebenswichtiger Bestandteil des Zellkernes. Chromosoma *11*: 263–96.

Brachet, J.   1960   The Biochemistry of Development. Pergamon Press, London.

Braun, A. C., and T. Stonier   1958   Morphology and physiology of plant tumors. Protoplasmatologia *10* (part 5a): 93.

Briggs, R., and T. J. King   1959   Nucleocytoplasmic interactions in eggs and embryos. The Cell *1*: 537–617. Academic Press, New York.

Caspari, E.   1958   Genetics of behavior. *In* Behavior and Evolution, A. Roe and G. G. Simpson, editors. Yale University Press, New Haven, Conn.

Clark, E., L. R. Aronson, and M. Gordon   1954   Mating behavior patterns in two sympatric species of xiphorphorin fishes: their inheritance and significance in sexual isolation. Bull. Am. Museum Nat. History *103*: 139–225.

Clever, U. and P. Karlson   1960   Induktion von Puff-Veränderungen in den Speicheldrüsenchromosomen von *Chironomus tentans* durch Ecdyson. Exptl. Cell Res. *20*: 623–6.

Costello, D. P.   1948   Ooplasmic segregation in relation to differentiation. Ann. New York Acad. Sc. *49*: 663–83.

Counce, S. J.   1956   Studies on female-sterility genes in *Drosophila melanogaster*. II The effects of the gene *fused* on embryonic development. Ztschr. ind. Abstamms-u. Vererbungsl. *87*: 462–81.

Dalton, H. C.   1950   Inhibition of chromoblast migration as a factor in the development of genetic differences in pigmentation in white and black axolotls. J. Exper. Zool. *115*: 151–74.

Dmochowski, L.   1959   Viruses and tumors. Bact. Rev. *23*: 18–40.

Ebert, J. D.   1959   The acquisition of biological specificity. The Cell *1*:619–93. Academic Press, New York.

Ebert, J. D., and F. H. Wilt   1960   Animal viruses and embryos. Quart. Rev. Biol. *35*: 261–312. (Contains an interesting discussion of parallels between enzyme repression and immunological tolerance.)

Failla, G.   1958   The aging process and cancerogenesis. Ann. New York Acad. Sc. *71*: 1124–40.

Fraser, R. C.   1959   Cytodifferentiation: protein synthesis in transition. Am. Naturalist *93*: 47–80.

Fuller, J. L., and W. R. Thompson   1960   Behavior Genetics. Wiley, New York.

Gruneberg, H.   1943   The Genetics of the Mouse. Cambridge University Press, Cambridge, England.

Gruneberg, H.   1960   Developmental genetics of the mouse, 1960. J. Cellular and Comparative Physiol. *56,* (Suppl.) *1*: 49–60.

Hadorn, E.   1948   Gene action in growth and differentiation of lethal mutants of *Drosophila*. Symposia Soc. Exper. Biol. *2*: 177–95.

Hadorn, E.   1958   The role of genes in developmental processes. *In* The Chemical Basis of Development, W. E. McElroy and B. Glass, editors. Johns Hopkins Press, Baltimore, Md.

Hadorn, E.   1961   Developmental Genetics and Lethal Factors. Translated by Ursula Mittwock. Methuen, London.

Hammerling, J.   1953   Nucleocytoplasmic relationships in the development of *Acetabularia*. Int. Rev. Cyt. *2*: 475–98.

Hannah-Alava, A.   1958   Developmental genetics of the posterior legs in *Drosophila melanogaster*. Genetics *43*: 878–905. (Discusses homeotic mutants.)

Hooker, D., and C. C. Hare, editors   1954   Genetics and the inheritance of integrated neurological and psychiatric patterns. Research Publications Vol. 33 of the Association for Research in Nervous and Mental Disease. Williams and Wilkins, Baltimore, Md.

Humphrey, R. R.   1960   A maternal effect of a gene (*f*) for a fluid imbalance in the Mexican axolotl. Devel. Biol. *2*: 105–28.

Hutt, F. B.   1949   Genetics of the Fowl. McGraw-Hill, New York.

Huxley, J.   1958   Biological Aspects of Cancer. Allen & Unwin, London.

Kallmann, F. J.   1953   Heredity in Health and Mental Disorder. Norton, New York.

King, R. C., A. C. Rubinson, and R. F. Smith   1956   Oogenesis in adult *Drosophila melanogaster*. Growth *20*: 121–57.

King, R. C., R. G. Burnett, and N. A. Staley   1957   Oogenesis in adult *Drosophila melanogaster*. IV. Hereditary ovarian tumors. Growth *21*: 239–61.

King, R. C., and R. G. Burnett   1957   Ibid. V. Mutations which affect nurse cell nuclei. Growth *21*: 263–80.

King, R. C.   1960   Ibid. IX. Studies on the cytochemistry and ultrastructure of developing oocytes. Growth *24*: 265–323.

King, R. C., E. A. Koch, and G. A. Cassens   1961   The effect of temperature upon the hereditary ovarian tumors of the *fes* mutant of *Drosophila melanogaster*. Growth *25*: 45–65.

Klein, G.   1959   Variation and selection in tumor cell populations. Canad. Cancer Congress *3*, R. W. Begg, editor. Academic Press, New York.

Krimm, S.   1960   Structure of Frizzle mutant feather keratin. J. Mol. Biol. *2*: 247–9.

Kroeger, H.   1960   The induction of new puffing patterns by transplantation of salivary gland nuclei into egg cytoplasm of *Drosophila*. Chromosoma *11*: 129–45.

Lees, A. D., and C. H. Waddington   1942   The development of the bristles in normal and some mutant types of *Drosophila melanogaster*. Proc. Roy. Soc. London *131B*: 87–110.

Lewis, I. F., and Walton, L.   1958   Gall-formation on *Hamamelis virginiana* resulting from material injected by the aphid *Hormaphis hamamelidis*. Trans. Amer. Micr. Soc. *77*: 146–200.

Lindauer, M. 1961 Communication Among Social Bees. Harvard University Press, Cambridge, Mass.

Macklin, M. T. 1959 Relative status of parity and genetic background in producing human breast cancer. J. Nat. Cancer Inst. *23*: 1179–89.

Markert, C. L., and F. Moller 1959 Multiple forms of enzymes: tissue, ontogenetic and species specific patterns. Proc. Nat. Acad. Sci. U. S. *45*: 753–63.

McClintock, B. 1956 Controlling elements and the gene. Cold Spring Harbor Symp. Quant. Biol. *21*: 197–216.

Needham, J. 1950 Biochemistry and Morphogenesis. Cambridge Universtiy Press, Cambridge, England.

Pardee, A. B., F. Jacob, and J. Monod 1959 The genetic control and cytoplasmic expression of "inducibility" in the synthesis of β-galactosidase in *E. coli.* J. Mol. Biol. *1*: 165–78.

Phinney, B. O., and C. A. West 1960 Gibberellins and the growth of flowering plants. *In* Developing Cell Systems and Their Control, D. Rudnick, editor. Ronald Press, New York.

Poulson, D. F. 1945 Chromosomal control of embryogenesis in *Drosophila.* Am. Naturalist *79*: 340–63.

Raven, C. P. 1960 An Outline of Developmental Physiology, 2nd. ed. Pergamon Press, London.

Rizki, M. T. M. 1960 Melanotic tumor formation in *Drosophila.* J. Morph. *106*: 147–58.

Scott, J. P. 1954 The effects of selection and domestication upon the behavior of the dog. J. Nat. Cancer Inst. *15*: 739–58.

Sinnott, E. W. 1960 Plant Morphogenesis. McGraw-Hill, New York.

Shor, R., and S. Krimm 1961 Studies on the structure of feather keratin. Biophysical J. *1*: 467–516.

Smith, H. H. 1958 Genetic plant tumors in *Nicotiana.* Ann. New York Acad. Sc. *71*: 1163–78.

Sonneborn, T. M. 1954 Patterns of nucleocytoplasmic integration in *Paramecium.* Proc. 9th. Int. Congr. Genet., Caryologia *6* (Suppl. I).

Sonneborn, T. M. 1960 The gene and cell differentiation. Proc. Nat. Acad. Sci. *46*: 149–65.

Spemann, H., and O. Schotte 1932 Über xenoplastische Transplantation als Mittel Zur Analyze der embryonalen Induktion. Naturwiss. *20*: 463–7.

Spemann, H., and H. Mangold 1924 Über Induktion von Embryonalanlagen durch Implantation artfremder Organisatoren. Arch. f. mikr. Anat. u. Entw. Mech. *100*: 599–638.

Stern, C. 1954 Two or three bristles. Amer. Sci. *42*: 213–47.

Stewart, S. E. 1960 The polyoma virus. Scientific American *203*: no. 5 pp 63–71.

Swanson, C. P.   1957   Cytology and Cytogenetics, Chap. 9. Prentice-Hall, Englewood Cliffs, N. J.

Thompson, D. W.   1948   On Growth and Form. Cambridge University Press,
Cambridge, England.

Van Overbeek, J.   1936   "Lazy," an a-geotropic form of maize. J. Hered. *27*: 93–6.

Von Frisch, K., and Lindauer, M.   1956   The "language" and orientation of the
honey bee. Ann. Rev. Entomology *1*: 45–58.

Weiss, P.   1959   Cellular dynamics. Rev. Mod. Physics *31*: 11–20.

Weiss, P., and A. C. Taylor   1960   Reconstitution of complete organs from single
cell suspensions of chick embryos in advanced stages of differentiation. Proc.
Natl. Acad. Sci. *46*: 1177–85.

Willier, B. H., P. Weiss, and V. Hamburger   1955   Analysis of Development.
Saunders, Philadelphia.

Wilson, L. P., R. C. King, and J. L. Lowry   1955   Studies on the tu[W] strain of *Drosophila melanogaster*. I. Phenotypic and genotypic characterization. Growth
19: 215–44.

Yamada, T.   1958   Embryonic induction. *In* The Chemical Basis of Development.
W. D. McElroy and B. Glass, editors. Johns Hopkins Press, Baltimore, Md.

Yokoyama, T.   1959   Silkworm Genetics Illustrated, 185 pp. Published by the
Japanese Society for the Promotion of Science, Ueno Park, Tokyo, Japan.

Zwilling, E.   1956   Genetic mechanism in limb development. Cold Spring Harbor
Symp. Quant. Biol. *21*: 349–54.

Chapter **17**

Evolution and Population Genetics

Introduction

"When on board H. M. S. 'Beagle,' as naturalist, I was much struck with certain facts in the distribution of organic beings inhabiting South America, and in the geological relations of the present to the past inhabitants of that continent. These facts, as will be seen in the latter chapters of this volume, seemed to throw some light on the origin of species—that mystery of mysteries, as it has been called by one of our greatest philosophers. On my return home, it occurred to me, in 1837, that something might perhaps be made out on this question by patiently accumulating and reflecting on all sorts of facts which could possibly have any bearing on it. After five years' work I allowed myself to speculate on the subject, and drew up some short notes; these I enlarged in 1844 into a sketch of the conclusions, which then seemed to me probable: from that period to the present day I have steadily pursued the same object. I hope that I may be excused for entering on these personal details, as I give them to show I have not been hasty in coming to a decision." This then is the way Charles Darwin opened his masterpiece *On the Origin of Species.* The work was published in 1859, and no biological treatise written before or since has produced an impact upon society equal to it.

Darwin's contribution was not only to document the phenomenon of evolution but to elaborate a theory which explained the mechanism of evolution. His theory of natural selection was based upon three facts and two deductions from these facts. The facts were (1) that organisms generally reproduce in a geometric ratio; (2) that the numbers in a given species remain relatively constant from generation to generation; and (3) that inherited modifications exist in all species. From the first two facts he deduced that there was a struggle for existence and from the third fact he concluded that a higher percentage of organisms with favorable variations survived to reproduce. Thus "nature" selected variations having an adaptive value. The result of this differential fertility between members of a species possessing adaptive characters and those without such advantages was "descent with change" or evolution.

That evolution has occurred is today a fact unchallenged by thinking scientists. The direct evidence for evolution comes from the fossil record as elucidated by paleontologists, and the indirect evidence comes from such sciences as comparative anatomy, comparative embryology, comparative physiology and biochemistry, comparative genetics and biogeography. The concept of evolution provides the foundation upon which is erected the taxonomic classification of all living things. Evolution has occurred in the past, and evidence will be presented in this chapter that evolution is occurring today. Current evolution will be shown to result by natural selection of adaptive mutations. The only hypothetical point is that the mechanism of past evolution is the same as the one operating today.

In Darwin's day there was no knowledge as to the mechanism whereby inherited variations were transmitted. We now know these inherited modifications as mutations, and believe that the first sign of evolution in a population is a change in the frequency of different alleles in response to selection. Thus mutation provides the raw material for evolution, and selection determines the direction which evolution will take. The study of fluctuations in gene frequencies in populations of sexually reproducing organisms is the domain of the population geneticist, and evolutionary mathematics may be said to have started with the rules set forth by G. H. Hardy and W. Weinberg.

The Hardy-Weinberg law

Hardy and Weinberg demonstrated independently in 1908 that both gene frequencies and genotype frequencies will remain constant from generation to generation in an infinitely large, interbreeding population in which mating is at random and there is no selection, migration, or mutation. To demonstrate that such is the case let us examine a hypothetical situation where the gene in which we are interested exists in but two allelic forms A and a in a sexually reproducing population sharing a common pool of genes. Let the frequency of germ cells carrying gene A equal p and the frequency of germ cells carrying gene a equal q. Obviously $p + q = 1$. If we consider the possible zygotes which can arise from the fertilization of A- and *a*-bearing eggs by *A*- and *a*-bearing sperm (see Fig. 17–1), we must conclude that in the F_1 population *AA*, *Aa*, and *aa* individuals occur at frequencies of p², 2 pq, and q² respectively. Thus if p = q = 0.5, the frequency of *AA*, *Aa*, and *aa* individuals will be 0.25, 0.50, and 0.25, respectively.

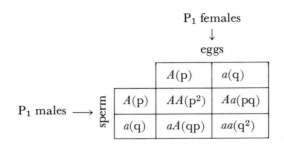

Figure 17–1

Now let us consider the frequency of *A*- and *a*-bearing gametes produced by the offspring:

$$A\text{-bearing gametes} = p^2 + \frac{2pq}{2} = p^2 + p(1 - p) = p^2 + p - p^2 = p$$

$$a\text{-bearing gametes} = q^2 + \frac{2pq}{2} = q^2 + q(1 - q) = q^2 + q - q^2 = q$$

Thus the frequencies of *A*- and *a*-bearing gametes in the next generation are p and q, just as they were in the succeeding generation. Therefore an equilibrium has been established with p and q remaining constant generation after generation. At equilibrium the frequencies of the genotypic classes are p²(*AA*): 2pq(*Aa*): q²(*aa*). The relationships between the frequencies of genes *A* or *a* and the frequencies of genotypes *AA*, *Aa*, and *aa* are shown graphically in Figure 17–2. One important point which can be brought home from an observation of this graph is how relatively common heterozygous "carriers" of a recessive gene are in situations where recessive homozygotes are rare. Thus when the frequency of gene *a* is 0.1, the frequency of *aa* individuals is 0.01, whereas the frequency of *Aa* individuals is 0.18. Thus individuals carrying one dose of the *a* gene are 18 times more abundant than those carrying two. When the frequency of gene *a* is 0.01, the frequency of *aa* individuals is 0.0001, whereas the frequency of *Aa* individuals is 0.0198. Here heterozygotes are 200 times more frequent than homozygous recessives.

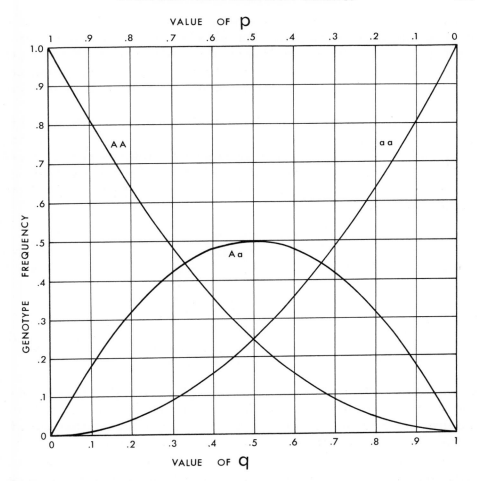

VALUE OF p

GENOTYPE FREQUENCY

VALUE OF q

Figure 17-2 The relationships between the frequencies of genes A or a and the frequencies of genotypes AA, Aa, and aa as predicted by the Hardy-Weinberg Law. (After Falconer.)

In nature, of course, populations of organisms are not infinitely large, mating may not occur at random, and selection, migration, and mutation do occur. Population geneticists led by Wright, Fisher, and Haldane have developed over the years mathematical models which describe the effects of the above factors upon gene frequencies in sexually reproducing populations sharing a common pool of genes ("Mendelian populations").

Random mating

An assumption that will underlie the discussions which follow is that mating is at random. This is generally true, and even applies for recessive deleterious traits, since the frequency of homozygous recessives is often so low that matings between phenotypically normal Aa individuals provide the major source of aa offspring. Situations do arise, however, where there is a tendency for phenotypically similar individuals to mate. This departure from random mating is called *assortative* mating. Tall people tend to choose tall mates, for example.

Inbreeding, the tendency of close relatives to mate, is another departure from random mating. Self-fertilization as sometimes found in monoecious plants and hermaphroditic animals generally constitutes the closest form of inbreeding. Let us consider the results of self-fertilization upon a hereditary line of organisms which originates from an individual of genotype Aa. Note the manner in which the

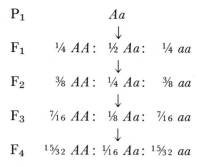

heterozygosity falls: $100\% \rightarrow 50\% \rightarrow 25\% \rightarrow 12.5\% \rightarrow 7.25\%$. Each generation one-half of the heterozygosity in the parents becomes homozygosity in the offspring. Note that the values of p and q remain 0.5 and that only the relative proportions of heterozygotes to homozygotes change.

In the case of inbreeding the frequencies of the three genotypes in a population are AA p² + F pq : Aa 2 pq (1 − F) : aa q² + F pq. In these equations F is defined as Wright's inbreeding coefficient, and the values for F are ½, ¼, ⅛, and ⅟₁₆ in the cases of self-fertilization, brother-sister matings, half-sib matings, and cousin matings, respectively. Half sibs are individuals who have one common parent, and cousins have a pair of common grandparents. In a randomly mating population F equals zero, and the above equations reduce to the usual Hardy-Weinberg formula.

Inbreeding per se is not deleterious, but it increases homozygosis which in turn leads to the unmasking of recessive genes (some of which may be deleterious). In the case of man the closest type of inbreeding observed with any frequency at the present time involves marriage between first cousins, and data from such consanguineous marriages have been used to estimate the number of recessive lethal mutations carried by phenotypically normal individuals in a human population. Records collected in France show that there is a 13 per cent excess in deaths before adulthood (including still births) among the offspring of cousins as contrasted to the children of unrelated parents. This increased mortality presumably is the result of the increased homozygosity of the children of related parents. It will be recalled that one-sixteenth of the heterozygosity is converted into homozygosity by cousin matings. By multiplying 0.13 by 16 we should find the mortality arising by complete homozygosity. The value obtained is 2, which indicates there are twice as many lethal genes as are necessary to kill. However, only half the deleterious genes will be detected by this method, since there is a 50 per cent probability that homozygosity may produce a double dose of the normal rather than the deleterious allele derived from a heterozygote. Taking this fact into consideration the estimate gives four as the average number of recessive lethals carried by each member of the population. Of course a genetic burden of eight recessive semilethals each of which when homozygous produced a 50 per cent probability of death before adulthood would give the same result. For this reason it is generally stated that the typical human carries four recessive *lethal equivalents*.

Meiotic drive

An assumption implicit in the Hardy-Weinberg law is that a heterozygote for alleles *A* and *a* produces gametes carrying each of these alleles with a frequency of 50 per cent. However, rare situations exist where such is not the case. The name *meiotic drive* has been coined by Sandler and Novitski to cover situations in which the frequencies of alleles in a population are altered as a consequence of peculiarities in the mechanics of the meiotic divisions. An example of meiotic drive is seen in certain races of *Drosophila pseudoobscura* in which an abnormal spermatogenesis occurs in males carrying a specific X-chromosome. The X- and Y-chromosomes fail to pair, the Y degenerates, and the X splits twice to form a bundle of four chromatids. Subsequently each secondary spermatocyte receives an X. As a consequence the population shows a preponderance of females.

Recurrent mutation

Let us assume that gene *A* mutates to its *a* allele at a constant rate u and that *a* mutates to gene *A* at a rate v. Thus if $u = 1 \times 10^{-5}$, then one out of 100,000 *A* genes will mutate to *a* between one generation and the next. If u and v are zero or if u and v are equal, then the equilibrium previously referred to will be maintained. However, if $v = 0$ and u is greater than 0, then the *A* gene will eventually be lost from the population by mutation to *a*. p_n, the frequency of *A* after *n* generations, is given by the equation $p_n = p_0 (1 - u)^n$, where $p_0 =$ the frequency of p at the start. With the rates of mutation generally observed, mutation alone can produce only very slow changes in gene frequency. If u and v are greater than zero and unequal to each other, then an equilibrium will be established. At equilibrium the frequency of a will be given by the equation $q_e = \dfrac{u}{u + v}$. Thus if $u = 2 \times 10^{-5}$ and $v = 1 \times 10^{-5}$, then $q_e = 0.666$. Given 10 million genes in a state of equilibrium, 3,333,333 will be A and 6,666,667 will be a. Between one generation and the next 66 A genes will mutate to a and 66 a genes will mutate to A.

It is generally found in nature that u is greater than v. That is, that reverse mutation from mutant to wild type occurs far less frequently than forward mutation. If such is the case, one would expect wild type alleles to be rarer than mutant alleles. Since this is certainly not the case in natural populations a second factor must be at work. This factor is selection.

Selection

Heretofore we have assumed that AA, Aa, and aa individuals have the same fitness. However, if individuals of differing genotype differ in their viability or fertility there will be differences in the proportionate contribution of individuals of different genotypes to the total offspring. That is, selection will be operating to varying degrees on the different phenotypes.

Let us define s as the selection coefficient against a specified genotype. Thus if $s = 1 \times 10^{-3}$, then one out of 1000 individuals of the genotype in question fails to reproduce. Consider the situation where there is selection only against aa individuals. Let p_1 equal the frequency of A after one generation of selection. Then $p_1 = \dfrac{p_0}{1 - sq_0{}^2}$. If all aa individuals die without reproducing (that is, if a is a homozygous lethal), then $s = 1$. If q_n is defined as the value of q after n generations of selection, then $q_n = \dfrac{q_0}{1 + nq_0}$.

By substituting values in this equation we can estimate the efficiency of 100 per cent selection against a recessive gene. From Table 17–1 we see that in two generations the frequency of the a gene can be halved. However, as selection proceeds it becomes progressively less efficient. It takes 20 generations to go from 0.5 to 0.05 and a further 180 generations to go from 0.05 to 0.005. On the other hand 100 per cent selection against a dominant gene would eliminate it in one generation. Thus the possibility of eliminating recessive deleterious genes from man or any other species by selection is small. It would be far more worthwhile to develop methods for detecting heterozygotes, for once this is done really efficient selection can be accomplished. The equation $n = \dfrac{1}{q_n} - \dfrac{1}{q_0}$ gives n the number of generations

TABLE 17–1

GENERATION	q
1	0.5
2	0.333
3	0.250
4	0.200
5	0.167
9	0.100
10	0.091
20	0.048
30	0.032
40	0.024
50	0.020
100	0.010
200	0.005
1000	0.001

required to reduce q from an original value q_0 to a desired value q_n under circumstances where there is 100 per cent selection against *aa* individuals.

Let us now consider the situation where heterozygotes are more fit than either homozygote. Under such circumstances once again after a number of generations an equilibrium will be reached such that the frequency of gene *a* will be given by the equation $p_e = \dfrac{s_2}{s_1 + s_2}$, where s_1 and s_2 are the selection coefficients against *AA* and *aa* individuals, respectively. Thus, if $s_1 = 0.20$ and $s_2 = 0.75$, $p_e = 0.79$. Thus at equilibrium *AA*, *Aa*, and *aa* individuals would make up 62.4, 33.2, and 4.4 per cent of the population, respectively.

Mutation and selection

Many instances have been recorded in man as well as other species in which a deleterious mutant gene is retained in a population because of recurrent mutation. Let us take as a model the situation where gene A mutates to an inactive allele a at a rate of u. The selection coefficients against AA, Aa, and aa individuals are 0, 0, and s respectively. Generally s is much greater than u. Under these circumstances an equilibrium will be reached eventually such that the frequency of gene a will be given by the equation $q_e = \sqrt{\dfrac{u}{s}}$. Note that if s = 1, that is, if gene a is lethal when homozygous, then $q_e = \sqrt{u}$. Remember, however, that $q^2 =$ the frequency of aa individuals. Thus if aa individuals survive long enough to be observed, then their frequency in the population is equivalent to the mutation rate of A to a.

Dominant deleterious mutations also arise by mutation. Thus if a mutates to A at a rate of v and the selection coefficients against AA, Aa, and aa individuals are s, s, and 0, respectively, then $p_e = \dfrac{v}{s}$. If s = 1, then $p_e = v$. In this case, if AA and Aa individuals survive long enough to be observed, the frequency of individuals showing the deleterious condition will be roughly equivalent to 2 v. The vast majority of such individuals will be heterozygotes. Note that the equilibrium value reached by the deleterious gene is far lower if the gene is dominant.

Migration

A change in gene frequency may be due to introduction of genes from other populations. The rate of change of gene frequency in any population subject to immigration obviously depends upon the immigration rate and the difference in gene frequency between the immigrants and the native population. The change in the frequency of gene a after one generation of immigration is given by the equation $q_1 - q_0 = m(q_m - q_0)$, where m is the frequency of immigrants per generation, q_m is the frequency of gene a among the migrants, q_0 is the frequency of gene a among the original population, and q_1 is the frequency of gene a in the combined population after one generation of immigration.

Population size

An assumption underlying all previous discussions is that the populations considered have been large, for in large populations gene frequencies are inherently stable. In small populations gene frequencies are subject to random fluctuations which are predictable in amount but not in direction. In such small populations the possibility arises that an allele can be fixed or lost purely by chance. Indeed neutral or deleterious alleles may be fixed in a population by this process. The chance fixation or loss of alleles in populations of small size is referred to as *random genetic drift* or the *Sewall Wright effect* (after the population geneticist who first called attention to the phenomenon).

Curt Stern has used the following hypothetical situation to illustrate genetic drift. Let us suppose that there exist 160 islands with identical environments and upon each of which live one man and one woman, both of genotype *Aa.* Thus p = q = 0.5. Each couple produces one girl and one boy, and these upon reaching sexual maturity become the progenitors of the subsequent populations of each island. Let us assume that the selection coefficients against *AA, Aa,* and *aa* individuals are zero in each case and that u and v are zero. The P_1 parents produce zygotes in the expected ratios of $1AA:2Aa:1aa$. However, we have specified that the F_1 generation will contain only two individuals, and consequently chance will produce the results shown in the checkerboard of Figure 17–3. Thus once in 16 times, or in 10 of the 160 islands, fixation of gene *A* will occur, and similarly in another 10 islands gene *a* will be fixed and gene *A* will be lost. Only in 60 out of 160 islands will p equal 0.5, the starting value. Thus a great variability in the value of p has arisen in the population of islands purely by chance; not by mutation or selection. The smaller the population size the greater the random fluctuations in gene frequencies and the less effective selection becomes. It should be recalled that the population size of many species may vary widely as a function of the season of the year, predation, parasitism, and other factors. The effective population size from the standpoint of genetic drift is much closer to the number of individuals observed during the period of maximal contraction than during maximum expansion.

Micro-evolution

In its earliest stages evolution can be detected by shifts in the frequencies of certain alleles in the gene pool of the population. Numerous examples can be given in which such shifts have occurred both in natural and laboratory populations. In a DDT-coated environment only that fly carrying a chance mutant gene which enables it to metabolize the poison to a non-toxic compound survives to reproduce. Our current problems with insecticide-resistant insects, antibiotic-resistant germs, and fungi which now attack hitherto resistant breeds of agriculturally important plants arise from present-day micro-evolution. In the laboratory, selection experiments have produced penicillin-resistant staphylococci, bacteriophage-resistant *E. coli*, D.D.T.-resistant *Drosophila,* etc.

MALE CHILDREN

		AA	Aa	aA	aa
	AA	AA AA 1	Aa AA 2	aA AA 3	aa AA 4
FEMALE CHILDREN	Aa	AA Aa 5	Aa Aa 6	aA Aa 7	aa Aa 8
	aA	AA aA 9	Aa aA 10	aA aA 11	aa aA 12
	aa	AA aa 13	Aa aa 14	aA aa 15	aa aa 16

COMPOSITION OF POPULATION OF ISLAND	EQUIVALENT TO SQUARE	p	FREQUENCY
both AA	1	1	$\frac{1}{16}$
one AA and one Aa	2,3,5,9	0.75	$\frac{4}{16}$
both Aa	6,7,10,11	0.50	$\frac{4}{16}$
one AA and one aa	4,13	0.50	$\frac{2}{16}$
one Aa and one aa	8,12,14,15	0.25	$\frac{4}{16}$
both aa	16	0	$\frac{1}{16}$

Figure 17-3   The chance distribution of pairs of children among the hypothetical islands as predicted by the checkerboard method.

Changes in the frequency of H^S in the Negro

A good example of a situation in which natural selection under certain circumstances has favored heterozygotes is seen in the case of sickle-cell anemia (see p. 219). It will be recalled that H^S/H^S individuals suffer from a severe form of hemolytic anemia, whereas H^A/H^S individuals appear perfectly healthy, although their erythrocytes contain both hemoglobins A and S. The frequency of heterozygotes is about 9 per cent in the Negro population of the United States, whereas in some regions of West Africa frequencies as high as 40 per cent are commonly found. In view of the severe disability characterizing sickle-cell anemics it is impossible to explain the high frequency of heterozygotes unless they have a substantially greater viability than H^A/H^A individuals. It appears that the H^A/H^S genotype confers at an early age a distinct resistance to certain forms of malaria. Indeed in locations where infection by *Plasmodium falciparum* is prevalent the frequency of H^A/H^S individuals is highest. Possibly the parasite cannot metabolize hemoglobin S efficiently or there is a premature destruction of parasitized erythrocytes in H^A/H^S individuals. The presence of the H^S gene in American Negroes is due to their African ancestry. In the United States where malaria is rare H^A/H^S individuals are no longer at an advantage over H^A/H^A individuals, and as a result the frequency of the H^S gene is declining.

Thus we see that a gene may be advantageous under certain circumstances and disadvantageous under others. In *Drosophila,* 15 different genes are known which reduce the size of the wing, and under most circumstances these mutations are deleterious. However, insects with large wings are readily carried aloft by air currents. Consequently on small, windy islands the mutations in question might be adaptive. Indeed, wingless insects are characteristic of small islands. The apterous condition is also advantageous to certain insects which live as ectoparasites and to others which continually burrow through the earth. Thus during their evolution the Anoplura (lice) and Siphonaptera (fleas) have lost their wings, and wings are lacking in the sterile castes of ants and termites.

Industrial Melanism

The best-documented and most spectacular evolutionary change as yet observed by naturalists is industrial melanism. The industrial revolution has led to the production of large amounts of factory smoke which have blanketed the country surrounding industrial areas with soot. Many animals escape from their predators because their concealing coloration blends so perfectly with the foliage upon which they lie. However, in polluted woods and meadows these same animals now stand out against the soot-darkened landscape and are subject to intense predation (see Fig. 17–4). Chance mutations which lead to a darkened coloration are of adaptive value and consequently are selected by nature.

In England more than 70 species of moths have been recorded which over the last century have altered their appearance toward a more somber coloration. The species studied most extensively is the Peppered Moth, *Biston betularia,* which prior to the middle of the nineteenth century had white and black specklings on the body and wings. However, about 1850

Figure 17-4   The ancestral (left) and melanic (right) form of the Peppered-Moth shown (in the upper drawing) resting upon lichen-covered bark in a nonpolluted woods and (in the lower drawing) resting upon soot-darkened bark.   (After Kettlewell.)

a black variety called *carbonaria* appeared in the area around Manchester. Today *carbonaria* makes up more than 95 per cent of the Peppered Moth population in many manufacturing districts.

The gene causing melanism in *B. betularia* today behaves as a dominant. It is assumed, however, that the original gene was recessive and that its present dominant condition has arisen through the selection of modifier genes. Perhaps the complementary action of genes at other loci led to more favorable concentrations and combinations of chemicals which normally serve as precursors for the pigment. As a result the pigment producing gene came to express itself fully in one rather than in two doses and consequently began behaving as a dominant.

Polymorphic species

The earth has great environmental diversity, and life has generally adopted two evolutionary means for filling all available environmental niches. One method involves the production of a polymorphic species. That is, a species which is subdivided into a number of specialized races. The second evolutionary method involves the formation of a variety of related species. The two methods are not mutually exclusive, for, as we shall see later, geographically isolated races may in time develop into new species. If the best utilization of the environment requires relatively few genotypes, the first method is used; whereas the second method is, if many diverse genotypes are required.

Man as a polymorphic species

The former method was taken by the human species, and it resulted in the production of a series of races the individuals of which differed from those of other races in various adaptive features (temperature tolerance, altitude adaptation, resistance to endemic diseases and the like). Certain adaptive mutations are so widespread as to constitute characters used to separate the species into major racial groups. The almond-shaped eyes of the Mongoloid ethnic group, for example, arise as a result of a fat-lined upper eyelid which serves to protect the eye in bitterly cold weather. Presumably the mutant was of adaptive value among the ancestors of the present Mongoloid group who originated in northern Asia. The isolated population which evolved into the Negro race developed in the sunny grasslands of northern Africa where pigmented skin was useful in screening out excessive amounts of damaging ultraviolet light. In cloudy northern Europe where the little available sunlight was not only acceptable but desirable pigment-producing genes were selected against. The Caucasoid group which resulted was relatively depigmented. There is good evidence that Paleolithic man existed in tribes numbering a hundred or less. Consequently genetic drift may have played an important role with the consequence that some genes with relatively little adaptive significance were fixed in the gene pool. The present-day human gene pool must contain not only genes of adaptive significance, but neutral genes of the type just discussed, and genes once of adaptive significance but of little value in our present-day environment.

It should be stressed that there exist no strict genetic boundaries between any of the races of mankind. Where the lines are drawn is arbitrary and the separations differ according to the criteria used. Neither have significant differences in the genetic capacities for intelligence been demonstrated in different ethnic groups nor has there been shown any mental or physical inferiority of racial hybrids as compared to the parental groups.

Chromosomal polymorphism in *Drosophila*

Perhaps the most elegant study of the evolution of adapted genotypes is that of T. Dobzhansky and his colleagues on *Drosophila pseudoobscura* and its relatives. Dobzhansky took samples from populations of *Drosophila pseudoobscura* residing in different regions throughout the western United States, southwest Canada, and Mexico. The insects were indistinguishable in terms of their external morphology. However, studies of the larval salivary chromosomes led to the discovery of a series of different gene arrangements for chromosome 3 characteristic for certain populations. One arrangement was chosen as the standard sequence, and all other arrangements were compared with it. Thus, if sequence A (see Fig. 17–5) is chosen as the standard, then the other sequences can be detected by the fact that in both the A/B and A/C heterozygotes chromosome 3 forms a simple, paracentric inversion loop; whereas in the B/C heterozygote it gives the double loop characteristic for an overlapping inversion system. Thus, it is obvious that the B sequence could not be converted to the C sequence by a single inversion. Once stocks homozygous for third chromosomes showing gene sequences A, B, and C are obtained they can be used to test the gene sequence of other chromosomes obtained from new collections. Eventually 15 third chromosomes in addition to standard (each characterized by a specific gene sequence) were obtained. These various sequences were named in accordance with the location where the flies possessing them were first collected (i.e. *Arrowhead,* British Columbia; *Pikes Peak,* Colorado; *Santa Cruz* island off California; *Chiricahua* mountains, Arizona; *Olympic* peninsula, Washington, etc.). Eight gene arrangements were detected in the related species *D. persimilis.*

By a systematic analysis of the configurations of the salivary gland chromosomes of larvae heterozygous for various third chromosomes, Dobzhansky was able to construct the chromosomal phylogenetic tree shown in Figure 17–6. Any gene sequences which lie adjacent to each other in this scheme when combined in a heterozygote produce a simple inversion loop. Thus in the example in Figure 17–5 A, B, and C could represent Standard, Pikes Peak, and Arrowhead, respectively. Note that the standard sequence is found not only in *Drosophila pseudoobscura* but is also in *D. persimilis.* The gene arrangement of the third chromosome of *D. miranda* is more like the hypothetical gene sequence postulated to fill the gap between Standard and Santa Cruz than any gene arrangement as yet discovered in either *D. pseudoobscura* or *D. persimilis.* It is impossible to decide just which gene

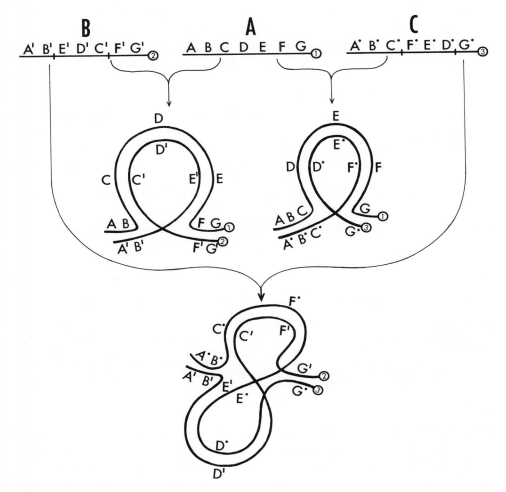

Figure 17-5 The types of inversion loops seen in different inversion heterozygotes.

arrangement is ancestral to the rest, but the *miranda* and Standard sequences are the most likely candidates. For this reason these gene sequences are connected by double arrows in Figure 17–6.

A study was made during the spring, summer, and fall of the frequency of various gene sequences in a population of *Drosophila pseudoobscura* in the Mount San Jacinto region of California. The frequency of Standard was high in March, dropped to a minimum value in June, and then rose steadily to a maximum value in October. Chiricahua behaved just the opposite with minima in March and October and a maximum frequency in June. Thus flies with Chiricahua gene sequence seem to do best during the hottest

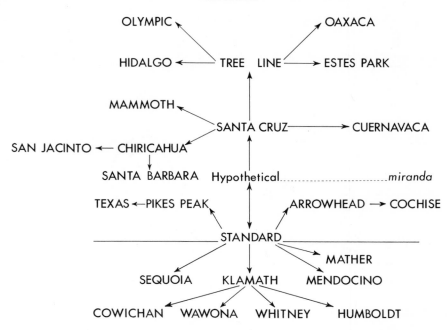

Figure 17–6 A phylogenetic chart showing how the various gene sequences in the third chromosome of *Drosophila pseudoobscura* and *D. persimilis* are related. Sequences connected by a single arrow differ from one another with respect to a single paracentric inversion. Sequences above the horizontal line occur only in *pseudoobscura*; those blow it only in *persimilis* (*Standard* is found in both).
(Redrawn from *Animal Cytology and Evolution* by M. J. D. White, 1954, Cambridge University Press.)

portion of the year, but those with Standard chromosomes excel during the spring and fall. In another experiment Dobzhansky contrasted the frequency of Standard and Arrowhead chromosomes in samples of flies collected at different elevations in the Sierra Nevada Mountains. Standard was most abundant at low altitudes, and Arrowhead was the most common sequence observed in alpine environments. Dobzhansky next raised populations of *Drosophila pseudoobscura* in the laboratory in population cages. The populations were reared at 25°C or 16°C with constantly replenished food supplies. At the start of the experiment equal numbers of Standard and Arrowhead chromosomes were present. In the 16°C population the Standard chromosome was eliminated; whereas in the 25°C environment an equilibrium value was reached where both Standard and Arrowhead chromosomes remained in constant proportions. Thus at 25°C the Standard/Arrowhead heterozygote appears to show the greatest fitness and at 16°C the Arrowhead homozygote is best adapted. In the experiments referred to above, the competing chromosomes came from the same natural population. In a situation in which flies containing Arrowhead and Standard chromosomes from different localities were placed in competition at 25°C Arrowhead was eliminated. Thus a balance is set up only when competing chromosomes come from the same natural population. It follows that Arrowhead chromosomes from different natural populations have different properties. Dobzhansky has concluded that the gene contents of the chromosomal types characteristic of a certain geographical region are mutually adjusted in such a way that the heterozygotes have a high degree of fitness. The biological role of the inversions is to prevent crossing over and thus preserve blocks of genes which are responsible for this harmonious situation. Along the west coast of the United States the Standard gene arrangement is the most common sequence found in the flies of the populations sampled. In western Mexico, Chiricahua is the commonest arrangement; whereas in the west central and central regions of the United States, Arrowhead and Pikes Peak, respectively, predominate.

The origin of the adaptive norm

A population of interbreeding organisms occupying a given area is adapted as a result of its evolutionary history to the variety of environmental conditions which commonly occur in that habitat. The array of genotypes (compatible with the demands of the environment) possessed by the population is defined by Dobzhansky as the "adaptive norm." The mode of origin of the adaptive norm constitutes one of the basic problems of population genetics.

According to the "classical" hypothesis the adaptive norm evolves by gradual substitution and eventual fixation of more favorable genes and gene arrangements in the place of inferior ones. Under this hypothesis *heterozygosity* should be *rare* and when present should arise from three sources: (1) deleterious mutations in the process of being eliminated; (2) advantageous mutations approaching fixation; and (3) mutations which are (a) advantageous at certain times and under certain conditions, (b) disadvantageous under other circumstances, and which exist in habitats where situations (a) and (b) are encountered frequently.

According to the "balance" hypothesis the adaptive norm is an array of genotypes heterozygous at numerous loci. *Homozygotes* occur *rarely* and are inferior. Natural selection leads to a harmonious balance between the components of the genotype of the population and rarely produces fixation of genes. The gene pool thus becomes organized, and each evolutionary change results in a repatterning of the entire system.

The hypotheses described above are not mutually exclusive, and presumably both mechanisms are involved in the evolution of the adaptive norm, although to different degrees in different species. Dobzhansky and his colleagues have demonstrated that in many natural populations of certain *Drosophila* species a large fraction of the chromosomes sampled when made homozygous in the laboratory by suitable breeding techniques produces effects deleterious to the insects (see Fig. 17–7). Thus in *D. pseudoobscura* over 90 per cent of the second and third chromosomes when homozygous caused a slight depression in viability, and in *D. willistoni* over 60 per cent of the second and third chromosomes when homozygous caused male sterility. It appears that these two species rely very heavily upon an array of balanced, co-adapted genotypes and as a result support a large load of mutations which are deleterious when homozygous. The heterozygotes appear to be very adaptable and have been shown in the laboratory to flourish under a much wider variety of environmental conditions than do homozygotes. *Drosophila prosaltans,* on the other hand, supports a relatively small mutational load, is less adaptable, and can live in only a few special-

<table>
<tr><th colspan="2"></th><th>*Drosophila prosaltans*</th><th>*Drosophila willistoni*</th><th>*Drosophila pseudoobscura*</th></tr>
<tr><td colspan="2">distribution</td><td>restricted</td><td>wide</td><td>wide</td></tr>
<tr><td colspan="2">ecology</td><td>specialized, limited habitats</td><td>able to exploit diverse habitats</td><td>able to exploit diverse habitats</td></tr>
<tr><td rowspan="16">percentages of the chromosomes which when homozygous produce certain phenotypic effects</td><td>Second chromosomes lethals and semi-lethals</td><td>32.6</td><td>41.2</td><td>?</td></tr>
<tr><td>subvitals</td><td>33.4</td><td>?</td><td>97.3</td></tr>
<tr><td>female sterility</td><td>9.2</td><td>40.5</td><td>17.5</td></tr>
<tr><td>male sterility</td><td>11.0</td><td>64.8</td><td>20.8</td></tr>
<tr><td>Third chromosomes lethals and semi-lethals</td><td>9.5</td><td>32.1</td><td>25.3</td></tr>
<tr><td>subvitals</td><td>14.5</td><td>?</td><td>93.5</td></tr>
<tr><td>female sterility</td><td>6.6</td><td>40.5</td><td>10.6</td></tr>
<tr><td>male sterility</td><td>4.2</td><td>66.7</td><td>8.3</td></tr>
</table>

Figure 17–7

ized natural habitats. Presumably the evolution of the adaptive norm of *D. prosaltans* has been dependent primarily upon substitution and fixation of adaptive genes.

The origin of species

In organisms which reproduce sexually, a species consists of one or more populations the individuals of which can interbreed but which in nature cannot exchange genes with members belonging to other species. Speciation involves the development of a variety of populations within a species followed by geographical isolation of the populations. Geographical isolation simply refers to any environmental factor which effectively prohibits the flow of genes between the two populations. Thus an earthquake or a lava flow from an erupting volcano might dam a river and cause the flooding of a valley. Populations of a species inhabiting the uplands to either side of the body of water so formed might thus be isolated from each other by a gap that could not be bridged. During the period of isolation the two geographical races would diverge genetically more and more as a result of the accumulation of different mutations and the exposure of each population to different selection pressures owing to the different conditions under which each exists. Given sufficient time, characters might develop which promote reproductive isolation once the barrier separating the two populations is removed. In this way the races would evolve into separate species.

The initial divergences between the two races generally involve genic ones. That is, certain genes will take up developmental functions different from their ancestral ones. We can get some idea as to how these transfers of function might occur by reviewing the action of suppressor genes (see p. 231). Eventually a point is reached where the evolved genotypes differ sufficiently so that haploid chromosomal sets from each race cannot function harmoniously together when combined in a hybrid. Hybrids between the races are thus rendered sterile or inviable. Since the two races are now reproductively isolated, they can be called true species. As a method of reproductive isolation, however, hybrid sterility and hybrid inviability are very wasteful. Consequently mutants will be selected which supplant these methods with more effective ones. The mechanisms found among related species occupying the same territory include ones that prevent hybridization because (1) mating does not occur since the behavioral patterns of the two species are sufficiently different or (2) copulation is mechanically impossible or (3) spermatozoa of one species fail to reach or penetrate eggs of the second species. Hybridization also may be prevented because the two species breed at different times of the year or exist in different ecological niches.

Chromosomal reorganization during the evolution of the genus Drosophila

The genus Drosophila probably contains at least 1500 species. The 700 described species have been distributed among eight subgenera. Extensive studies of the cytogenetics of about 300 members of this genus have led to an encyclopedic body of information much of which has been summarized in a book by two of the principal researchers in the field, J. T. Patterson and W. S. Stone.

It appears that the haploid ancestral chromosomal configuration consisted of five rods and a dot. Muller has called these chromosomal elements

SUBGENERA	SPECIES	CHROMOSOMAL ELEMENTS A	B	C	D	E	F	N	METAPHASE CHROMOSOMES
SOPHOPHORA	*melanogaster*	X	2L	2R	3L	3R	4	4	1R, 2V, ID
SOPHOPHORA	*simulans*	X	2L	2R	3L	3R	4	4	1R, 2V, ID
SOPHOPHORA	*pseudoobscura*	XL	4	3	XR	2	5	5	3R, 1V, 1D
SOPHOPHORA	*persimilis*	XL	4	3	XR	2	5	5	3R, 1V, 1D
SOPHOPHORA	*miranda*	XL	4	X_2	XR	2	5	5	3R, 1V, 1D
SOPHOPHORA	*affinis*	XL	4	3	XR	2	5	5	1R, 2V, 1J, 1D
SOPHOPHORA	*algonquin*	XS	C	A	X*L*	B	D	5	1R, 1V, 2J, 1D
SOPHOPHORA	*azteca*	XS	C	A	X*L*	B	D	5	1V, 3J, 1D
DROSOPHILA	*hydei*	X	4	3	5	2	6	6	4R, 1V, 1D
DROSOPHILA	*virilis*	X	4	5	3	2	6	6	5R, 1D
DROSOPHILA	*novamexicana*	X	4	5	3	2	6	6	5R, 1D
DROSOPHILA	*montana*	X	4	5	3	2	6	6	4R, 1v, 1D
DROSOPHILA	*lacicola*	X	4	5	3	2	6	6	4R, 1v, 1D
DROSOPHILA	*americana*	X ⟷	4	5	3 ⟷	2	6	4	1R, 2V, 1D
DROSOPHILA	*texana*	X	4	5	3 ⟷	2	6	5	3R, 1V, 1D
DROSOPHILA	*littoralis*	X	4 ⟵	5	⟶ 3	2	6	5	2R, 1J, 1V, 1D

Figure 17–8 Chromosomal homologies between various species of Drosophila (after Patterson and Stone). R, L, *L*, or S represent the right, left, long, or short arms of a given chromosome. The column under N gives the haploid chromosome number. R. V, J, and D represent rod-, V-, J-, and dot-shaped chromosomes, respectively. Small V-shaped chromosomes are represented by v.

A, B, C, D, E, and F and has arranged them to correspond to the X-chromosome, the left arm of chromosome 2, the right arm of chromosome 2, the left arm of chromosome 3, the right arm of chromosome 3 and chromosome 4, respectively, of *Drosophila melanogaster*. Sufficient cytological and genetic information is available to homologize the chromosomal elements of a number of species belonging to the subgenera Sophophora and Drosophila (see Fig. 17–8). Note that *Drosophila virilis* and *D. novamexicana* show the ancestral karyotype of five rods and one dot. In the case of *D. montana* and *D. lacicola* one of the rods has been converted into a small v, presumably as the result of a pericentric inversion. The two v-shaped chromosomes of *D. americana* have arisen by fusion of elements A with B and D with E, whereas only D and E have fused in *D. texana*. In *D. littoralis* the fusion involved elements B and D. As in the case of *D. americana* the V-shaped chromosomal elements of *D. melanogaster* must have arisen from whole arm fusions with the result that the chromosome number was reduced from six to four. Such whole arm fusions are the consequence of eucentric reciprocal translocations between two rod-shaped chromosomes where the break in one chromosome is immediately in front of the centromere and the break in the second chromosome immediately behind the centromere (see Fig. 17–9). Note that one of the arms of the sex-determining chromosomes of

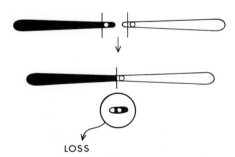

LOSS

Figure 17–9   A whole arm transfer resulting from a eucentric reciprocal translocation.

D. pseudoobscura, D. persimilis, D. miranda, D. affinis, D. algonquin, and *D. azteca* is homologous with the left arms of the third chromosomes of *D. melanogaster* and *simulans*. In *D. miranda* one of the original C-chromosomes has become a sex chromosome, while the other C-chromosome has become incorporated into the Y and has lost many of its genes.

A total of 30 pericentric inversions, 40 shifts of heterochromatin, 60 chromosomal fusions, and 600 paracentric inversions has been shown to have occurred in a group of species which make up only about one-twenty-fifth of the total for the genus. Thus a vast amount of reshuffling of genes has occurred during the millions of years this genus has existed on our planet.

Rates of evolution

Sewall Wright has pointed out that an organism with a genetic machinery comprised of but 100 genes, each of which could exist in as few as ten allelic states, has the potentialities of forming 10^{100} homozygous genotypes. This figure which is far larger than the number of neutrons, electrons, and protons in the known universe implies that there is an inconceivably great amount of potential variability upon which natural selection can work. Wright has demonstrated that the difficulty with evolution lies not in a lack of raw material with which to operate at any one time but in finding a path from one harmonious gene combination to another, through a system of potential combinations, against the enormous, conservative pressure of selection. Thus evolution may proceed at a very slow rate under certain circumstances and result in organisms like the present-day coelacanths which resemble closely their Devonian ancestors. Under exceptionally favorable circumstances, however, evolutionary advance is possible at a rapid rate. The evolution of the primates is an example of such an acceleration.

Human evolution

About two million years ago, early in the Pleistocene period in Africa, small-brained, plains-living, vegetarian apes began a limited bipedal form of locomotion. Presumably this adaptation left the hands sufficiently free so that stones and sticks could be manipulated and eventually used as tools and weapons. The success of this new way of life led to selection pressures which resulted in great changes, particularly with respect to the pelvis, teeth, hands, and brain. The brain doubled in size, and those areas concerned with mental faculties such as memory and speech expanded greatly. These changes in turn made possible the more skillful production and effective use of more types of tools and weapons, the development of language, and the domestication of fire. The result of this evolutionary sequence was ancient man belonging to the genus *Homo* living about 500,000 years ago.

The possession of dexterous hands, intelligence, the abilities to vocalize, communicate, and imitate, all these tremendously advantageous faculties depended upon the production of larger and more complex brains. However, an upper limit to the size of the brain was set by the size of the bony birth canal. This obstacle was surmounted, however, by the delivery of a fetus at a much earlier stage of development followed by a prolonged period of maternal care. A major factor in the initial organization of human society was this maternal obligation to a slowly developing infant. Thus the possession of the faculties referred to above resulted in the production of a culture, but the modes of life made accessible through a culture gave increasing opportunities for the effective use of these and other skills. In competition, the survivors were those individuals, families, and groups of families in which characteristics such as intelligence and resourcefulness were best developed. Thus cultural and biological evolution operated concurrently for many generations—in fact, until very recently.

Eventually man came to control his environment to such a degree that natural selection became relatively inefficient, and indeed today man stands apart from all other species in the minor degree to which his evolution is determined by natural selection. Furthermore man, unlike any other species, continues to undergo social evolution. Just as adaptive genes are transmitted from generation to generation, so in man useful information gathered during one generation is transmitted to the next. Furthermore the rate at which knowledge is accumulating and the efficiency by which it is transmitted is increasing rapidly. As a result man is evolving at a speed transcending that of all other species and is the dominant form of life on earth.

However, the fact that natural selection operates so inefficiently in modern man has led to the accumulation of deleterious mutations at an accelerated rate. As the modes of inheritance of the major genetic diseases and handicaps are worked out and methods are developed for detecting heterozygotes, knowledge will be available which will make possible genetic counseling on a large scale. If a trend is established whereby those burdened with hereditary defects voluntarily adopt rather than father their own children, a type of consciously directed selection will be put into operation which will act to the benefit of our species far more rapidly than natural selection. Under these conditions our species will continue to evolve socially while our biological foundation will remain unimpaired.

17–1. Describe the mechanisms whereby new species arise.

17–2. Give evidence for micro-evolution from the laboratory and nature.

17–3. Mutants obtained from wild populations and cultured in the laboratory often appear to be deleterious, yet their frequency in wild populations remains constant. Give at least three reasons why this might occur.

17–4. Darwin, in Chapter 1 of *On the Origin of Species,* describes in considerable detail the varieties of domesticated dogs, pigeons, sheep, horses, etc., which have been produced by breeders. What was his point in doing this?

17–5. Discuss Dobzhansky's studies of chromosomal polymorphism in *Drosophila pseudoobscura.* What is the experimental evidence for the postulate that flies carrying different chromosomal types are not ecologically equivalent? Indicate how a chromosomal phylogenetic tree can be erected. What is the biological role of the inversions so characteristic of this species?

17–6. Contrast the "classical" and the "balance" hypotheses in explaining the origin of the adaptive norm.

17–7. Under what conditions is the frequency of individuals homozygous for a gene equal to the mutation rate to that gene?

17–8. Albinos (see p. 216) occur in the human population at a frequency of 0.000067. What is the frequency of individuals heterozygous for the recessive, albino gene?

17–9. Assume gene A mutates to a at a rate of 1×10^{-5}. What will be the frequency of the A gene after 10; 100; 1000; 10,000; 100,000; and 1,000,000 generations?

17–10. Consider the situation where $p = q = 0.5$ and there is selection only against homozygous recessive individuals. What will be the values for p_1, if $s = 1, 0.6, 0.1, 0.01,$ and 0?

17–11. From the information that one American Negro child in 500 suffers from sickle-cell anemia calculate the frequency of the H^S gene. Assuming that in West Africa $s_1 = 0.20$ and $s_2 = 0.75$, what is the frequency of H^S there? Assuming that in the United States the selection coefficients against H^A/H^A, H^A/H^S and H^S/H^S individuals are 0, 0, and 1, respectively, how many generations would be required to reduce q from 0.21 to 0.045? What do you conclude from your calculation, if you assume that a human generation is roughly 25 years?

17–12. Make the appropriate calculations to enable you to fill in the blanks in the following table.

mutation	rate	selection coefficient	against	number of individuals at equilibrium			population size	genes lost by selection	genes gained by mutation
				AA	Aa	aa			
$A \rightarrow a$	1×10^{-5}	1×10^{-3}	aa				1×10^7		
$a \rightarrow A$	1×10^{-5}	1×10^{-3}	AA and Aa				1×10^7		

17–13. What will be the frequency of gene *a* after one generation of immigration, if the frequency of new immigrants per generation is $\frac{1}{100}$ and the frequencies of gene *a* among the immigrants and natives are 0.7 and 0.5, respectively?

17–14. Mimicry often involves situations where resemblances between two or more species have evolved. In the case of Batesian mimicry the model has conspicious warning coloration and is distasteful to predators. The mimic is edible, occurs in the same area as the model, is much less common than the model, and bears a very close resemblance to the model in terms of size, color pattern, and behavior. In the case of Mullerian mimicry one warning pattern is used by a number of distasteful species inhabiting the same area. Consider the possible adaptive significance and method of origin of both types of mimicry. Subsequently refer to Chapter 10 of Sheppard's book.

17–15. Demonstrate that the children resulting from a first-cousin marriage have one chance in 64 of being homozygous for a given recessive lethal carried heterozygously by one of the common great-grandparents. The incidence of the phenylketonuria in the human population is one in 25,000. Compute the expected incidence of the disease among the offspring of first-cousin marriages.

17–16. In a number of laboratories it has been demonstrated that amino acids and other biochemicals can be formed if a mixture of simple inorganic compounds of carbon, hydrogen, oxygen, and nitrogen are provided with energy in the form of heat or ultraviolet radiation. S. Fox and his colleagues have heated to 70°C a dry mixture containing phosphoric acid and 18 amino acids (with dicarboxylic amino acids present in excess amounts). They recovered amino acid polymers with molecular weights as high as 10,000. These "proteinoids" are acted upon by proteolytic enzymes, have nutritive value for bacteria, but are nonantigenic. They show a tendency to form microspheres having diameters around two microns which appear to have osmotic properties. What do you suppose is the point of experiments of the type described above?

17–17. Can you conceive of a situation in which: (a) speciation could occur which was not preceded by geographical isolation; (b) selection might operate before fertilization; (c) Wright's inbreeding coefficient would be 1; and (d) a mutation which lowered fecundity might be beneficial?

17–18. *Drosophila pseudoobscura* and *D. persimilis* do not hybridize at 25°C, but will at 16°C. Koopman introduced *pseudoobscura* and *persimilis* into a population cage at 16°C and demonstrated that after a series of generations the species became sexually isolated. What do you conclude from these findings?

17–19. Let us assume that two recessive deleterious genes exist (*a* and *b*) each of which when homozygous causes a fatal disease (the "a" and the "b" syndromes). In population A gene *a* has a frequency of 0.05 and gene *b* is virtually absent. In population B gene *b* has a frequency of 0.04 and gene *a* is virtually absent. Assume intermingling occurs between two equally sized sub-populations of A and B. If one assumes that mating occurs at random, how will the frequency of individuals in the new population suffering from the "a" or the "b" syndrome compare to the frequency of individuals afflicted in the original populations.

Does miscegenation under these circumstances have a deleterious or a beneficial effect?

17–20. A hereditary paralytic disease called Kuru is found extremely often among the Fore natives of New Guinea, but is unknown elsewhere. According to Bennett males and females homozygous for the *Ku* gene generally contract the disease during childhood. Heterozygous females become affected as adults; whereas heterozygous males are unaffected. How could such a deleterious gene become so widespread in a human population?

BIBLIOGRAPHY

Bateman, N.   1960   Selective fertilization at the T-locus of the mouse. Genetical Research *1*: 226–38.

Bennett, J. H., F. A. Rhodes, and H. N. Robson   1959   A possible genetic basis for Kuru. Am. J. Human Genet. *11*: 169–87.

Boyd, W. C.   1950   Genetics and the Races of Man. Little, Brown, Boston.

Cain, A. J.   1954   Animal Species and Their Evolution. Hutchinson's University Library, London.

Carter, C. S.   1957   A Hundred Years of Evolution. Macmillan, New York.

Chetverikov, S. S.   1926   Concerning certain aspects of the evolutionary process from the standpoint of modern genetics. Zhurnal Experimentalnoi Biologii *2*: 3–54. Partially translated from the Russian in Cold Spring Harbor Symp. Quant. Biol. *24*: 27–30.

Clark, W. E. L.   1955   The Fossil Evidence for Human Evolution. University of Chicago Press, Chicago.

Clark, W. E. L.   1960   The Antecedents of Man: An Introduction of the Evolution of the Primates. Quadrangle Books, Chicago.

Coon, C. S.   1959   Race and ecology in man. *In* Genetics and Twentieth Century Darwinism. Cold Spring Harbor Symp. Quant. Biol. *24*: 153–9.

Cott, H. B.   1940   Adaptive Coloration in Animals. Methuen, London.

Crow, J. F.   1960   Genetics Notes. Burgess Publ. Co., Minneapolis, Minn.

Darwin, C. R.   1958   The Voyage of the *Beagle*. Bantam Books, New York.

Darwin, C. R.   1956   The Origin of Species, 6th ed. Oxford University Press, Oxford, England.

Darwin, C. R., and A. R. Wallace   1958   Evolution by Natural Selection. Cambridge University Press, Cambridge, England.

Dobzhansky, Th.   1944   Contributions to the genetics, taxonomy, and ecology of *Drosophila pseudoobscura* and its relatives. Carnegie Inst. of Washington Publ. No. 554, Washington, D. C.

Dobzhansky, Th.   1951   Genetics and the Origin of Species. Columbia University Press, New York.

Dobzhansky, Th.   1955   A review of some fundamental concepts and problems of population genetics. Cold Spring Harbor Symp. Quant. Biol. *20*: 1–15.

Dodson, E. O.   1960   Evolution: Process and Product. Reinhold, New York.

Falconer, D. S.   1960   Introduction to Quantitative Genetics. Ronald Press, New York.

Fisher, R. A.   1930   The Genetical Theory of Natural Selection. Clarendon Press, Oxford, England.

Fox, S. W.   1960   How did life begin? Science *132*: 200–208.

Glass, B.   1954   Genetic changes in human populations, especially those due to gene flow and genetic drift. Adv. Genet. *6*: 95–139.

Glass, B., O. Temkin, and W. L. Straus, Jr.   1959   Forerunners of Darwin, 1745–1859. Johns Hopkins Press, Baltimore, Md.

Hardy, G. H.   1908   Mendelian proportions in a mixed population. *In* Classic Papers in Genetics, J. A. Peters, editor   1959   Prentice-Hall, Englewood Cliffs, N. J.

Huxley, J.   1940   The New Systematics. Oxford University Press, Oxford, England.

Huxley, J.   1942   Evolution, the Modern Synthesis. Harper, New York.

Irvine, W.   1955   Apes, Angles, and Victorians. McGraw-Hill, New York.

Johnson, T.   1961   Man-guided evolution in plant rusts. Science *133*: 357–62.

Kettlewell, H. B.   1956   Further selection experiments on industrial melanism in the Lepidoptera. Heredity *10*: 287–301.

Kettlewell, H. B.   1961   The phenomenon of industrial melanism in Lepidoptera. Ann. Rev. Entomology *6*: 245–62.

Koopman, K. F.   1950   Natural selection for reproductive isolation between *Drosophila pseudoobscura* and *Drosophila persimilis*. Evolution *4*: 135–48.

Lederberg, J.   1960   Exobiology, experimental approaches to life beyond the earth. *In* H. K. Kallmann Bijl, editor. Proc. 1st International Space Science Symposium, pp. 1153–70. North Holland Publ. Co., Amsterdam, Holland.

Lerner, I. M.   1954   Genetic Homeostasis. Wiley, New York.

LIFE   1955   The World We Live In. Time, Inc., New York.

LIFE   1960   The Wonders of Life on Earth. Time, Inc., New York.

Mayr, E.   1942   Systematics and the Origin of Species. Columbia University Press, New York.

Morton, N. E., J. Crow, and H. J. Muller   1956   An estimate of the mutational damage in man from data on consanguineous marriages. Proc. Nat. Acad. Sc. *42*: 855–63.

Motulsky, A. G.   1960   Metabolic polymorphism and the role of infectious diseases in human evolution. Human Biol. *32*: 28–62.

Muller, H. J.   1955   Life. Science *121*: 1–9.

Muller, H. J.   1961   Human evolution by voluntary choice of germ plasm. Science *134*: 643–9.

Patterson, J. T., and M. R. Wheeler   1949   A catalogue of described species belonging to the genus *Drosophila* with observations on their geographical distribution. U. of Texas Publ. 4920.

Patterson, J. T., and W. S. Stone   1952   Evolution of the Genus *Drosophila*. Macmillan, New York.

Pontecorvo, G.   1943   Viability interactions between chromosomes of *Drosophila melanogaster* and *Drosophila simulans*. J. Genet. *45*: 51–66.

Sandler, L., and E. Novitski   1957   Meiotic drive as an evolutionary force. Am. Naturalist *91*: 105–10.

Scholander P. T., T. H. Hammel, J. S. Hart, D. H. Le Messuier, and J. Steen   1958   Cold adaptation in Australian aborigines. J. Appl. Physiol. *13*: 211–18.

Sheppard, P. M.   1959   Natural Selection and Heredity. Hutchinson's University Library, London.

Simpson, G. G.   1944   Tempo and Mode in Evolution. Columbia University Press, New York.

Simpson, G. G.   1945   The principles of classification and a classification of mammals. Bull. Am. Mus. Nat. Hist. *85*: 1–350.

Slatis, H. M., R. H. Reis, and R. E. Hoene   1958   Consanguineous marriages in the Chicago region. Am. J. Human Genetics *10*: 446–64.

Stern, C.   1949   Principles of Human Genetics, Chap. 27. Freeman, San Francisco.

Sturtevant, A. H., and E. Novitski   1941   The homologies of the chromosome elements of the genus *Drosophila*. Genetics *26*: 517–41.

Sturtevant, A. H.   1942   The classification of the genus *Drosophila* with a description of nine new species. U. of Texas Publ. No. 4213: 5–51.

Tax, S., editor   1960   Evolution after Darwin, Vols. 1–3. University of Chicago Press, Chicago.

Ward, H.   1927   Charles Darwin: the Man and His Welfare. Bobbs-Merrill, Indianapolis, Ind.

Weinberg, W.   1908   Über den Nachweis der Vererbung beim Menschen. Jahreshefte Verein f. vaterl. Naturk. in Wurttemberg *64*: 368–82.

White, M. J. D.   1954   Animal Cytology and Evolution, 2nd. ed. Cambridge University Press, Cambridge, England.

Wright, S.   1922   Coefficients of inbreeding and relationship. Am. Naturalist *56*: 330–38.

Wright, S.   1931   Evolution in Mendelian populations. Genetics *16*: 97–159.

Wright, S.   1948   On the roles of directed and random changes in the genetics of populations. Evolution *2*: 279–94.

APPENDIX

A. Chronology

Genetics has received stimulation from both related and quite independent sciences. In many cases the development of a particular physical instrument or technique has led to a golden age of discovery. Often the various areas of genetics have advanced in nonsynchronous spurts, and consequently it is difficult to develop a course in genetics from a strictly historical standpoint. The student, however, should have some idea of the chronological order in which certain events having a bearing on genetics took place. The following chronology will fill this need, even though every professional geneticist will complain about the inclusion of some events and the omission of others. Furthermore, a decade from now some of the recent discoveries may be relegated to less prominant positions. The student should keep the following thought in mind when perusing this catalogue. In science a great unifying concept generally does not spring full-blown from the mind of a single individual. Rather when the time is ripe perhaps a dozen authorities may grope about for an explanation, and all may be on the verge of the answer. However, often one man may first express the unifying concept in a clear fashion, and as a matter of convenience he is the one listed as the progenitor of the idea.

1590	Z. and H. Janssen combine two double convex lenses in a tube and produce the first compound microscope.
1651	W. Harvey puts forward the concept that all living things (including man) originate from eggs.
1657	R. de Graaf discovers follicles in the human ovary; interprets them incorrectly as eggs.
1665	R. Hooke publishes *Micrographia* in which he gives the first description of cells.
1677	A. van Leeuwenhoek observes sperms of man and other mammals; regards them as wild animalcules.
1680	F. Redi disproves the theory of spontaneous generation of maggots.
1694	R. J. Camerarius conducts early pollination experiments and reports the existence of sex in flowering plants.
1761	J. G. Kolreuter shows the semen of mammals and the pollen of flowers are essential for fertility.
1798	T. R. Malthus publishes anonymously an *Essay on Population*. This essay later suggests the concept of the struggle for existence and of the survival of the fittest to Darwin.
1809	J. B. Lamarck puts forward the view that species can change gradually into new species through a constant strengthening and perfecting of adaptive characteristics, and that these acquired characters are transmitted to the offspring.
1822	T. A. Knight, J. Goss, W. Herbert, and A. Seton initiate early work in plant hybridization.
1824	Prevost and Dumas discover that the fertilizing element in the mammalian semen is not the fluid itself but the spermatozoa.
1825	F. V. Raspail founds the science of histochemistry by using the iodine reaction for starch.

1830   G. B. Amici shows that the pollen tube grows down the style and into the ovule of the flower.

1831   R. Brown introduces the word "protoplasm." He also notes nuclei within cells.

1838   G. J. Mulder discovers proteins.

1838–9 M. J. Schleiden and T. Schwann develop the cell theory, a great generality of biology equaled only by the theory of evolution. Schleiden notes nucleoli within nuclei.

1841   A. Kölliker shows sperm to be sex cells which arise by transformation of cells in the testis.

1846   L. Quetelet publishes the *Theory of Probabilities*. He shows that a group of individuals gives a distribution which takes the form of the well-known binomial theorem of Newton.

1849   C. F. von Gaertner calls attention to the equivalence of reciprocal crosses.

1854   J. Dzierzon reports that drones hatch from unfertilized eggs; worker and queen bees from fertilized eggs.

1855   R. Virchow states the principle that new cells come into being only by division of previously existing cells.

1859   C. Darwin publishes *On the Origin of Species*.

1860   Laplace, Gauss, and Poisson found the mathematical theory of probability with researches initiated at this time.

1866   G. Mendel publishes "Experiments in Plant-Hybridisation."

1867   LaValette St. George discovers the cytoplasmic element later called the Golgi apparatus.

1869   F. Galton publishes *Hereditary Genius,* and so founds the scientific study of human heredity.
       F. Miescher isolates nucleoprotein.

1870   W. His invents the microtome.

1873   A. Schneider gives the first account of mitosis.

1875   O. Hertwig concludes from a study of the reproduction of the sea urchin that fertilization in both animals and plants consists of the physical union of the two nuclei contributed by the male and female parents.

1877   E. Abbe begins to publish important contributions to microscopic optics.
       H. Fol sees starfish spermatozoan penetrate an ovum.

1879   W. Flemming shows that nuclear division involves a longitudinal splitting of the chromosome and a migration of the daughter halves to the daughter nuclei. In 1882 he coins term mitosis.

1879   L. de Vilmorin establishes the progeny test.

1881   E. G. Balbiani discovers the giant salivary chromosomes in *Chironomus* larvae.

1883   E. van Beneden shows that the gametes of round worms contain half as many chromosomes as the body cells. He also describes fertilization in mammals.

1884   E. Strasburger describes fertilization in seed plants.

1887   W. Roux postulates that the chromosomes within the nucleus are the bearers of the hereditary factors.

1888   T. Boveri describes the centriole.
       W. Waldeyer names the chromosomes.

1892   T. Boveri describes meiosis in *Ascaris* (including synapsis).
       A. Weismann stresses the independence of the germ plasm from the body proper. He contradicts Lamarck by asserting that the only inherited variations arise in the germ plasm.

1894   E. Strasburger postulates that a periodic reduction in chromosome number must occur in all sexual organisms.

1895   W. C. Roentgen discovers X-rays.

1898   C. Benda discovers the mitochondria.
       K. Pearson develops the chi square technique.

1899   J. Loeb produces artificial parthenogenesis.

1900   De Vries, Correns, and Tschermak rediscover Mendel's paper.

        K. Landsteiner discovers the blood agglutination phenomenon in man.

1901   H. de Vries postulates the occurrence of spontaneous and discrete alterations in the hereditary material which are expressed as "sports" or mutations (the result of work with evening primroses, *Oenothera*).

1902   C. E. McClung describes sex chromosomes.

        W. S. Sutton advances the chromosome theory of heredity.

        T. Boveri shows experimentally that qualitative differences exist between chromosomes.

1902–09   W. Bateson introduces the terms allele, homozygote, heterozygote, F_1, F_2, and epistatic genes.

1903   E. Buchner receives the Nobel Prize for discovering the first enzyme.

1907   R. G. Harrison invents tissue culture.

        The Faraday medal is given to E. Fisher who separated and isolated 19 of the 20 amino acids making up proteins.

1908–09   The Hardy-Weinberg law is formulated.

1908–10   Nilsson Ehle puts forward the multiple factor hypothesis.

1909   G. H. Shull advocates the use of self-fertilized lines in production of commercial seed corn. The hybrid corn program which resulted created an abundance of foodstuffs worth over a billion dollars.

        W. Johannsen coins the words gene, genotype, phenotype.

        A. E. Garrod publishes *Inborn Errors in Metabolism,* the earliest study of the biochemical genetics of man (or any other species).

        F. A. Janssens suggests that exchanges between nonsister chromatids produce chiasmata.

1910   T. H. Morgan discovers white eye and consequently sex linkage in *Drosophila. Drosophila* genetics begins.

1913   A. H. Sturtevant provides the experimental basis for the linkage-distance concept.

1918   H. J. Muller discovers the balanced lethal phenomenon.

1920   A. F. Blakeslee discovers trisomics in *Datura.*

1921   C. B. Bridges describes triploid intersexes in *Drosophila.*

1922   C. B. Bridges discovers duplications, deficiencies, and translocations.

1924   S. Wright, R. A. Fisher, J. B. S. Haldane initiate advances in the mathematics of population genetics.

        R. Feulgen and H. Rossenbeck describe the cytochemical test which currently is most used for DNA localization.

        H. Spemann demonstrates that a living part of an embryo can exert a morphogenetic stimulus upon another part, bringing about its morphogenetic differentiation.

1925   E. B. Wilson publishes *The Cell in Development and Heredity.*

        A. H. Sturtevant analyzes the Bar phenomena in *Drosophila,* and discovers position effect. He finds the first inversion in 1926.

        F. Bernstein suggests that the A B O blood groups are determined by a series of allelic genes.

1926   S. S. Chetverikov initiates the genetic analysis of wild populations.

        J. B. Sumner isolates the first enzyme in crystalline form and shows it to be a protein.

1927   H. J. Muller reports the artificial induction of mutations in animals by X-rays.

1928   L. J. Stadler reports the same finding in plants.

1930   K. Landsteiner receives the Nobel Prize for his studies in immunology.

1931   C. Stern, and H. B. Creighton and B. McClintock provide the cytological proof of crossing over.

1932   M. Knoll and E. Ruska describe the prototype of the modern electron microscope.

1933   T. S. Painter initiates cytogenetic studies on the salivary gland chromosomes of *Drosophila.*

T. H. Morgan gets the Nobel Prize for his development of the theory of the gene.

1935   F. Zernicke describes the principle of the phase microscope.

G. W. Beadle and B. Ephrussi work out the genetics of eye-pigment production in *Drosophila.*

1936   J. Schultz notes the relation of the mosaic expression of a gene to its position relative to heterochromatin.

T. Caspersson uses cytospectrophotometric methods to investigate the quantitative chemical composition of cells.

1937   T. Dobzhansky publishes *Genetics on the Origin of Species.*

1938   T. M. Sonnenborn discovers the killer factor of *Paramecium.*

1940   K. Landsteiner and A. S. Wiener discover the Rh factor.

1941   G. W. Beadle and E. L. Tatum publish their classic study on the biochemical genetics of *Neurospora.*

1942   R. Schoenheimer publishes *The Dynamic State of Body Constituents.*

1944   O. T. Avery, C. M. MacLeod, and M. McCarty (1944) describe the pneumococcus transforming principle. The fact that it is DNA suggests that DNA and not protein is the hereditary chemical.

T. Dobzhansky describes the phylogeny of the gene arrangements in the third chromosome of *Drosophila pseudoobscura* and *D. persimilis.*

1946   H. J. Muller gets the Nobel Prize for his contributions to radiation genetics.

M. Delbruck and W. T. Bailey demonstrate genetic recombination in bacteriophage.

J. Lederberg and E. L. Tatum demonstrate genetic recombination in bacteria.

1948   A. Boivin, R. Vendrely, and C. Vendrely show that in the different cells of an organism the quantity of DNA for each haploid set of chromosomes is constant.

1949   M. M. Green and K. C. Green describe crossing over between alleles at the *lz* locus of *Drosophila.*

L. Pauling, H. A. Itano, S. J. Singer, and I. C. Wells show the H^S gene produces an abnormal hemoglobin.

1950   B. McClintock discovers the *Ac, Ds* system in maize.

1952   D. Mazia and K. Dan isolate the mitotic apparatus and start work on its biochemical characterization.

N. D. Zinder and J. Lederberg describe transduction in *Salmonella.*

R. Briggs and T. J. King transplant living nuclei from blastula cells into enucleated frog's eggs. They later demonstrate that nuclei undergo differentiation.

A. D. Hershey and M. Chase demonstrate that only the DNA of phage enters the host, whereas the protein remains behind.

1953   J. D. Watson and F. H. C. Crick propose a model for DNA comprised of two helically intertwined chains tied together by hydrogen bonds between the purine and pyrimidines.

1955   S. Benzer works out the fine structure of the genetic material of phage T_4 of *E. coli,* and coins the terms cistron, recon, and muton.

1956   M. Demerec and P. E. Hartman show that the order of certain metabolically related genes on the chromosome of *Salmonella typhimurium* is in the same sequence as the biochemical steps the genes control.

F. Jacob and E. L. Wollman are able to experimentally interrupt the mating process in *E. coli* and show that a piece of chromosome is slowly inserted from one bacterium into another.

Groups lead by S. Ochoa and A. Kornberg succeed in the *in vitro* enzymatic synthesis of polymers of ribonucleotides and deoxy-ribonucleotides, respectively. Thus a giant step is made toward the artificial synthesis of genetic material.

H. Fraenkel-Conrat and R. C. Williams reconstitute "hybrid" tobacco mosaic virus from nucleic acid and protein components arising from different sources.

C. O. Miller and his co-workers isolate and determine the chemical structure of kinetin, a substance promoting cell division.

P. I. Marcus, S. J. Cieciura, and T. T. Puck succeed in growing clones of human cells *in vitro.*

1957   J. H. Taylor, P. S. Woods, and W. L. Hughes make the first attempt to determine the mechanism of chromosomal duplication using tritiated thymidine for high resolution autoradiography.

1958   G. W. Beadle, E. L. Tatum, and J. Lederberg receive the Nobel Prize in biology and medicine for their contributions to genetics.

F. Sanger receives the Nobel Prize in chemistry for being the first to determine the sequence of amino acids in a protein molecule (insulin).

1959   S. Ochoa and A. Kornberg receive the Nobel Prize.

1960   P. B. Medawar and F. M. Burnett receive the Nobel Prize for their studies on immunological tolerance.

B. Periodicals which often contain articles oriented toward genetics and cytology

Acta Genetica et Statistica Medica
Acta Geneticae Medicae et Gemellologiae
Archiv der Julius Claus Stiftung für Vererbungsforschung
Acta Psychiatrica et Neurologica Scandinavica
Advances in Genetics
Advances in Virus Research
American Journal of Human Genetics
American Journal of Psychiatry
American Naturalist
Annals of Human Genetics
Annual Review of Microbiology
Bacteriological Reviews
Bibliographia Genetica
Biological Reviews of the Cambridge Philosophical Society
Canadian Journal of Genetics and Cytology
Carnegie Institution of Washington—Year Book
Caryologia
La Cellule
Chromosoma
Cold Spring Harbor Symposia in Quantitative Biology
Cytologia
Eugenics Quarterly
Eugenics Review
Evolution
Experimental Cell Research
Genetica
Genetical Research
Genetics
Growth
Hereditas

Heredity
Human Biology
International Review of Cytology
Japanese Journal of Human Genetics
Japanese Journal of Genetics
Journal de Genetique
Journal of Biophysical and Biochemical Cytology
Journal of Cellular and Comparative Physiology
Journal of Chronic Diseases: Medical Genetics
Journal of Experimental Zoology
Journal of Embryology and Experimental Morphology
Journal of Genetics
Journal of Heredity
Journal of Histochemistry and Cytochemistry
Journal of Molecular Biology
National Academy of Sciences, Proceedings of the
Nature
The Nucleus
Protoplasma
Quarterly Journal of Microscopical Science
Quarterly Review of Biology
Radiation Botany
Radiation Research
Resumptio Genetica
Revue Suisse de Zoologie
Royal Society of Edinburgh, Proceedings of the (Series B)
Stain Technology
Virology
Zeitschrift für induktive Abstammungs-und Vererbungslehre
Zeitschrift für menschliche Vererbungs-und Konstitutionslehre
Zeitschrift für Zellforschung und mikroskopische Anatomie

C. Some laboratories engaged in studies of human genetics throughout Canada, Mexico, and the United States

Canada

Province	City	Institution	Investigator in charge
Manitoba	Winnipeg	Hospital for Sick Children	Dr. I. Uchida
Ontario	Toronto	Dept. of Genetics, Hospital for Sick Children	Dr. N. F. Walker
Quebec	Montreal	Children's Memorial Hospital	Dr. F. C. Fraser

Mexico

Mexico	City	Institution	Investigator in charge
	Mexico City	Comision Nacional de Energia Nuclear	Dr. A. L. de Garay

United States

State	City	Institution	Investigator in charge
California	Berkeley	Dept. of Zoology, University of California	Dr. C. Stern

State	City	Institution	Investigator in charge
California	Los Angeles	Los Angeles Medical Center, University of California	Dr. S. Wright
	Palo Alto	Stanford University Medical School	Dr. N. Kretchmer
District of Columbia	Washington	Genetics Counseling Research Center, George Washington University Hospital	Dr. N. C. Myrian-thopoulos
Hawaii	Honolulu	University of Hawaii	Dr. J. B. Smith
Illinois	Chicago	Children's Memorial Hospital	Dr. D. Hsia
Louisiana	New Orleans	Tulane University School of Medicine	Dr. H. W. Kloepfer
Maryland	Baltimore	Moore Clinic, Johns Hopkins University	Dr. V. McKusick
Massachu-setts	Boston	Dept. of Immunochemistry, Boston University Medical School	Dr. W. C. Boyd
	Boston	Cancer Research Institute, New England Deaconess Hospital	Dr. W. E. Knox
Michigan	Ann Arbor	Dept. of Human Genetics, University of Michigan	Dr. J. V. Neel
	East Lansing	Genetic Clinic, Michigan State College	Dr. K. A. Stiles
Minnesota	Minneapolis	Dight Institute for Human Genetics, University of Minnesota	Dr. S. C. Reed
	Rochester	The Mayo Clinic	Dr. J. S. Pearson
North Carolina	Chapel Hill	Dept. of Pathology, School of Medicine, University of North Carolina	Dr. J. Graham
	Winston-Salem	Dept. of Medical Genetics, Bowman Gray School of Medicine	Dr. C. N. Herndon
New York	New York	Albert Einstein College of Medicine	Dr. H. Ranney and Dr. S. Gluecksohn-Waelsch
		New York State Psychiatric Institute, Columbia University	Dr. F. J. Kallmann
		Rockefeller Institute	Dr. A. G. Bearn
Ohio	Cleveland	Dept. of Biology, Western Reserve University	Dr. A. G. Stein-berg
Olkahoma	Norman	Dept. of Genetics, University of Oklahoma	Dr. P. R. David
Rhode Island	Providence	Institute for Research in Health Services, Brown University	Dr. G. W. Hagy
Texas	Austin	Genetics Foundation, University of Texas	Dr. C. P. Oliver
Utah	Salt Lake City	Laboratory of Human Genetics, University of Utah	Dr. C. L. Woolf
Virginia	Charlottes-ville	School of Medicine, University of Virginia	Dr. R. F. Shaw
	Richmond	Dept. of Biology and Genetics, Medical College of Virginia	Dr. B. L. Hanna
Washington	Seattle	Dept. of Medicine, University of Washington	Dr. A. Motulsky
Wisconsin	Madison	Dept. of Medical Genetics, University of Wisconsin	Dr. J. F. Crow

D. *Drosophila* culture

Living *Drosophila* of various mutant types are available for classroom use from various biological supply houses.

There are as many media used for rearing *Drosophila* as there are workers in the field. The following formula is as good as any: Propionic acid, 40 ml; agar, 85 g; rolled oats, 170 g; Brewer's yeast, 210 g: corn syrup, 840 ml; molasses (unsulphured), 840 ml; cornmeal, 680 g; water, 7650 ml. The dry ingredients are stirred until a homogeneous mixture results. The liquid ingredients are added, and the whole conglomeration is heated to boiling. The mixture is stirred constantly and allowed to boil for 15 minutes. It is then dispensed into sterile bottles, sterile cotton wadding is added, and the bottle is plugged with a sterile cardboard milk bottle cap. The bottles are refrigerated until they are used. The above formula will make about 100 one-half pint cultures. Each one-half pint culture takes about 50 ml of medium.

The propionic acid (CH_3CH_2COOH) serves as a fungicide. Other fungicides often used are: sodium orthophenylphenate (Dowicide A) and methyl-p-hydroxybenzoate (also called methyl parasept, tegosept M, or Nipagin). Mold growth rapidly destroys cultures which do not contain a fungicide. Old cultures should be washed up as soon as possible to prevent multiplication of mites.

E. Motion pictures or film strips which illustrate material covered in specific chapters.

Chapter	Film
2	McGraw-Hill Film 38 (J. D. Watson—DNA Structure and Replication)[1]
2	McGraw-Hill Film 42 (J. Schultz—Chromosome Chemistry & Genetic Activity)[1]
2	M. Chevremont and J. Frederic: Les chondriosomes (the mitochondria) (Silent)[2]
3	A Bajer and J. Mole-Bajer: Mitosis in endosperm. I. (Silent)[2]
3	C. M. Pomerat: The HeLa cell strain.[2]
3	A. S. Fraser: Meiosis[3]
3	K. Michel: Spermatogenesis in the grasshopper. (Silent)[2]
4	The basic nature of sexual reproduction[4]
4	McGraw-Hill Film 44 (J. Lederberg—Bacterial Genetics: Sexual Reproduction)[1]
4	McGraw-Hill Film 45 (J. Lederberg—Bacterial Genetics: Genetic Transduction)[1]
5	McGraw-Hill Film 9 (C. Stern—Allelism and Lethals)[1]
5	McGraw-Hill Film 10 (C. Stern—Pleiotropism, Penetrance and Expressivity)[1]
7	McGraw-Hill Film 8 (J. F. Crow—Multiple Factor Inheritance)[1]
9	McGraw-Hill Film 16 (G. W. Beadle—Crossingover in Terms of Meiosis)[1]
9	McGraw-Hill Film 17 (G. W. Beadle—Crossing, Chiasmata, and Genetic Maps)[1]
10	McGraw-Hill Film 20, 21 (H. J. Muller—Structural Changes in Chromosomes I, II)[1]
11	McGraw-Hill Film 19 (H. J. Muller—Chromosome Addition and Subtraction)[1]
11	McGraw-Hill Film 18 (H. J. Muller—Changes in Genome Number)[1]
12	McGraw-Hill Films 13, 14 (C. Stern—Sex Determination I, II)[1]
13	McGraw-Hill Film 23 (H. J. Muller—Mutagen-induced Gene Mutation)[1]
13	McGraw-Hill Film 37 (R. A. Brink—Variegated Pericarp, an Unstable Allele in Maize)[1]
14	McGraw-Hill Films 39, 40 (G. W. Beadle—Biochemical Genetics I, II)[1]
14	McGraw-Hill Film 36 (E. B. Lewis—Pseudoallelism)[1]

14   McGraw-Hill Film 46 (J. Lederberg—Virus Genetics: Bacteriophage)[1]
15   McGraw-Hill Film 34 (T. M. Sonneborn—Cytoplasmic Heredity)[1]
15   McGraw-Hill Film 35 (T. M. Sonneborn—Nucleo-cytoplasmic Relations in *Paramecium*)[1]
16   McGraw-Hill Films 32, 33 (L. C. Dunn—Developmental Genetics I, II)[1]
17   Darwin's World of Nature[5]
17   McGraw-Hill Film 30 (J. F. Crow—Inbreeding and Heterosis)[1]
17   McGraw-Hill Film 27 (T. Dobzhansky—The Genetics of Race)[1]
17   McGraw-Hill Film 28 (G. L. Stebbins—The Origin of Species)[1]
17   McGraw-Hill Film 48 (J. Lederberg—Biochemical Origin of Terrestrial Life)[1]

[1] Available from the Visual Aids Service, University of Illinois, Champaign, Ill.
[2] Films available from Dr. D. C. Hetherington, Duke Hospital, Durham, N. C.
[3] Films available from the International Film Bureau, 57 E. Jackson Blvd., Chicago, Ill.
[4] Films available from the Audiovisual Center, Indiana University, Bloomington, Indiana
[5] Nine film strips available from Time-Life Bldg., Rockefeller Center, New York 20, N. Y.

Useful Material for Laboratory Use and Vendor

Carolina Biological Supply Co., Elon College, N. C.
  Drosophila cultures
  Mormoniella cultures
General Biological Supply Co., 8200 South Hoyne Ave., Chicago 20, Ill.
  Drosophila cultures, corn ears showing segregating kernel populations, *Acetabularia*.
  Stained microscope slides: grasshopper spermatogenesis, lily microsporogenesis, onion root tip mitosis, crayfish spermatogenesis, amphibian larval epidermal mitosis, cleaving whitefish eggs, *Drosophila* salivary gland smears.
A. E. Galiger, Box 63, Albany Station, Berkeley, Calif.
  Stained microscope slides: squash bug spermatogenesis, *Batrachoseps* spermatogenesis, *Ascaris* fertilization, maturation, and cleavage.
M. Demerec and B. P. Kaufman 1961 Carnegie Institution of Washington, 1530 P St. N. W., Washington 5, D. C., 25¢.
  The Drosophila Guide — Introduction to the Genetics and Cytology of *Drosophila melanogaster*.
Mann Instrument Co., San Francisco, Calif.
  Ishihara Colorblindness Test Charts.

INDEX

NOTE: Page references to tables and figures are indicated in bold face type.

A B O blood group system, 228; legal aspects, 243
Aberrations, chromosomal, 129–54, 198–200
Ac (locus), 186–88
Acentric chromosomes, 33, 136
Acetabularia, 272, **273**
Acospores, 53, 123, **124**
Acridine dyes, 209
Acrosomes, 37–38
Activator (locus), 186–88
Adaptive norm, 313–15
Adenosine triphosphate (ATP), 16, 129
Aegilops ovata, 260
Aegilops speltoides, 156
Aegilops squarrosa, 157
Aegilops umbellulata, 157
Afibrinogenemia, 225
Agglutination of blood cells, 227–29
Albinos, 216, 320
Aleurone, 51; pigmentation, 81–82, **82,** 87, 186, **187**
Alkaptonuria, 215
Allelism, 65, 69, 185; test for, 233
Allium, 198
Allopolyploidy, 166
Allotetraploids, 156, 161–62
Alpha particle, 191–92, **192**
Altenberg, E., 188
Amorphic allele, 69
Amphidiploid, 156
Amyloplasts, 16
Anemia, sickle-cell, 220–22, **220, 221,** 306–7
Aneucentric translocation configuration, **142**
Aneuploidy, 143, 148, 155, 162–65, **162**
Ångström unit, defined, 191n

Annuli, of nuclear envelope, 14
Antibodies, 225–31
Antigens, 225–31
Antimutagens, 189
Apis mellifera, 285; *see also* Bees
Apomixis, 180
Arithmetic mean, 96n
Arrhenotokous parthenogenesis, 40, 178
Arrowhead sequence, 310–13
Ascogonium, **52**
Ascospores, 53, 124, **124**
Asexual reproduction, **62,** 180
Aspergillus nidulans, 126, 176
Assortative mating, 300
Attached-X females, 108
Auerbach, C., 188
Autogamy, 55
Autopolyploidy, 166
Autoradiography, 9–11, **10**
Autosomes, 106
Autotetraploids, 158–62, **159–61**
Auxotrophs, 56
Avery, O. T., 190

ba (gene), 181
Back cross, 76–77
Bacteria: lysogenized, 60; transformed, 190
Bacteriophages, 56–61, **59**
"Balance" hypothesis for origin of the adaptive norm, 313
Balanced lethal systems, 146–49, **147**
"Balancing" chromosomes, 137–38, **137**
Baldness, 111
Baltzer, F., 176
Bar (gene), 133–34, **133, 134,** 149–51, **150, 151**

Batesian mimicry, 321
Beadle, G. W., 127, 241
Beale, G. H., **54**
Beermann, W., 25, 232, 290
Bees: behavior patterns, 285; parthenogenesis in, 40
Behavior: and genetics, 285–88; "retiring," 289
Bennett, J. H., 322
Benzer, S., 238, **239**, 240, 245
Bernstein, F., 228
Beta particle, **192**
Bilateral gynandromorphs, 173, **174**, 241
Billingham, R. E., 260
Bisexuality, and polyploidy, 173–75
Biston betularia, 307–8
Bittner, J. J., 253
Bivalents, 35
Blakeslee, A. F., 163, **163**
Blindness, due to hereditary causes, 205
Blood: coagulation, 225; groups, 227–31; hemoglobin types, 219–25, 232; transfusions, 227–29
Bobbed (gene), 175
Bombyx mori (silkworm), 262, 282
Bonellia viridis, 176, **177**
Bonner, D. M., 218
Boycott, A. E., 259
Bracon brevicornis (synonym for *Habrobracon juglandis*), **179**
Brassica oleracea, 166
Breakage-fusion-bridge cycles, **140**, 141
Breeding, selective, 97–99, 288
Brenner, S., 209
Bridges, C. B., **23**, 124, 129, 131, 132, 168, **170**
Bridges, P. N., 131
Briggs, R., 267, **268**
Brink, R. A., 187–88
Bristles, of *Drosophila,* 284–85, front endpaper
Brock, T. D., 175
Burnet, F. M., 227
Burst size, 58

C l B technique, 195–96, **196**
Callan, H. G., **22**, 23, 232
Cancer, 253–55, 264–67
Carbohydrates, in tissues, 13

Carbon dioxide, sensitivity of *Drosophila* to, 251–52
cardinal (mutant), 216
carnation (gene), 149–51, **150**
Carcinogens, 289
Cartilage, formation of, 290
Cats, coat color in, 110, 182
Caucasoid ethnic group, 309
'Cecidomyia' serotinae, **26**
Cells, control of proliferation of, 264–67, 271; division of, 32–33, methods for studying, 3–12; number in infant, 65; nurse, 49; sensitivity to radiation of, 195, 201–2; structure of, 13–27; *see also* Chromosomes; Genes; Nuclei
Centrioles, 31, 37
Centromeres, 20, **20**, 33, 42, 195
Centrosome, 17, 31, **39**
Cesium[137], 206
Chemical mutagens, 188–90
Chemostat, 188, 189, 207
Chi-square method, 84–86, **84, 85**
Chiasmata, 36, 113
Chickens: broodiness, 288; comb shape, 83–84, **83;** Frizzle feather mutation, 77, 291; plumage, 77, 87; "sex reversals," 110
Chiricahua sequence, 310–13
Chironomus, **24, 25**
Chlorophyll inheritance, 255–57
Chloroplasts, 16, 255–57, **256**
Christmas disease, 107, 225
Chromatids, 32–33, 36; double *Bar,* 133, **133,** exchanges, 113–26, **114, 123,** 138, 139; separation of, 159–60, **159**
Chromocenter, 27
Chromonemata, 19, 20, 202–4, **203**
Chromoplasts, 16
Chromosomal phylogenetic tree, **312**
Chromosomes, 17–27, **21–27,** 31–43, 65; aberrations, 129–54, **131, 139, 148, 150, 151,** 198–200; 310, **311;** appearance at anaphase, 33, 42; "balancing," 137–38, **137;** broken, 198–200; of *'Cecidomyia' serotinae,* **26;** doubling, 155–56; of *Drosophila,* 23, **23, 27,** 136–37, **136, 151,** 316–18, **316;** duplications, 133–34; dynamics of, 31–43; giant, 21–27; haploid, 35,

62; irradiation of, 195; in meiosis, 35–40; of midge, **24;** in mitosis, 32–33; of newt, **32;** number, variations in, 155–67; polymorphism, 310–13; replication, 31–32; rod-shaped, 126; segregation during gametogenesis, **73;** transfer of bacterial, **57;** X-chromosomes, 106–9, 116, **116,** 120–21, 122, **131,** 136, **136,** 168–75; Y-chromosomes, 106–8, **106,** 136, 168–75; *see also* Genes

Chronology of scientific discoveries, 325–29

Chronomeres, 20–23, **21**

Cilia, 37

cinnabar (gene), 216

Cis configuration, 235–36, **236**

Cistrons, 233, 235–36, 238–40, **239**

claret (gene), 103–4

Clark, E., 289

"Classical" hypothesis for origin of the adaptive norm, 313

Clever, U., 291

Coe, W. R., 177, **178**

Coefficient of coincidence, 116

Coefficient of variation, 92

Colchicine, 33, 155–56

Coli-phage system, 55–56

Comparison of reproduction: man, *Drosophila*, maize, *Neurospora*, *Paramecium*, *E. coli*, 62

Complementation, 237–40

Compound eyes, in *Drosophila*, 133–34, **134,** 216–18, 241, front endpaper

Conidia, 51

Conjugation, *Paramecium*, 53–55, **54**

Conklin, E. G., 263

Constitutive enzymes, 270

Corn. *See* Maize

Coupling configuration, 106

Cousin matings, 301, 321

Creeper (gene), 279–80

Creighton, H. B., 151

Crepidula, 177, **178**

Cretinism, 215–16

Cricetulus griseus, 173

Cross agglutination tests, 227, **228**

Crosses: autotetraploid, 160, **160, 161;** back, 76–77; dihybrid, 69–74, 77–78, 80; in *Drosophila*, **106,** 107, 110–11, 114, **115, 250,** 259, *ebony claret,* 103–5, **104, 105;** monohybrid, 67–69; multifactor, 75–76; reciprocal, 105–6, 249, **250;** test, 76, 105–6; tetraploid dihybrid, 160, **161**

Crossing over, 36, **62,** 113–28; between *Bar* and *carnation,* 150–51, **150;** classes, 105–6, 114–16; cytological proof of, 149–51; double, 114–22; factors affecting, 124–25; and inversions, 136, 138–41; sexual differences in, **124;** somatic, 125–26; and tetrad stage, 123–24, **123;** three-point cross, 114–20; unequal, 133, **133**

Crossover mapping. *See* Genetic mapping

Crossover units, defined, 116

Crowther, J. A., 193

Cucurbita pepo, 83

Curly (mutant), 77, 103

Cytochemistry of chromosomes, 20

Cytokinesis, 33

Cytological mapping, 131–32; *see also* **Fig. 10-4**

Cytophotometry, 7–8

Cytoplasm, 14–17; irradiation of, 195; and nuclear differentiation, 271–72; organelles of, 15–17; self-regulation, 272

Dalton, H. C., 283

Danforth's short tail (gene), 278

Darwin, Charles, 296–97, 320

Das, N. K., 33

Datura stramonium, 163, **163,** 164

Davenport, C. B., 101

Deafness due to hereditary causes, 205

Deficiencies: chromosomal, 129–32, **131,** 138, **139**

Deformities, hereditary, 205

Degrees of freedom, **84, 85,** 86

Delayed expression of mutations, 208

Delbruck, M., 58

De Marinis, F., 133

Demerec, M., 186, 236, 237

Deoxyribose, 17

Deoxyribose nucleic acid (DNA), **9, 10,** 17–25, **19,** 28–29, 32, 56, 174, 190, 205, 207, 222–24, **223, 224,** 245, frontispiece

Devine, R. L., 37
Dicentric chromosomes, 33, 136, 141
Dihybrid cross, 69–74, 77–78, 80; tetraploid, 160, **161**
Dihydroxyphenylalanine (DOPA) 213, **214**
Diploids, **162,** 163–64; "double," 156
Diplotene stage, 36
Dippell, R. V., 252
Discoveries, chronological list of scientific, 325–29
Dissociation (locus), 186–88
Dizygotic twins, 61
Dobzhansky, T., 310–14, 320
Dogs, selective breeding of, 288
Dominance, concept of, 67; origin of, 308
Dosage compensation, 175, 182
Dotted (gene), 186–87, **187**
Double *Bar,* 133, **133**
Double crossover, 114–22
"Double diploids," 156
Double exchanges, 121–22
Driesch, H., 263
Drosophila (genus), culture of, 332; evolution of, 316–18, **316**
Drosophila buskii, 272
Drosophila hydei, 264
Drosophila Information Service, 45
Drosophila melanogaster, 44–49; adult morphology, front end paper, **47;** allelism test, 233–34; aneuploidy, 162–63; attached-X females, 108; *Bar,* 133–34, **133, 134,** 149–51, **150, 151;** bilateral gynandromorph, 173, **174,** 241; bristle pattern, 284–85; and chi-square method, 84–86, **84, 85;** chromosomes, 23, **23, 27,** 136–37, **136, 151,** 316–18, **316, Fig. 10-4;** crosses, **106,** 107, 107n, 110–11, 114, **115, 250,** 259; crossing over, 113, **114, 125,** 126; *Curly,* 77, 103; dosage compensation, 175, 182; *dumpy,* 77; egg production, 168, **169;** embryogenesis, 274–75, **275;** eyes of, 87, 133–34, **134,** 216–18, 241; *fes* sterility factor, 111; *fused,* 250–51, 265; hereditary virus, 251–52; heritability values, **99;** homeotic mutants, 280, **281;** intersexes, 168–71, **170;** larvae, 45–47, **46, 284;** life cycle, 45–49; mapping of genes on chromosomes, **117-20,** 121, 131–32, **Fig. 10-4;** meiosis, 138; mutants, 103, 108–9, **108,** 117–21, 263, 277, 285; mutation, 186, 195–98, **197;** offspring, 168–71, **169,** 173, 181; oocytes, **263;** ovarian tumors, 265, 266; pseudoallelism, 234–36, **234-36;** pseudotumors, 283, **284;** radiation genetics of, 195–98, 200, 202–3, 208; reproductive system, **48, 49;** *rosy,* 274; salivary glands, 131–32, **Fig. 10-4;** sex chromosomes, 106; supersexes, 168–71, **170;** *transformer,* 171, 285, 288; translocations, 142–46, **144-46,** 149–51, **200, 201;** and tryptophan, 216
Drosophila miranda, 310
Drosophila persimilis, 310, **312,** 321
Drosophila prosaltans, 314–15, **314**
Drosophila pseudoobscura, 175, 301, 310–14, **312, 314,** 321
Drosophila simulans, 259
Drosophila subobscura, 259
Drosophila willistoni, 252, 314, **314**
Drosopterins, 216, 241
Ds (locus), 186–88
Dt (gene), 186–87, **187**
Duplex autotetraploids, 158–60, **159**
Duplications, chromosomal, 133–34
Dwarfism, 66–68, **66,** 216, 280, **282**
Dyads, 36–37

East, E. M., 94, 95
Ebony body (mutant), 103
Ebony claret cross, 103–5, **104, 105**
Ebony-sooty (mutant), 103
Ecdysone, 291
Edington, C. W., 198
Eggs: enucleation of, 267–69, **268;** produced by *Drosophila,* 168, **169**
Elaioplasts, 16
Electron microscope, 4, **5**
Electron volt, defined, 192n
Embryo, development of, 262–91
Embryo sac, 50, back endpaper
Embryonic fields, 284
Emerson, R. A., 94, 127

Endoplasmic reticulum, **15,** 16
Endosperm, 50–51, back endpaper
Enucleation, of eggs, 267–69, **268**
Environment: and determination of sex, 176–77; and mutation, 188; and quantitative inheritance, 89; influence on intelligence, 288
Enzymes, 213–18, 225, 231, 270
Ephestia kühniella, 249, **250**
Ephrussi, B., 241, 257
Episomes, 61
Epistacy, 80, 88
Erythroblastosis fetalis, 230
Escherichia coli, 55–56, **57,** 190, 207; metabolism in, 270; *r* II mutants, 238–40, **239;** reproduction of, **62**
Eucentric reciprocal translocations, 141–49, **142,** 317, **317**
Euchromatin, 25–27
Euploidy, 148, 155
Evolution, 296–324; of *Drosophila,* 316–18, **316;** human, 318–19; microevolution, 305–8; through polyploidy, 162; rates of, 318
Exchanges, chromatid, 113–26, **114, 123,** 138, **139**
Excitation, process of, 191
Exconjugants, 55
Eyes: of *Drosophila,* 87, 133–34, **134,** 216–18, 241; transplantations of primordia, 241–42

F_1 individuals, 66–67
F_2 generation, 66–67
Falconer, D. S., 98, **99, 299**
Fallout, 206, 208
Fankhauser, G., 41
female-sterile (gene), 111, 265, **266**
Female gonadal dysgenesis, 171
Fertilization, 39–40, **39,** 67, 143, **145;** self-fertilization, 180
Fetus: hemoglobin of, 232; incompatibilities with mother, 229–30
Feulgen, R., 29
Feulgen test, 20
Fibrinogen, 225
Ficq, A., **10**
Film strips for teaching aids, 332–33
Fisher, R. A., 299

5-Bromouracil, 208–9
Fixative, 4
Flies. *See Drosophila*
Flagellum, 37, **38**
Flower pigmentation, inheritance of, 77
Formyl kynurenine, 216, **217**
Fox, A. L., 78
Fox, S., 321
Fraenkel-Conrat, H., 245
Fraser, A. C., 127
Freemartins, 181
Freese, E., 209
Frequency distributions, **91,** 92–4
Frizzle feather mutation, 77, 291
Frogs, egg enucleation in, 267–69, **268**
Fruit fly. *See Drosophila melanogaster*
Fujii, S., 232
Fukasawa, H., 260
fused (gene), 250–51, 265, 289

Galactosides, metabolism in *E. coli,* 270
Gall, J. G., **22,** 23
Galls, on plants, 290
Gametes: aneuploid, 143; gametogenesis, 35–39, 72, **73;** male and female, **71,** 74, **74,** 75; mutation, 185–86, **186;** X- and Y-bearing, 107
Gametocytes, 148
Gametophytes, 50
Gamma rays, 191, **192**
Gastrula nuclei, 268–69
Gastrulation, 277
Genes, 213–48; action, time of, 273–74; active, 65–66; and aleurone color in maize, 81–82, 87, 186, **187;** and cellular dynamics, 276–77; compensator, 175; complementary, 81; and cytological processes, 264–67; and developmental processes, 274–75; dispensable, 218–19; frequencies, 297–305; and growth hormones, 280–82; H^s, in Negroes, 306–7, 320; Hardy-Weinberg law, 297–305, **299;** inactive, 65–66; indispensable, 218–19; interaction of, 80–84; interaction with cytoplasmic factors, 249–61; intergenic regulation, 270–71; linked, 103–11; migration, 304; nature of, 233–34;

Genes (*continued*)
    and organizer systems, 278–80, **279;** recessive, 181, 256; suppressor, 231–33; transfer between species, 157–58; *transformer,* 171, 285, 288; *see also* Chromosomes; Lethals; Mutation

Genetic drift, 305

Genetic mapping, 113–21; *Drosophila melanogaster,* mutants of, **117–20,** 121; *D. melanogaster,* salivary gland chromosomes of, 131–32, **Fig. 10–4;** maize, 127; *r* II region of T$_4$ phage 238–40, **239;** X-chromosome, 116, **116**

Genetic ratios, **74;** modification of, 79–88

Genomes of wheat, 156–57

Genotype, 66; classes, 71–76, **74;** and comb shape, **83;** and fruit shape, 83; masking expression of, 79–82; prediction of frequencies by Hardy-Weinberg law, 297, 298, **299;** and selection, 302

Geometric mean, 96n

Germarium, 48

Gibberellic acid, 280

Golgi apparatus, **15,** 16–17, 37

Gordon, M., **265,** 289

Grandchildless (gene), 259

Grasshopper, spermatogenesis in, **34,** 35

Green, M. M., 234

Growth hormones, 280–82

Gynandromorphs, bilateral, 173, **174**

Gynandromorphs, bilateral, 173, **174** 241

H^S gene, in Negroes, 306–7, 320

Habrobracon juglandis (synonym for *Bracon brevicornis*), 178, **179**

Hadorn, E., 274, 275

Hair pigment, of mice, 87

Hairless (gene), 272–73

Haldane, J. B. S., 110, 299

Half life, defined, 206n

Hammerling, J., 272

Hamsters, 173–74

Hannah-Alava, A., 284, 285

Hansenula wingei, 175–76

Haplodiploidy, 178

Haploidy, 35, 65, 155

Hardy-Weinberg law, 297–305, **299**

Health, and radiation, 205–6

Hemizygosity, 107

Hemoglobin, 219–25, **223,** 232

Hemophilia, 110, 225

Hemophilus influenzae, 190

Heredity, 65–77; chlorophyll inheritance, 255–57; interaction of genic and nongenic units, 249–61; maternal inheritance, 249–51, **250;** and mental and physical deficiencies, 205–6; quantitative inheritance, 89–102; transmission of self-reproducing particles, 251–57

Heritability, 98–99, **99**

Hermaphrodites, 177

Heterobrachial inversions, 134

Heterocaryons, 51, 53, 219

Heterochromatic blocks, 138–41

Heterochromatin, 25–27, 138–41, 146, 270

Heterchromosomes, 27, 106

Heterogametic sex, 107

Heterogenote, 56

Heteropyknosis, 41

Heterosis, 149

Heterosomal aberrations, 141

Heterozygotes, 66–69; paracentric inversion, **135,** 136; translocation, **147**

Hidden breaks in DNA, 207

High frequency of recombination (Hfr), strain of *E. coli,* 56, **57**

Himalayan strain of rabbits, 291

Hiraizumi, Y., 188

Histocompatibility loci, 226

Histone, 19

Homeotic mutants, 280, **281**

Homo sapiens. See Man

Homobrachial inversions, 134

Homogametic sex, 107

Homosomal aberrations, 129

Homozygotes, 65–69

Horowitz, N. H., 218

Hotchkiss, R. D., 190

Hughes-Schrader, S., 181

Humphrey, R. R., 290

Hutt, F. B., 288

Huxley, J., 264

Hybrid inviability, 315

Hydroperoxyl radicals, 192

Hydroxy kynurenine, 216, **217**
Hydroxyl radicals, 192
Hyphae, 51
Hypomorphic allele, 69

Imaginal discs, 47
Immigration of genes, 304
Immunization, transplacental, 230
Immunological tolerance, 226–27
Inbreeding, 300–301
Independent assortment of gene pairs, 73
Induced chromosomal aberrations, 198–200, **199, 200**
Inducible enzymes, 270
Industrial melanism, 307–8
Ingram, V. M., 222
Inheritance. *See* Heredity
Instar, 45n, **46**
Insulin, 243
Intelligence, of twins, 288
Interchromosomal aberrations, 141–51,
Interference, 116, 120
Interphase cells, 31
Intersexes, 168–71, **170**
Intrachromosomal aberrations, 129–41
Intramitochondrial fluid, 16
Inversions, chromosomal, 134–41, 196, 310, **311**
Ionizing radiations, 191–93
Isoelectric point, defined, 219n
Isotopes, radioactive, 9–10, 9n

Jacob, F., 61, 294
James, A. P., 205
Jimson weed, 163

Kappa particles, 252–53, **254**
Karlson, P., 291
Karpechenko, G. D., 166
Kellner, A., 210
Keratin, 291
Kettlewell, H. B., **308**
Killer paramecia, 252–53, **254**
Kinetin, 33
Kinetochore, 20n
King, R. C., 202, 263, 265, 289
Klinefelter's syndrome, 171

Knipling, E. F., 208
Kornberg, A., 18, 29
Krimm, S., 291
Kroeger, H., 272
Kühn, A., **250**
Kuru disease, 322
Kynurenine, 216, **217**, 249

LET value, defined, 192
Laboratories of human genetics, 330–31
Lampbrush chromosomes, 21, **22**
Landsteiner, K., 227
Lang, A., 87
Larvae, of *Drosophila melanogaster,* 45–47, **46**
Lawler, S. D., 111
Lazy (mutant), 282, **283**
Lea, D. E., 198
Lederberg, J., 227
Lees, A. D., 273
Lethal equivalent, 301
Lethals: amount of normal development in various homozygous, **275;** balanced, 146–49, **147;** sex-linked recessive, 195–98, **196, 197;** translocation homozygote, 145
Levitan, M., 152
L'Héritier, P. L., 251
Light microscope, 3, **4**
Lilium, 198
Lillie, F. R., 181, 263
Lima-de-Faria, A., 32
Limnea peregra, 259
Lindsley, D. L., 198
Linkage: complete and incomplete, 113; groups, 103–11; sex, 106–7
Linkage maps. *See* Genetic mapping
Linked genes, 103–11; in man, 111, 244
Lipids, 13
Liturgosa, 181
lozenge alleles, 234, **235**
Lymphoid cells, 227
Lynch, C., **250**
Lysogenized bacteria, 60

McCarty, M., 190
McClintock, B., **140,** 141, 151, 186, 187, 188, 270
MacLeod, C. M., 190

Macroconidia, 51
Macronuclei, 53–55, 271
Magnifying systems, 3–4
Maize, 50–51; aleurone pigmentation, 81–82, **82**, 87, 186, **817**, breakage-fusion-bridge cycle, **140**, 141; *Dissociation-Activator* system, 186–88; ear length, 94–95, **94**, **96**, 97, 100; growth, 282, **283**; life cycle, back endpaper; mutants, 264; pollen, 257–58; recessive genes, 181, 256; reproduction, **62**; spontaneous mutation rates, **186**
Mammary tumor agent (MTA), 253–55
Man: evolution of, 318–19; hemoglobin types, 219–25, 232; lethal radiation dose, 201–2, 201n; as object for genetic research, 61–62; phenylalanine-tyrosine metabolism, 213–16; as polymorphic species, 309–10; sex determination, 171; trisomy and triploidy, 164–65
Mangold, H., 277
Mapping. *See* Cytological mapping; Genetic mapping
Mate killers, 253
Maternal inheritance, 249–51, **250**
Mating: assortative, 300; of cousins, 301, 321; random, 299–301; types, 176
Mazia, D., 33
Medawar, P. B., 227
Mediterranean flour moth, 178
Megaspores, 50
Meiosis, 35–37, **Fig. 3–3**
Meiotic drive, 301
Melandrium album, 172, **172**
Melanism, industrial, 307–8
Mendel, Gregor, 67–74, 79
Mendelian populations, 299
Merogonic hybrids, 289
Mesocricetus auratus, 174
Metacentric chromosomes, 33
Metamorphosis, 45
mi-3 mutant strain, 257
Mice: dwarfs, 280, **282;** hair pigment, 87; mammary cancer, 253–55; mutation rate higher than *Drosophila,* 202; skin grafting, 226–27
Microbeam irradiations, 195
Microconidia, 51

Micro-evolution, 305–8
Micron, defined, 3n
Micronuclei, 53–55
Microscopes: electron, 4, **5;** light, 3, **4; phase-contrast, 11
Microspectrophotometry, 8, **8**
Microspores, 50
Microtome, 4, 5
Midge, chromosome of, **24**
Migration of genes, 304
Millimicron, defined, 3n
Mimicry, 321
Miscegenation, 322
Mitchell, H. K., 257
Mitochondria, 15–16, **15,** 257
Mitosis, 32–33, **Fig. 3–1**
Modal class, 90
Monads, 37
Mongoloidism, 164–65
Mongoloid ethnic group, 309
Monod, J., 294
Monoecious plants, 50
Monohybrid cross, 67–69
Monosaccharides, 13
Monosomic diploids, **162,** 163
Monozygotic twins, 61; cancer incidence, 267
Morgan, T. H., 263
Moscona, A., 290
Moses, M. J., 174
Mother-fetus incompatibilities, 229–30
Motion pictures useful for teaching, 332–33
Mu particles, 253
Muller, H. J., 116, 137, 173, 175, 188, 195, **196,** 198, **201,** 316
Mullerian mimicry, 321
Multi cistron-assembly line hypothesis, 236
Multifactor crosses, 75–76
Multiple factor hypothesis, 94–96
Multiple sexuality, 176
Multiple strand exchanges, 121–22, **122, 135**
Multirecon-cistron hypothesis, 235–36
Mutagens: chemical, 188–90; radiations as, 190–94; ultraviolet light as, 204–5
Mutants: of *Drosophila,* **117–20;** affecting cytological processes, 264; as-

signment to linkage groups, 108–9; *r* II type of T₄ phage, 238–40, **239;** subvital, 198

Mutation, 185–212; by chemical means, 188–90; dispensable and indispensable, 218–19; factors influencing, 186–88; by radiations, 190–98, **197;** rates, **186,** 188; recessive lethal, 195–98, **196, 197;** recurrent, 301–2; and selection, 303–4; spontaneous, 185–86, **186;** suppressor mutations, 231–33; and ultraviolet light, 204–5; *see also* Genes

Muton, 233

Mycelium, 51

Myelencephalic blebs gene, 277

Nail-patella syndrome, 111

*narrow*² gene, 265

Natural selection, theory of, 296–97

Nebenkern, 37

Negative interference, 120

Negroes: *H*ˢ gene in, 306–7; 320; pigmentation, 101, 309

Neurospora crassa, 51–53, **52, 62,** 123, **124,** 218, 257

Newcombe, H. B., 205

Nilsson-Ehle, H., 95

Nitrous acid, action on nucleic acid, 245

Nondisjunction, 164

"Nonsense RNA," 28

Notch mutation, 129–32, **130, 131**

Novick, A., 188, 189, 207

Novitski, E., 301

Nuclei, 14, **15;** aneuploid, 155; chemistry of, 17–20; euploid, 155; polar, 38–39, **39;** sensitivity to radiation, 195; transplantation of, 267–69; *see also* Cells; Chromosomes; Genes

Nucleic acids, 7, 17; *see also* DNA; RNA

Nucleolus: irradiation of, 195; nucleolusless zygotes, 290; organizer, 20–21, **21**

Nucleoproteins, 13

Nucleoplasm, 14, **15**

Nucleosides, 18

Nucleotides, 18; pairs, **19,** frontispiece

Nurse cells, 49

Ocelli, 249

Ochoa, S., 18

Oenothera, 149

Oksala, T., 138, 141

Olsen, N. W., 111

Olympic sequence, 310

One gene-one enzyme hypothesis, 218, 225

One gene-one polypeptide chain hypothesis, 225

Oocytes, 39, 49, 263–64, **263**

Oogenesis, 38–39, 263–64

Oogonial chromosomes, **23**

Organelles, cytoplasmic, 15–17

Organizer systems, 278–80, **279**

Origin of life, 321

Ottolenghi, E., 190

Ovarioles, 48, **48**

Oxygen concentration: effect on radiosensitivity, 204

Paeonia californica, 149

Paracentric inversions, 134–36, **135**

Parachromatin, 188

Paramecium aurelia, 53–55, **54, 62,** 252, 253, **254,** 271

Paramecium bursaria, 176

Paranemic coiling, 28

Parasexuality, 176

Pardee, A. B., 294

Parentage disputes, 243–44

Paroral cone, 55

Parthenium argentatum, 181

Parthenogenesis, 40, 42, 178

Patau, K., 33

Patterns, genetic control of, 282–85

Patterson, J. T., 145, 316, **316**

Pauling, Linus, 219

Pavan, C., **10**

Pearson, Karl, 84

Pedigree, sample, **61**

Peppered moth, 307–8, **308**

Pericarp, 51

Pericentric inversions, 134, **134**

Periodical list, 329–30

Perithecium, 53

Petite colonies, 257

Phages. *See* Bacteriophages

Phase-contrast microscope, 11
Phenotype, 66; ratios, 71–75, **74, 160**
Phenotypic variance, 98
Phenylalanine, 213–16, **214,** 241
Phenylketonuria, 215, 321
Photon, defined, 191n
Photoreactivation, 204–5
Pi particles, 252–53
Pigmentation: *Drosophila,* 87, 216–18, 241; flowers, 77; maize, 81–82, **82,** 87, 186, **187;** mice, 87; rabbits, 291; racial differences, 101, 309; spread of, 260
Pikes Peak sequence, 310–13
Pipkin, S. B., 181
Pisum sativum, 67
Plaques, 58, **59**
Plasmodium falciparum, 307
Plastids, 16, 255–56
Platyfish, 289
Plectonemic coiling, 28
Pleiotropic genes, 277
Ploidy, 155–62
Plough, H. H., 124
Pneumococcus, 190
poky (mutant), 257
Polar nuclei, 38–40
Pollard, E., 207
Pollen abortion, 257–58
Polymorphic species, 309–13
Polyoma virus, 291
Polyploidy, 155–62, 173–74
Polysaccharides, 13
Polysomics, in plants, 163–64
Polytene chromosomes, 23–27
Pontecorvo, G., 125, 176
Populations: comparison of, 90–93; Mendelian, 299; population genetics, 297–305; size of, 304–5; of a species, 315
Position effect, 134, 237
Potter DNA kit, 29
Poulson, D. F., 274, **275**
Powers, L., 181
Prepatterns, 284–85
Primer DNA, 29
Proasci, **52,** 53
Prophages, 59–60
Protamine, 19
Proteins: chains, 219; in cytoplasm, 14; synthesis of, **224,** 269; in tissues, 13
Protentor, 107, **107**

Protoperithecia, 52
Pseudoallelism, 234–37, **234–36**
Pseudotumors, 283, **284**
Puccinia triticina, 157
Puck, T. T., 64, 201
Puff formation, 25, **25**

Quantitative inheritance, 89–102
Quantum, defined, 191n

r II region, 238–40, **239**
Rabbits, pigmentation of, 291
Racial differences, in pigmentation, 101, 309
Rad, defined, 191
Radiation: and cells, 195, 201–2; chemistry, 191–93; and chromosomal aberrations, 198–200; and *Drosophila,* 200, 202–3, 208; from fallout, 206; and health, 205–6; lethal dose for man, 201–2, 201n; as mutagens, 190–94; and recessive lethal mutations, 195–98, **197;** sensitivity to, 202–4, **203;** sickness from, 202; and survival, 193–94, **194;** threshold dose rate, 204; and translocations, 199–200, **200, 201**
Radicals, hydroxyl and hydroperoxyl, 192
Radioactive isotopes, 9–10, 9n
Radioactivity, and mutations, 197
Radiosensitivity, 202–4, **203**
Rana pipiens, 267, **268**
Random genetic drift, 305
Random mating, 299–301
Raphanobrassica, 166
Raphanus sativa, 166
Rats, maze-learning ability of, **286–87**
Recessive lethal mutations, 195–98, **196, 197**
Recessiveness, concept of, 67
Reciprocal crosses, 105–6, 249, **250**
Reciprocal tranlocations, 141–49, **142,** 317, **317**
Recon, 233
Recurrent mutation, 301–2
Reductional divisions, *See* Meiosis
Reeve, E. C. R., 149
Refractive index, 11n
Renwick, J. H., 111

Repressor genes, 270
Reproduction: asexual, **62,** 180; comparison of, **62;** in *Drosophila,* 48–49, **48, 49;** self-reproducing particles, 251–57
Reproductive isolation, 259, 315, 321
Repulsion configuration, 106
Resolving power, of magnifying systems, 3–4
"Retiring" behavior, 289
Rhesus system, 230–31
Rhoades, M. M., 186, 256
Rhoeo discolor, 149
Rhynchosciara angelae, **10**
Ribose, 17
Ribose nucleic acid (RNA), 17–25, 28, **224,** 245; template (messenger) RNA, 224, 245; transfer (acceptor, adaptor) RNA, 224
Ribosomes, **15,** 16, **224,** 245
Ring gland, 280
Ris, H., 7
Rizki, M. T. M., 283
Robertson, F. W., 149
Robson, J. M., 188
Roentgen, defined, 191
Roentgen equivalent physical (*rep*), **201**
Rossenbeck, H., 29
rosy (mutant), 274
Russell, W. L., 202

Saccharomyces cerevisiae, 257
Salivary glands, of *Drosophila,* 131–32, **Fig. 10-4**
Salmonella typhimurium, 236–37
Sandler, L., 188, 301
Sang, J. H., 45
Sanger, F., 243
Santa Cruz sequence, 310
scarlet (mutant), 216
Schiff's reagent, 20, 29
Schotté, O., 290
Schwartz, D., 126
Scott, J. P., 288
Scutellum of maize, 51
Sears, E. R., 157, 158, 164
Seed capsules of Datura, 163
Segregation, in autotetraploids, 158–60; of *Neurospora* ascospores, 123–24, **124**
Selection, 302–4; and breeding, 97–99, 288, 320; natural, 296–97

Seminiferous tubule dysgenesis, 171
Serial nuclear transplantations, **268,** 269
Sewall Wright effect, 305
Sex chromosomes. *See* X-chromosomes; Y-chromosomes
Sex determination, 168–84
Sex linkage, 106–7
"Sex reversal," in chickens, 110
Sexual cycle, of *Neurospora,* **52**
Sexual differences, in crossing over, **124**
Sexual isolation, 321
Sexual reproduction, **62,** 180
Sexuality, among unicellular organisms, 175–76
Shell coiling, inheritance of, 259
Sheppard, P. M., 321
Shifts, 138, **140**
Shigella paradysenteriae, 190
Sickle-cell anemia, 220–22, **220, 221,** 306–7
Sigma (viruslike agent), 251, 259
Sinnott, E. W., **27**
Sister chromatid exchanges, 126
Skin grafting, in mice, 226–27
Skoog, F., 33
Slizynski, B. M., 131
Somatic crossing over, 125–26
Sonneborn, T. M., 252, 271
Sparrow, A. H., **199,** 202, **203**
Species: origin of, 315; polymorphic, 309–13
Spector, W. S., 31
Spemann, H., 263, 277, 278, 290
Spencer, W. P., 196, 197, **197**
Spermatids, 37, **38**
Spermatocytes, **34,** 35, 36
Spermiogenesis, **34,** 35, 37–38, **38**
Spontaneous mutations, 185–86, **186**
Sporophyte, 50
Spurway, H. S., 259
Squash, fruit shape in, 83
Standard error, 93
Standard sequence, 310–13, **312**
Stebbins, S. G., 166
Steffensen, D., 42, 204
Sterility: in cows, 181; *fes* factor, 111; in man, 171
Stern, C., 125, 127, 149, 151, 196, 197, **197,** 198, 284, 285, 305
Stewart, S. E., 291
Stone, W. S., 316, **316**
Strontium[90], 206

Sturtevant, A. H., 133, 134, 138, 171, 241, 259
Subatomic particles, **190**
Submetacentric chromosomes, 33
Subvital mutants, 198
Supersexes, 168–71, **170**
Suppressor mutations, 231–33
Survival, as a function of radiation dose, 193–94, **194**
Suskind, S. R., 218
Swift, H., 7
Swordtail, 289
Synapsis, 35; of quadrivalents, 161
Syngamy, **39,** 40
Szilard, L., 188, 207

T₄ bacteriophage, **58,** 238–40, **239**
Tahmisian, T. N., 37
Target theory, 193–94
Tatum, E. L., 218
Taylor, J. H., 32, 126
Telocentric chromosomes, 33
Telomeres, 20
Temperate phages, 59
Templates, 20, **224**
Terminalization, 36, **Fig. 3–3**
Test crosses, 76, 105–6
Tetrads, 36; and crossing over, 123–24; **123, Fig. 3–3**
Tetraploid dihybrid crosses, 160, **161**
Thalassemia, 231–32
Thelytoky, 42
Three-point cross, 114–20
Threshold dose rate, 204
Thrombin, 225
Tissue: components of, 13–14; preparation for observation, 4–7
Tobacco, inheritance of leaf number, 100–101
Tobacco mosaic virus (TMV), 245
tra (gene). *See transformer*
Traction fiber, 20, 20n
Tradescantia, 198
Trans configuration, 235–37, **236**
Transduction, 60, 237
Transformed bacteria, 190
transformer (gene), 171, 285, 288
Translocations, 141–51, **142–47;** 317, **317;** frequency of, 199–200, **200,**

201; viability of homozygote, **146**
Transplacental immunization, 230
Trichogynes, 52
Trillium, 198, **199,** 202, **203**
Triploids, offspring of, 168–71, **169**
Triploidy, in man, 164–65
Trisomic method, 164
Trisomy, in man, 164–65
Triticum, 156–58, 166, 260
Tritium, 9–10
Tryon, R. C., **286**
Tryptophan, 216–18, **217,** 236–37
Tryptophan synthetase, 218
ts (gene), 181
Tsugita, A., 245
Tumors, 264–67, **265, 266,** 291
Turner's syndrome, 171
Twins, 61–62; and cancer, 267; intelligence of, 288
Tyrosine metabolism, 213–16
Tyrosinosis, 215

Ultramicrotome, 4, **6**
Ultraviolet light, 8, **9,** 190–91, 204–5

Van Overbeek, J., 282, **283**
Variance, defined, 97n
Variegation, 141, 146
Vegetative state, 56
vermilion (gene), 216
Vicia, 198
Victoria, Queen, 110
Viruses, **58,** 245, 251–52
Visconti, N., 58
Vitellogenesis, 39, 263–64
Vogt, M., 291
Von Fritsch, K., 285
Von Halle, E. S., 198

Waddington, C. H., 273, 280
Wasps, 178, **179**
Water, reactions with ionizing radiation, 192
Watson-Crick DNA helix, 18, 19, 28, 222, frontispiece
Weinberg, W., 297
Weinstein, A., 122

Weiss, P., 276, 290
Wettstein, D. von, 256
Wheats, 156–58
White, M. J. D., **26,** 42
White forelock, 111
White Leghorn chickens, 87
White Plymouth Rock chickens, 87
Whiting, P. W., 178
Whole arm transfer, **317**
Wilson, L. P., 263
Witkin, E. M., 205
Woodward, D., 237
Wolff, S., 129, 200
Wright, S., 299, 305, 318
Wright's inbreeding coefficient, 300

X-chromosomes, 106–9, **131,** 136, **136,**
   168–75
X-rays, 191, 195–98, 206
Xantha 3 (mutant), 256
Xanthommatin, 216, **217**
Xiphophorous, **265**

Y-chromosomes, 106–8, **106,** 136, 168–75
Yerganian, G., 174

Zea mays. See Maize
Zirkle, R. E., 195
Zwilling, E., 280